INSTRUCTOR'S SOLUTIONS MANUAL

JAMES LAPP

USING AND UNDERSTANDING MATHEMATICS
A QUANTITATIVE REASONING APPROACH
FIFTH EDITION

Jeffrey Bennett
University of Colorado at Boulder

William Briggs
University of Colorado at Denver

Addison-Wesley
is an imprint of

The author and publisher of this book have used their best efforts in preparing this book. These efforts include the development, research, and testing of the theories and programs to determine their effectiveness. The author and publisher make no warranty of any kind, expressed or implied, with regard to these programs or the documentation contained in this book. The author and publisher shall not be liable in any event for incidental or consequential damages in connection with, or arising out of, the furnishing, performance, or use of these programs.

Reproduced by Pearson Addison-Wesley from electronic files supplied by the author.

ISBN-13: 978-0-321-65293-5
ISBN-10: 0-321-65293-2

1 2 3 4 5 6 BB 14 13 12 11 10

Addison-Wesley
is an imprint of

www.pearsonhighered.com

Table of Contents

UNIT 1A

TIME OUT TO THINK

Pg. 17. Not guilty does not mean innocent; it means not enough evidence to prove guilt. If defendants were required to prove innocence, there would be many cases where they would be unable to provide such proof even though they were, in fact, innocent. This relates to the fallacy of appeal to ignorance in the sense that lack of proof of guilt does not mean innocence, and lack of proof of innocence does not mean guilt.

Pg. 18. Opinions will vary. One argument is that character questions should be allowed in court if answers to those questions may show bias or ulterior motives for testimony given by a witness. This would be a good topic for a discussion either during or outside of class.

QUICK QUIZ

1. **a**. By the definition used in this book, an argument always contains at least one premise and a conclusion.
2. **c**. By definition, a fallacy is a deceptive argument.
3. **b**. An argument must contain a conclusion.
4. **a**. Circular reasoning is an argument where the premise and the conclusion say essentially the same thing.
5. **b**. Using the fact that a statement is unproved to imply that it is false is appeal to ignorance.
6. **b**. "I don't support the President's tax plan" is the conclusion because the premise "I don't trust his motives" supports that conclusion.
7. **b**. This is a personal attack because the premise (I don't trust his motives) attacks the character of the President, and says nothing about the substance of his tax plan.
8. **c**. This is limited choice because the argument does not allow for the possibility that you are a fan of, say, boxing.
9. **b**. Just because *A* preceded *B* does not necessarily imply that *A* caused *B*.
10. **a**. By definition, a straw man is an argument that distorts (or misrepresents) the real issue.

DOES IT MAKE SENSE?

5. Does not make sense. Raising one's voice has nothing to do with logical arguments.
6. Does not make sense. Logical arguments always contain at least one premise and a conclusion.
7. Makes sense. A logical person would not put much faith in an argument that uses premises he believes to be false to support a conclusion.
8. Makes sense. There's nothing wrong with stating the conclusion of an argument before laying out the premises.
9. Does not make sense. One can disagree with the conclusion of a well-stated argument regardless of whether it is fallacious.
10. Makes sense. Despite the fact that an argument may be poorly constructed and fallacious, it still may have a believable conclusion.

BASIC SKILLS AND CONCEPTS

11. a. *Premise:* Apple's iPhone outsells all other smart phones. *Conclusion:* It must be the best smart phone on the market.
    b. The fact that many people buy the iPhone does not necessarily mean it is the best smart phone.
12. a. *Premise:* The current recession began just a few years after large tax cuts. *Conclusion:* Tax cuts cause recessions.
    b. The fact that tax cuts preceded a recession does not imply that tax cuts cause recessions.
13. a. *Premise:* Fifty years of searching has not revealed life on other planets. *Conclusion:* Life in the universe must be confined to Earth.
    b. Failure to find life does not imply that life does not exist.
14. a. *Premise:* Federal deficits have increased under Republican presidents and decreased under Democratic presidents. *Conclusion:* Only Democrats can balance the federal budget.
    b. The conclusion is based on relatively little evidence.
15. a. *Premise*: He refused to testify. *Conclusion*: He must be guilty.
    b. There are many reasons that someone might have for refusing to testify (being guilty is only one of them), and thus this is the fallacy of limited choice.
16. a. *Premise:* Thousands of unarmed people, many of them children, are killed by firearms every year. *Conclusion:* The sale of all guns should be banned.
    b. The conclusion is reached on the basis of an emotional statement.
17. a. *Premise:* The Senator doesn't have a religious affiliation. *Conclusion:* He can't have the personal values required to represent me.
    b. The conclusion is based on a personal allegation.
18. a. *Premise:* Illegal immigration is against the law. *Conclusion:* Illegal immigrants are criminals.
    b. The conclusion is a restatement of the premise.
19. a. *Premise:* Good grades are needed to get into college, and a college diploma is necessary for a good career. *Conclusion:* Attendance should count in high school grades.

b. The premise (which is often true) directs attention away from the conclusion.

20. a. *Premise:* The mayor wants to raise taxes to fund social programs. *Conclusion:* She must not believe in the value of hard work.

    b. The mayor is characterized (perhaps wrongly) by one quality, on which the conclusion is based.

21. *Premise:* Obesity and video game sales have increased steadily for the last decade. *Conclusion:* Video games are compromising the health of Americans. This argument suffers from the **false cause** fallacy. It's true obesity and video game sales have increased steadily for the last decade, but we cannot conclude that the former caused the latter simply because they happened together.

22. *Premise:* The Republican candidate leads by a 2 to 1 margin. *Conclusion:* You should vote for the Republican. This is a blatant **appeal to popularity**. No argument concerning the platform of the candidate is given.

23. *Premise:* All the mayors of my home town have been men. *Conclusion:* Men are better qualified for high office than women. The conclusion has been reached with a **hasty generalization**, because a small number of male mayors were used as evidence to support a claim about all men and women.

24. *Premise:* My father says I should exercise daily. *Premise:* He never exercised when he was young. *Conclusion:* I don't need to take his advice. This is a **personal attack** on the father's past transgressions, which should play little part in the child's logical decision about whether to exercise.

25. *Premise:* My baby was vaccinated and later developed autism. *Conclusion:* I believe that vaccines cause autism. **False cause** is at play here, as the vaccination may have nothing to do with the development of autism, even though both are occurring at the same time.

26. *Premise:* The state has no right to take a life. *Conclusion:* The death penalty should be abolished. Both the premise and conclusion say essentially the same thing; this is **circular reasoning**.

27. *Premise:* Shakespeare's plays have been read for many centuries. *Conclusion:* Everyone loves Shakespeare. Both the premise and conclusion say essentially the same thing; this is **circular reasoning**.

28. *Premise:* It's not a good idea to have your seat belt on if your car is on fire or underwater. *Conclusion:* The studies about the risks of driving without seat belts are flawed. Using two scenarios where wearing a seat belt is dangerous to come up with a conclusion about all seat belt use in general is **hasty generalization**. It can also be seen as an

appeal to ignorance: the lack of examples of scenarios where seat belts are beneficial does not mean that they are not.

29. *Premise:* After I last gave to a charity, an audit showed that most of the money was used to pay its administrators in the front office. *Conclusion:* I will not give money to the tsunami relief organization.. This is a **personal attack**, on charities. It can also be seen as an **appeal to ignorance**: the lack of examples of charities passing donations onto to the intended recipients does not mean that a charity will not pass on donations.

30. *Premise:* Democrats don't care about taxpayers' money. *Conclusion:* It's not surprising that the President's budget contains spending increases. This is **limited choice**: the premise does not allow for the possibility that the Democrats do care about taxpayers' money.

31. *Premise:* The Congressperson is a member of the National Rifle Association. *Conclusion:* I'm sure she will not support a ban on assault rifles. This is a **personal attack** on members of the National Rifle Association. The argument also distorts the position of the National Rifle Association (not all members would oppose a ban on assault rifles); this is a **straw man**.

32. *Premise:* My three friends who drink wine have never had heart attacks. *Premise:* My two friends who have had heart attacks are non-drinkers. *Conclusion:* Drinking wine is clearly good therapy. The conclusion has been reached with a **hasty generalization**, because a small number of wine drinkers were used as evidence to support a claim about drinking wine.

33. *Premise*: The Republicans favor repealing the estate tax, which falls most heavily on the wealthy. *Conclusion*: Republicans think the wealthy aren't rich enough. (Implied here is that you should vote for Democrats). The argument distorts the position of the Republicans (none of whom would say the rich need to be richer); this is a **straw man**.

34. *Premise*: The Wyoming toad has not been seen outside of captivity since 2002. *Conclusion*: It is extinct in the wild. **Appeal to ignorance** is used here – the lack of proof of the existence of the woodpecker does not imply it is extinct.

35. *Premise*: My boy loves dolls, and my girl loves trucks. *Conclusion*: There's no truth to the claim that boys prefer mechanical toys while girls prefer maternal toys. Using one child of each gender to come up with a conclusion about all children is **hasty generalization**. It can also be seen as an **appeal to ignorance**: the lack of examples of boys

enjoying mechanical toys (and girls maternal toys) does not mean that they don't enjoy these toys.

36. *Premise*: The Democrats want to raise gas mileage requirements on new vehicles. *Conclusion*: Democrats think the government is the solution to all of our problems. The argument distorts the position of the Democrats (none of whom would claim government is the solution to all of our problems); this is a **straw man**.

UNIT 1B

TIME OUT TO THINK

Pg. 26. We needed 8 rows for 3 propositions; adding a fourth proposition means two possible truth values for each of those 8 rows, or 16 rows total. The conjunction is true only if all four propositions are true.

Pg. 28. The precise definitions of logic sometimes differ from our "everyday" intuition. There is no possible way that Jones could personally eliminate all poverty on Earth, regardless of whether she is elected. Thus, at the time you heard her make this promise, you would certainly conclude that she was being less than truthful. Nevertheless, according to the rules of logic, the only way her statement can be false is if she is elected, in which case she would be unable to follow through on the promise. If she is not elected, her claim is true (at least according to the laws of logic).

QUICK QUIZ

1. **c.** This is a proposition because it is a complete sentence making a claim, which could be true or false.
2. **a.** The truth value of a proposition's negation (*not p*) can always be determined by the truth value of the proposition.
3. **c.** Conditional statements are, by definition, in the form of *if p, then q*.
4. **c.** The table will require eight rows because there are two possible truth values for each of the propositions *x, y,* and *z*.
5. **c.** Because it is not stated otherwise, we are dealing with the inclusive *or* (and thus either *p* is true, or *q* is true, or both are true).
6. **a.** The conjunction *p and q* is true only when both are true, and since *p* is false, *p and q* must also be false.
7. **c.** The inclusive disjunction *Calcutta or Bombay* allows for either or both (i.e. at least one) of these words to appear in the article.
8. **a.** In this case, all of the words means both of them (as there are just two), and the conjunction

Calcutta and Bombay means you want both of the words to appear in the article.

9. **b.** Statements are logically equivalent only when they have the same truth values.
10. **a.** Rewriting the statement in *if p, then q* form gives, "if you want to win, then you've got to play."

DOES IT MAKE SENSE?

7. Does not make sense. Propositions are never questions.
8. Does not make sense. The professor's stance on torture may not have much to do with his level of compassion.
9. Makes sense. If restated in *if p, then q* form, this statement would read, "If we catch him, then he will be dead or alive." Clearly this is true, as it covers all the possibilities. (One could argue semantics, and say that a dead person is not caught, but rather discovered. Splitting hairs like this might lead one to claim the statement does not make sense).
10. Does not make sense. The first statement is in the *if p, then q* form, and the second is the converse (i.e. *if q, then p*). Since the converse of an *if...then* statement is not logically equivalent to the original statement, this doesn't make sense.
11. Does not make sense. Not all statements fall under the purview of logical analysis.
12. Does not make sense. The converse of a statement is not always false if the original statement is true.

BASIC SKILLS AND CONCEPTS

13. Since it's a complete sentence that makes a claim (whether true or false is immaterial), it's a proposition.
14. No claim is made with this statement, so it's not a proposition.
15. No claim is made with this statement, so it's not a proposition.
16. This is a complete sentence that makes a claim, so it's a proposition.
17. Questions are never propositions.
18. This is a proposition as we can assign a truth value to it, and it's a complete sentence.
19. Asia is not in the northern hemisphere. The statement is true; the negation is false.
20. Spain is not in North America. The statement is false; the negation is true.
21. The Beatles were a German band. The statement is true; the negation is false.
22. Brad Pitt is an American actor. The statement is false; the negation is true.
23. Sarah did go to dinner.

24. The Senator is comfortable with demonstrations. Whether he approves of them is debatable, given the limited information.
25. The Congressman voted in favor of discrimination.
26. The Senate failed to push the bill to stop logging through (it did not overturn the President's veto), so logging will continue.
27. Paul appears to support building the new dorm.
28. Since the mayor was trying to strike down a law prohibiting cell phones in public meetings, the mayor appears to oppose the use of cell phones in public meetings.
29. This is the truth table for the conjunction *q and r.*

q	*r*	*q and r*
T	T	T
T	F	F
F	T	F
F	F	F

30. This is the truth table for the conjunction *p and s.*

p	*s*	*p and s*
T	T	T
T	F	F
F	T	F
F	F	F

31. "Cucumbers are vegetables" is true. "Apples are fruit" is true. Since both propositions are true, the conjunction is true.
32. "12 + 6 = 18" is true, but "3 × 5 = 8" is false. The conjunction is false because both propositions in a conjunction must be true for the entire statement to be true.
33. "The Mississippi River flows through Louisiana" is true. "The Colorado River flows through Arizona" is true. Since both propositions are true, the conjunction is true.
34. "Bach was a composer" is true, but "Bono is a violinist" is false. The conjunction is false because both propositions in a conjunction must be true for the entire statement to be true.
35. "Some people are happy" is true (in general), as is "Some people are short," so the conjunction is true.
36. "Not all dogs are black" is true. "Not all cats are white" is also true, so the conjunction is true.

37. This is the truth table for *q and r and s.*

q	*r*	*s*	*q and r and s*
T	T	T	T
T	T	F	F
T	F	T	F
T	F	F	F
F	T	T	F
F	T	F	F
F	F	T	F
F	F	F	F

38. This is the truth table for *p and q and r and s.*

p	*q*	*r*	*s*	*p and q and r and s*
T	T	T	T	T
T	T	T	F	F
T	T	F	T	F
T	T	F	F	F
T	F	T	T	F
T	F	T	F	F
T	F	F	T	F
T	F	F	F	F
F	T	T	T	F
F	T	T	F	F
F	T	F	T	F
F	T	F	F	F
F	F	T	T	F
F	F	T	F	F
F	F	F	T	F
F	F	F	F	F

39. *Or* is used in the exclusive sense because you probably can't dress in both red and blue.
40. *Or* is used in the exclusive sense because you probably can't have both the salad and soup.
41. The exclusive *or* is used here as it is unlikely that the statement means you might travel to both countries during the same trip.
42. Oil changes are good for either 3 months or 3,000 miles, whichever comes first, so this is the exclusive use of *or.*
43. *Or* is used in the inclusive sense because you probably would be thrilled to attend both concerts or the theater while in New York.
44. Most insurance policies that cover "fire or theft" allow for the coverage of both at the same time, so this is the inclusive *or.*
45. This is the truth table for the disjunction *r or s.*

r	*s*	*r or s*
T	T	T
T	F	T
F	T	T
F	F	F

46. This is the truth table for the disjunction *p or r*.

p	r	p or r
T	T	T
T	F	T
F	T	T
F	F	F

47. This is the truth table for *p and (not p)*.

p	not p	p and (not p)
T	F	F
F	T	F

48. This is the truth table for *q or (not q)*.

q	not q	q or (not q)
T	F	T
F	T	T

49. This is the truth table for *p or q or r*.

p	q	r	p or q or r
T	T	T	T
T	T	F	T
T	F	T	T
T	F	F	T
F	T	T	T
F	T	F	T
F	F	T	T
F	F	F	F

50. This is the truth table for *p or (not p) or q*.

p	(not p)	q	p or (not p) or q
T	F	T	T
T	F	F	T
F	T	T	T
F	T	F	T

51. "Oranges are vegetables" is false. "Oranges are fruits" is true. The disjunction is true because a disjunction is true when at least one of its propositions is true.

52. Both "3 × 5 = 15" and "3 + 5 = 8" are true, and thus the disjunction is true, as all you need is one proposition or the other to be true for the statement to be true.

53. "The Nile River is in Africa" is true. "China is in Europe" is false. The disjunction is true because a disjunction is true when at least one of its propositions is true.

54. "Bachelors are married" is false. "Bachelors are single" is true. The disjunction is true because at least one of the propositions is true.

55. "Trees walk" is false. "Rocks run" is also false. Since both are false, the disjunction is false.

56. "France is a country" is true. "Paris is a continent" is false. The disjunction is true because at least one of the propositions is true.

57. Use option **a**, and search for *economic* AND *depression* AND *America*.

58. Use options **b**, and search for *natural disasters* AND *Japan*.

59. Use options **b** and **c**, and search for *politicians* AND (*Ohio* OR *Indiana*) AND *Jones*.

60. Use options **b** and **c**, and search for (*17th century* OR *18th century*) AND *German* AND *composers*.

61. This is the truth table for *if p, then r*.

p	r	if p, then r
T	T	T
T	F	F
F	T	T
F	F	T

62. This is the truth table for *if r, then s*.

r	s	if r, then s
T	T	T
T	F	F
F	T	T
F	F	T

63. *Hypothesis:* Eagles can fly. *Conclusion:* Eagles are birds. Since both are true, the implication is true, because implications are always true except in the case where the hypothesis is true and the conclusion is false.

64. *Hypothesis:* London is in England. *Conclusion:* Chicago is in America. Since both are true, the implication is true.

65. *Hypothesis:* London is in England. *Conclusion:* Chicago is in Bolivia. Since the hypothesis is true, and the conclusion is false, the implication is false (this is the only instance when a simple *if p, then q* statement is false).

66. *Hypothesis:* London is in Mongolia. *Conclusion:* Chicago is in America. Since the hypothesis is false, the implication is true, no matter the truth value of the conclusion (which, in this case, is true).

67. *Hypothesis:* Pigs can fly. *Conclusion:* Fish can brush their teeth. Since the hypothesis is false, the

implication is true, no matter the truth value of the conclusion (which, in this case, is false).

68. *Hypothesis:* $2 \times 3 = 6$ *Conclusion:* $2 + 3 = 6$. Since the hypothesis is true, and the conclusion is false, the implication is false.

69. *Hypothesis:* Butterflies can fly. *Conclusion:* Butterflies are birds. Since the hypothesis is false, the implication is true, no matter the truth value of the conclusion (which, in this case, is false).

70. *Hypothesis:* Butterflies are birds. *Conclusion:* Butterflies can fly. Since the hypothesis is false, the implication is true, no matter the truth value of the conclusion (which, in this case, is true).

71. If a creature is a monkey (p), then that creature is a mammal (q).

72. If a person is a resident of Tel Aviv (p), then that person is a resident of Israel (q).

73. If you are eating (p), then you are alive (q).

74. If you are alive (p), then you eat (q).

75. If you are bald (p), then you are a male (q).

76. If she is an art historian (p), then she is educated (q).

77. *Converse:* If José owns a Mac, then he owns a computer. *Inverse:* If José does not own a computer, then he does not own a Mac. *Contrapositive:* If José does not own a Mac, then he does not own a computer. The converse and inverse are always logically equivalent, and the contrapositive is always logically equivalent to the original statement.

78. *Converse:* If the patient is breathing, then the patient is alive. *Inverse:* If the patient is not alive, then the patient is not breathing. *Contrapositive:* If the patient is not breathing, then the patient is not alive. The converse and inverse are always logically equivalent, and the contrapositive is always logically equivalent to the original statement.

79. *Converse:* If Teresa works in Massachusetts, then she works in Boston. *Inverse:* If Teresa does not work in Boston, then she does not work in Massachusetts. *Contrapositive:* If Teresa does not work in Massachusetts, then she does not work in Boston. The converse and inverse are always logically equivalent, and the contrapositive is always logically equivalent to the original statement.

80. *Converse:* If the lights are on, then I am using electricity. *Inverse:* If I am not using electricity, then the lights are not on. *Contrapositive:* If the lights are not on, then I am not using electricity. The converse and inverse are always logically equivalent, and the contrapositive is always logically equivalent to the original statement.

81. *Converse:* If it is warm outside, then the sun is shining. *Inverse:* If the sun is not shining, then it is not warm outside. *Contrapositive:* If it is not warm outside, then the sun is not shining. The converse and inverse are always logically equivalent, and the contrapositive is always logically equivalent to the original statement.

82. *Converse:* If the oceans rise, then the polar ice caps will have melted. *Inverse:* If the polar ice caps do not melt, then the oceans will not rise. *Contrapositive:* If the oceans do not rise, then the polar ice caps will not have melted. The converse and inverse are always logically equivalent, and the contrapositive is always logically equivalent to the original statement.

83. If you die young, then you are good. Opinions will vary on whether these are true.

84. If a man hasn't discovered something that he will die for, then he isn't fit to live. Opinions will vary on whether this is true.

85. If a free society cannot help the many who are poor, then it cannot save the few who are rich. Opinions will vary on whether this is true.

86. If a man reads nothing at all, then he is better educated than the man who reads only newspapers. Opinions will vary on whether this is true.

87. "If Sue lives in Cleveland, then she lives in Ohio," where it is assumed that Sue lives in Cincinnati. (Answers will vary). Because Sue lives in Cincinnati, the hypothesis is false, while the conclusion is true, and this means the implication is true. The converse, "If Sue lives in Ohio, then she lives in Cleveland," is false, because the hypothesis is true, but the conclusion is false.

88. "If $2 + 2 = 4$, then $3 + 3 = 6$." (Answers will vary). The implication is true, because the hypothesis is true and the conclusion is true. The converse, "If $3 + 3 = 6$, then $2 + 2 = 4$" is also true for the same reason.

89. "If Ramon lives in Albuquerque, then he lives in New Mexico" where it is assumed that Ramon lives in Albuquerque. The implication is true, because the hypothesis is true and the conclusion is true. (Answers will vary). The contrapositive, "If Ramon does not live in New Mexico, then he does not live in Albuquerque", is logically equivalent to the original conditional, so it is also true.

90. "If Delaware is in America, then Maryland is in Canada." (Answers will vary). The hypothesis is true, while the conclusion is false, and this means the implication is false. In the inverse, "If Delaware is not in America, then Maryland is not in Canada," the hypothesis is false, while the conclusion is true, and this means the implication is true.

91. a. The book would be on the list because the search finds all entries with either *Steinbeck* or *grapes* (or both).

b. The book would be on the list because the search finds all entries with *Grapes of Wrath*.

c. The book would be on the list because the search finds all entries with both *grapes* and *Steinbeck*.

d. The book would be on the list because the search would find all entries with *Steinbeck* (it would also find entries with *Hemingway*).

e. The book would not be on the list because the search would find only those items that have both *Hemingway* and *grapes*.

f. The book would be on the list because the search would find all entries with *Steinbeck* and *grapes* (it would also find all items with *Hemingway* and *grapes*).

92. (1) If the payer does not know that you remarried, then alimony you receive is taxable.

(2) If the payer knows that you remarried, then alimony you receive is not taxable.

(3) If you pay alimony to another party, then it is not deductible on your return.

93. Believing is sufficient for achieving. Achieving is necessary for believing.

94. Our species being alone in the universe is sufficient for the universe having aimed rather low. The universe having aimed rather low is necessary for our species being alone in the universe.

95. Loving until it hurts is sufficient for there being no hurt but only more love. There being no hurt but only more love is necessary for loving until it hurts.

96. Needing both of your hands for whatever it is you're doing is sufficient for your brain being in on it too. Your brain being in on it too is necessary for needing both of your hands for whatever it is you're doing.

97. Following is a truth table for both *not (p and q)* and *(not p) or (not q)*.

p	q	*p and q*	*not (p and q)*	*(not p) or (not q)*
T	T	T	F	F
T	F	F	T	T
F	T	F	T	T
F	F	F	T	T

Since both statements have the same truth values (compare the last two columns of the table), they are logically equivalent.

98. Following is a truth table for both *not (p or q)* and *(not p) and (not q)*.

p	q	*p or q*	*not (p or q)*	*(not p) and (not q)*
T	T	T	F	F
T	F	T	F	F
F	T	T	F	F
F	F	F	T	T

Since both statements have the same truth values (compare the last two columns in the table), they are logically equivalent.

99. Following is a truth table for both *not (p and q)* and *(not p) and (not q)*.

p	q	*p and q*	*not (p and q)*	*(not p) and (not q)*
T	T	T	F	F
T	F	F	T	F
F	T	F	T	F
F	F	F	T	T

Note that the last two columns in the truth table don't agree, and thus the statements are not logically equivalent.

100. Following is a truth table for *not (p or q)* and *(not p) or (not q)*.

p	q	*p or q*	*not (p or q)*	*(not p) or (not q)*
T	T	T	F	F
T	F	T	F	T
F	T	T	F	T
F	F	F	T	T

Note that the last two columns in the truth table don't agree, and thus the statements are not logically equivalent.

101. Following is a truth table for *(p and q) or r* and *(p or r) and (p or q)*.

p	q	r	*p and q*	*(p and q) or r*	*p or r*	*p or q*	*(p or r) and (p or q)*
T	T	T	T	T	T	T	T
T	T	F	T	T	T	T	T
T	F	T	F	T	T	T	T
T	F	F	F	F	T	T	T
F	T	T	F	T	T	T	T
F	T	F	F	F	F	T	F
F	F	T	F	T	T	F	F
F	F	F	F	F	F	F	F

Since the fifth and eighth column of the table don't agree, these two statements are not logically equivalent.

102. Following is a truth table for *(p or q) and r* and *(p and r) or (q and r)*.

p	q	r	p or q	(p or q) and r	p and r	q and r	(p and r) or (q and r)
T	T	T	T	T	T	T	T
T	T	F	T	F	F	F	F
T	F	T	T	T	T	F	T
T	F	F	T	F	F	F	F
F	T	T	T	T	F	T	T
F	T	F	T	F	F	F	F
F	F	T	F	F	F	F	F
F	F	F	F	F	F	F	F

Since the fifth and eighth columns agree, the statements are logically equivalent.

UNIT 1C

TIME OUT TO THINK

Pg. 35. The set of students in the mathematics class could be described by writing each student's name within the braces, separated by commas. The set of countries you have visited would be written with the names of the countries within the braces. Additional examples will vary.

Pg. 41. The student should see that the statement some teachers are not men leaves both questions posed in the Time Out unanswered. Thus, from the statement given, it is not possible to know whether some teachers are men. From this, it also follows that we cannot be sure that none of the teachers are men.

Pg. 42. Changing the circle for boys to girls is fine, since a teenager is either one or the other. It would also be fine to change the circle for employed to unemployed. But the set girls, boys, and unemployed does not work because it offers no place to record whether the teenager is an honor student.

Pg. 43. This question should convince the student that the variety of colors on TVs and monitors is made from just red, green, and blue. Higher-resolution monitors use smaller or more densely packed pixels (or both).

Pg. 44. The two sets in this case are the opposites of the two sets chosen for Figure 1.24, so they work equally well.

Pg. 52. Clear market research would be the best evidence on which to build the case. For example, use focus groups to react to the story, or show sample movie clips to groups of typical viewers.

QUICK QUIZ

1. **b.** The ellipsis is a convenient way to represent all the other states in the U.S. without having to write them all down.
2. **c.** 3.5 is a rational number (a ratio of two integers), but it is not an integer.
3. **a.** When the circle labeled C is contained within the circle labeled D, it indicates that C is a subset of D.
4. **b.** Since the set of boys is disjoint from the set of girls, the two circles should be drawn as non-overlapping circles.
5. **a.** Because all apples are fruit, the set A should be drawn within the set B (the set of apples is a subset of the set of fruits).
6. **c.** Some cross country runners may also be swimmers, so their sets should be overlapping.
7. **a.** The X is placed in the region where *business executives* and *working mothers* overlap to indicate that there is at least one member in that region.
8. **c.** The region X is within both *males* and *athletes*, but not within *Republicans*.
9. **a.** The central region is common to all three sets, and so represents those who are male, Republican, and an athlete.
10. **c.** The sum of the entries in the column labeled Low Birth Weight is 32.

DOES IT MAKE SENSE?

7. Does not make sense. More likely than not, the payments go to two separate companies.
8. Makes sense. A Venn diagram displays the relationship between sets, and we don't need to comprehend the labels used for the sets to understand the relationship between their members.
9. Does not make sense. The number of students in a class is a whole number, and whole numbers are not in the set of irrational numbers.
10. Makes sense. The number of students in a class is a whole number, and whole numbers are a subset of the real numbers.
11. Does not make sense. A Venn diagram shows only the relationship between members of sets, but does not have much to say about the truth value of a categorical proposition.
12. Does not make sense. A Venn diagram is used to show the relationship between members of sets, but it is not used to determine the truth value for an opinion.

BASIC SKILLS & CONCEPTS

13. 23 is a natural number.
14. −45 is an integer.

15. 2/3 is a rational number.
16. −5/2 is a rational number.
17. 1.2345 is a rational number.
18. 0 is a whole number.
19. π is a real number.
20. $\sqrt{8}$ is a real number.
21. −34.45 is a rational number.
22. $\sqrt{98}$ is a real number.
23. $\pi/4$ is a real number.
24. 123/456 is a rational number.
25. −13/3 is a rational number.
26. −145.01 is a rational number.
27. $\pi/129$ is a real number.
28. 13,579,023 is a natural number.
29. {Sunday, Monday, Tuesday, Wednesday, Thursday, Friday, Saturday}
30. {10, 12, 14, . . . , 60, 62}
31. {New Mexico, Oklahoma, Louisiana}
32. {4, 7, 10, 13, 16, 19}
33. {36, 49, 64, 81, 100, 121}
34. The set has no members.
35. {3, 9, 15, 21, 27}
36. {a, e, i, o, u}
37. Because some women are veterinarians, the circles should overlap.

38. Because some nurses are skydivers, the circles should overlap.

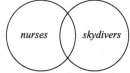

39. All verbs are words, and thus the set of verbs is a subset of the set of words. This means one circle should be contained within the other.

40. No reptile is a bacteria, so these sets are disjoint, and the circles should not overlap.

41. Some painters are also musicians, so the circles should overlap.

42. No atheist is a Catholic bishop, so these sets are disjoint, and the circles should not overlap.

43. No negative integer is a natural number, so these sets are disjoint, and the circles should not overlap.

44. All limericks are poems, so one circle should be placed within the other.

45. The subject is *widows*, and the predicate is *women*.

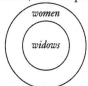

46. The subject is *worms*, and the predicate is *birds*.

47. All U.S. presidents are people over 30 years old. The subject is *U.S. presidents*, and the predicate is *people over 30 years old*.

48. All children are people that sing. The subject is *children*, and the predicate is *people who can sing*.

49. No monkey is a gambling animal. The subject is *monkeys*, and the predicate is *gambling animals*.

50. No plumbers are people who cheat. The subject is *plumbers*, and the predicate is *people who cheat*.

51. All winners are people who smile. The subject is *winners*, and the predicate is *people who smile*.

52. The subject is *movie stars*, and the predicate is *redheads*.

53.

54.

55.

56.

57.

58.

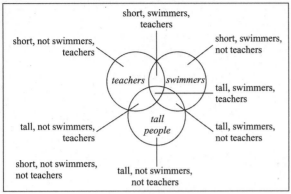

59. a. There are 31 women at the party that are under 30.
b. There are 22 men at the party that are not under 30.
c. There are 44 women at the party.
d. There are 81 people at the party.

60. a. There are 15 men at the party that are under 30.
b. There are 28 women at the party who are over 30.
c. There are 37 men at the party.
d. There are 50 people at the party that are not under 30.

61. a. There are 20 people at the conference that are unemployed women with a college degree.
b. There are 22 people at the conference that are employed men.
c. There are 8 people at the conference that are employed women without a college degree..
d. There are 34 people at the conference that are men.

62. a. There are 6 people at the conference that are employed men without a college degree.
b. There are 24 people at the conference that are unemployed women.
c. There are 3 people at the conference that are unemployed men without a college degree..
d. There are 74 people at the conference.

63.

64.

FURTHER APPLICATIONS

65. 15 comedies received unfavorable reviews, and 10 non-comedies received favorable reviews.

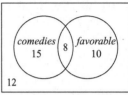

66. 18 cyclists that tested negative did not finish in the top 10, and 43 cyclists were tested.

67.

68.

69.

70. a.

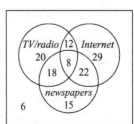

b. The region common to both *TV/radio* and *newspapers* shows that 26 people use at least

TV/radio and *newspapers* (some of these also use the *Internet*).

c. Count the number of people that are in all of the regions contained within the two circles *TV/Radio* and *Internet*. There are 109 such people.

d. Use the regions that are contained in the *TV/radio* and *Internet* circles, but not contained in the *newspapers* circle. There are 61 such people.

e. Count the number of people that are in the *Internet* circle, but outside of the *TV/radio* circle, and add them together to arrive at 51 people.

f. Count the number of people that are in the *TV/radio* circle, but outside of the *newspaper* circle, and add them together to arrive at 32 people.

71. a.

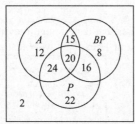

b. Add the regions that are contained in the *A* and *BP* circles, to find that 95 people took antibiotics or blood pressure medication.

c. Count the number of people that are in the *BP* circle, but outside the *P* circle, and add them together to arrive at 23 people.

d. Count the number of people that are in the *P* circle. There are 82 such people.

e. Use the region that is common to the *A* and *BP* circles, but not contained in the *P* circle, to find that 15 people took antibiotics and blood pressure medicine, but not pain medication.

f. Add the regions that are common to all three circles, to find that 117 people took antibiotics or blood pressure medicine or pain medicine.

72. Because there are three different brands and two possible responses for each brand (acceptable or not acceptable), a three-circle diagram is needed.

73.

74.

75.

76.

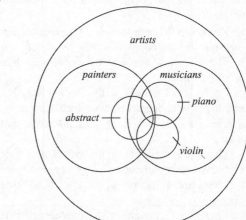

77. The two-way table should look like this:

	Vegetarian	Meat/Fish	Total
Wine	20	40	60
No wine	45	15	60
Total	65	55	120

78. The two-way table should look like this:

	Women	Men	Total
No claims	30	20	50
At least one claim	20	40	60
Total	50	60	110

79. a. 47% of households (in the survey) have fewer than three television sets?
b. There is not enough information to determine the answer.
c. 27% of households do not have a VCR?
d. There is not enough information to determine the answer.
e. About 60 million households have three or more television sets.

80. a.

	Women	Men
Flu	80	60
Anemia	50	50
Both	20	10
Total	150	120

b.

81. a.

b.

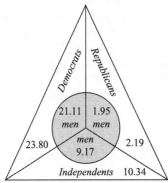

82. As shown in the diagram, the sets *hairy animals* and *fish* do not overlap (because all hairy animals are mammals, and no mammal is a fish). Since some mammals can swim, and hairy animals are mammals, there may be hairy animals that swim. There is nothing in the propositions that excludes the possibility of walking mammals, and thus there may be walking mammals, and for the same

reason, there may be hairy animals that walk on land.

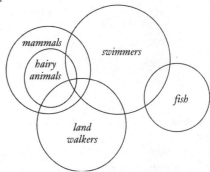

83. Since beans are contained within the set of plants, and meat and dairy products are outside of the set of plants, beans and dairy products are disjoint sets, and thus no bean is a dairy product. There is nothing in the propositions that prohibits the overlap of meat and dairy products, so there could be a meat that is a dairy product. No dairy product is a plant, because it is disjoint from that set. There could be plants that contain protein.

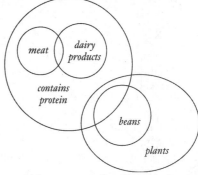

84. There could be conservative Democrats, and there could be liberal Green Party members, because there is nothing in the propositions to prohibit this. No liberal is a Republican, because the set of Republicans is a subset of the set of conservatives, and no liberal is a conservative (which means those sets are disjoint).

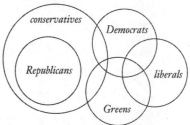

85. a. It is implied here that no Democrat is a Republican, and thus those sets are disjoint, as shown in the diagram.

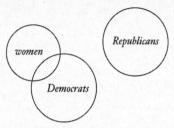

b. Yes, it is possible to meet such a woman, as there is nothing in the propositions to exclude that possibility.

c. Yes, there may be men who are Republicans (if there are any Republicans in attendance, they must be men).

86. a.

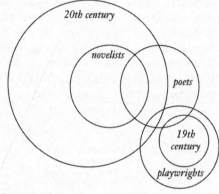

b. No, all of the novelists were born in the 20th century.

c. There is nothing in the facts you noticed that excludes the possibility of a poet born in the 19th century, so, yes, you may have studied such a poet.

d. Yes, there's nothing stated that excludes this possibility.

87. a. There are 16 different sets of options: choose nothing, A, B, C, D, AB, AC, AD, BC, BD, CD, ABC, ABD, ACD, BCD, and ABCD.
   b.

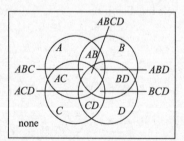

c. There are no regions for A and D only, and for B and C only.

d. There are 32 different sets of options: choose nothing, A, B, C, D, E, AB, AC, AD, AE, BC, BD, BE, CD, CE, DE, ABC, ABD, ABE, ACD, ACE, ADE, BCD, BCE, BDE, CDE, ABCD, ABCE, ABDE, ACDE, BCDE, and ABCDE.

e. Notice that with four options, there are $2^4 = 16$ different sets of options, and that with five options, there are $2^5 = 32$ different sets of options. It turns out that this pattern continues so that with N options, there are 2^N different sets of options.

UNIT 1D

TIME OUT TO THINK

Pg. 53. Answers will vary. Recall that inductive arguments make a case for a general conclusion from more specific premises, while deductive arguments make a case for a specific conclusion from more general premises. This would be a good topic for a discussion either during or outside of class.

Pg. 58. Changing from heroin to aspirin does not affect the argument's structure, so it is still valid. It is now also sound, because this change makes both premises true.

QUICK QUIZ

1. **b.** The only way to prove a statement true beyond all doubt is with a valid and sound deductive argument.

2. **c.** A deductive argument that is valid has a logical structure that implies its conclusion from its premises.

3. **c.** If a deductive argument is not valid, it cannot be sound.

4. **a.** Premise 1 claims the set of *knights* is a subset of the set of *heroes*, and Premise 2 claims Paul is a hero, which means the X must reside within the *hero* circle. However, we cannot be sure whether the X should fall within or outside the *knights* circle, so it belongs on the border.

5. **c.** Diagram *a* in question 4 is the correct diagram for its argument, and since X lies on the border of the *knights* circle, Paul may or may not be a knight.

6. **b.** The argument is of the form *denying the conclusion*, and one can always conclude *p* is not true in such arguments. (Whether the argument is sound is another question).

7. **c.** This argument is of the form *affirming the conclusion*, and it is always invalid, which means we can conclude nothing about *p*.

8. **c.** A chain of conditionals from *a* to *d* is necessary before we can claim the argument is valid.

9. **b.** The side opposite the right angle in a right triangle is always the longest, and it's called the hypotenuse.

10. **b.** The Pythagorean theorem states that $c^2 = 4^2 + 5^2 = 16 + 25 = 41$.

DOES IT MAKE SENSE?

9. Does not make sense. One cannot prove a conclusion beyond all doubt with an inductive argument.
10. Makes sense. An inductive argument is judged on its strength.
11. Makes sense. As long as the logic of a deductive argument is valid, if one accepts the truth (or soundness) of the premises, the conclusion necessarily follows.
12. Does not make sense. A deductive argument which is valid is not necessarily sound, and therefore the conclusion may not be true.
13. Does not make sense. This argument is of the form *affirming the conclusion*, and it is always invalid.
14. Does not make sense. Mathematicians generally do not claim a theorem to be true until it is proved with a valid and sound deductive argument.

BASIC SKILLS & CONCEPTS

15. This is an inductive argument because it makes the case for a general conclusion based on many specific observations.
16. This is a deductive argument because a specific conclusion is deduced from more general premises.
17. This is an inductive argument because it makes the case for a general conclusion based on many specific observations.
18. This is a deductive argument because a specific conclusion is deduced from more general premises.
19. This is an inductive argument because it makes the case for a general conclusion based on many specific observations.
20. This is a deductive argument because a specific conclusion is deduced from more general premises.
21. This is an inductive argument because it makes the case for a general conclusion based on several specific observations.
22. This is a deductive argument because a specific conclusion is deduced from more general premises.
23. The premises are true and the argument is moderately strong The conclusion is correct.
24. The premises are generally true, and the argument is weak. The conclusion may not be true (it is possible to pay more and not receive quality).
25. The premises are true, the argument seems moderately strong, and the conclusion is false.

26. The premises are true, the argument seems moderately strong, and the conclusion is true.
27. The premises are true, and the argument is moderately strong. The conclusion is true.
28. The premises are true, though the argument is weak (it speaks to only four of many composers). The conclusion is false.
29. Premise: All European countries are countries that use the euro as currency. The diagram shows the argument is valid. However, it is not sound as the first premise is false.

30. Premise: All dairy products are foods containing protein. The diagram shows the argument is invalid, even though the premises are true. Because it is invalid, the argument cannot be sound.

31. Premise: All states west of the Mississippi River are not in the eastern time zone. The argument is valid, and the premises are true, so the argument is also sound.

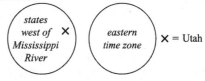

32. As shown in the diagram, the argument is not valid because we cannot place the X within the *presidents* circle based on the second premise alone. Though the premises are true, the argument is not sound.

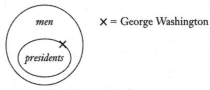

33. As shown in the diagram, the argument is not valid because we cannot place the X within the *Best Actor Award* circle based on the second premise alone. Though the premises are true, the argument is not sound.

= Sean Penn

34. The argument is valid. Since the first premise is not true, the argument is not sound.

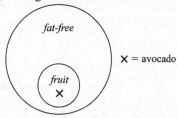

= avocado

35. The diagram shows the argument is valid, and it is sound if we believe the premises to be true (there's room for disagreement on that count as we can't be sure all opera singers can whistle, nor can we be sure they know Mozart).

= Pavarotti

36. Premise: All countries are non-islands. The argument is valid. The first premises is not true, so the argument is not sound.

= Iceland

37. Affirming the hypothesis – this form is always valid, as confirmed by the diagram. The premises are true, and thus the argument sound.

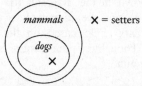

= setters

38. Affirming the hypothesis – this form is always valid, as confirmed by the diagram. The premises are true, and thus the argument sound.

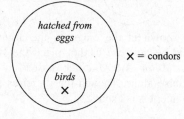

= condors

39. Denying the hypothesis – this form is always invalid, as confirmed by the diagram. Since it is invalid, it cannot be sound.

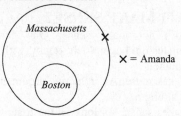

= Amanda

40. Affirming the conclusion – this form is always invalid, as confirmed by the diagram. Since it is invalid, it cannot be sound.

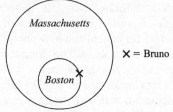

= Bruno

41. Denying the conclusion – this form is always valid, as confirmed by the diagram. Since it is invalid, it cannot be sound.

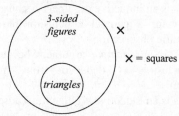

= squares

42. If you are a nurse, then you must know CPR. Affirming the hypothesis – this form is always valid, as confirmed by the diagram. To the extent that the premises are true, the argument is sound.

= Tom

43. Premise: If a novel was written in the 19th century, then it was not written on a word processor. Denying the hypothesis – this form is always invalid, as confirmed by the diagram. Since it is invalid, it cannot be sound.

= Jake's novel

44. Affirming the conclusion – this form is always invalid, as confirmed by the diagram. Since it is invalid, it cannot be sound.

45. The argument is in standard form, and it is valid as there is a clear chain of implications from the first premise to the conclusion.

46. The argument is in standard form, but it is invalid as there is no chain of implications from the premises to the conclusion.

47. The second premise and conclusion should be written as follows to put the argument in standard form. Premise: If taxpayers have less disposable income, the economy will slow down. Conclusion: If taxes are increased, then the economy will slow down. The argument is valid as there is a clear chain of implications from premises to conclusion.

48. The conclusion should be written as: "If taxes are cut, then the deficit will increase." The argument is valid as there is a clear chain of conditionals from premises to conclusion.

49. The statement is true.

50. The statement is not true (consider $c = 0$).

51. The statement is not true (consider negative numbers, or just about any other pair of numbers).

52. The statement is true.

FURTHER APPLICATIONS

53. Answers will vary. An example:
Premise: All living mammals breathe.
Premise: All monkeys are mammals.
Conclusion: All living monkeys breathe.

54. A sound argument must be valid, so this combination is impossible.

55. Answers will vary. An example:
Premise: All mammals fly. (false)
Premise: All monkeys are mammals. (true)
Conclusion: All monkeys fly. (false)

56. Answers will vary. An example:
Premise: All mammals swim. (false)
Premise: All fish are mammals. (false)
Conclusion: All fish swim. (true)

57. Answers will vary. An example:
Premise: All mammals breathe. (true)
Premise: All mammals have hair. (true)
Conclusion: All hairy animals breathe. (true)

58. An example of *affirming the hypothesis* (valid):
Premise: If I am in Phoenix, then I am in Arizona.
Premise: I am in Phoenix.
Conclusion: I am in Arizona.

59. An example of *affirming the conclusion* (invalid):
Premise: If I am in Phoenix, then I am in Arizona.
Premise: I am in Arizona.
Conclusion: I am in Phoenix.

60. An example of *denying the hypothesis* (invalid):
Premise: If I am in Phoenix, then I am in Arizona.
Premise: I am not in Phoenix.
Conclusion: I am not in Arizona.

61. An example of *denying the conclusion* (valid):
Premise: If I am in Phoenix, then I am in Arizona.
Premise: I am not in Arizona.
Conclusion: I am not in Phoenix.

62. Answers will vary, though it's unlikely you'll discover any counter-examples, and thus a strong inductive argument can be made.

63. a. Ford will be punished by the market.
b. Toyota did not take market share from Ford
c. No conclusion can be made since this scenario is not covered by the premises.

64. a. People who live on flood plains are far less likely to purchase flood insurance.
b. There were floods in the immediate past.
c. No conclusion can be made since this scenario is not covered by the premises.

65. a. Their vast remaining dollar holdings would plummet in value.
b. Chinese officials did not pull assets out of the U.S.
c. No conclusion can be made since this scenario is not covered by the premises.

UNIT 1E

TIME OUT TO THINK

Pg. 66. The pre-election polls suggest that the confusion affected the two sides differently, since the outcome was different from what polls suggested. Of course, the polls may not have been valid.

Pg. 68. Selling tickets in advance guarantees the airline that the seats are sold, so it is worthwhile to provide an incentive for advance sales. The cancellation penalty helps prevent the airline from losing what it thought were sold seats.

Pg. 70. Answers will vary. Possible topics could include that the United States and the Soviet Union have had proxy conflicts in other countries and the economic interdependency of countries in the modern world. This would be a good topic for a discussion either during or outside of class.

QUICK QUIZ

1. **b**. A vote for C implies a property tax reduction.

2. **c**. An argument that doesn't clearly spell out all of its premises is weak in logical structure.

3. **c**. With unknown application fees, it's not clear which bank has the better offer.

4. **b**. It's a good deal if you get six haircuts at this shop (and that you remember to get your card punched), but it's a bad deal otherwise.

5. **c**. $20/100 min = 20¢/min.

6. **a**. As long as you remember to get the 50% refund coming to you, you'll spend $200.

7. **c**. Both Jack's argument and this one make a huge leap from premises to conclusion: here's a few examples when *A* happened, so *A* must happen all the time.

8. **b**. You can't compute how much you'll spend with each policy without knowing the number and cost of collisions over the span of a year.

9. **a**. The teacher is assuming that students will do fine without spell checkers, which implies that traditional methods of teaching spelling are effective.

10. **c**. If it did not rain, and today is a Saturday, the Smiths would have a picnic. Since they did not, it must not be a Saturday.

DOES IT MAKE SENSE?

5. Makes sense. The double negative means the insurance company accepted his claim.

6. Does not make sense. Survivors are not typically buried after plane crashes.

7. Does not make sense. If Sue wants to save time, she should take the Blue Shuttle, and save ten minutes.

8. Does not make sense. With a 10% surcharge, Alan will spend $36.30 through Ticketmaster, which is a worse deal than $35 through the box office.

9. Makes sense. Both the duration and mileage of the first warranty is the better deal.

10. Does not make sense. There are other factors besides collision insurance that one must consider when purchasing auto insurance.

BASIC SKILLS & CONCEPTS

11. He has 2 bagels left as he ate the rest.

12. No, it's not possible, as a man who has a widow is dead.

13. Neither person, roosters don't lay eggs.

14. You must chose 4 apples, once you have chosen three, the next must be the same kind as one already chosen.

15. You must meet five people, as the first four might all be Canadians or Americans.

16. You must meet three people. The first and second might be from different countries, in which case by the third person, you will have met two from the same country.

17. You must meet six people, as the first four might all be Americans.

18. The surgeon is the boy's mother.

19. Suzanne might go bowling 1, 2, 3, or 4 days per week.

20. one minute and forty seconds is 100 seconds.

21. No it does not follow. Some of the communications majors may be men.

22. Yes, it does follow that one quarter of the exports consist of corn from Caldonia.

23. a. A person can serve for three consecutive terms of four years, or 12 years.
b. The councilmember would have to wait 8 years.
c. No; the councilmember must only wait 8 years if he or she has served for three consecutive terms.
d. The councilmember could serve for three more consecutive terms since this is not prohibited by the charter.

24. a. The state constitution is less strict than the U.S. Constitution since the initiative's purpose is to restrict the state court from interpreting the right of free expression more broadly under the state constitution than under the First Amendment to the U.S. Constitution.
b. A *yes* vote would tighten (strengthen) laws against obscenity.
c. *False*; the initiative would give the state the power to make stricter laws, but does not require the state to do so.

25. (1) The interest rate remains the same. (2) No withdrawals or additional deposits are made.

26. (1) The money you give is spent on worthwhile causes and not on overhead. (2) There are not other perhaps more worthwhile causes.

27. (1) The Senator will keep her promise. (2) There are no overriding reasons *not* to vote for the Senator.

28. (1) America needs a stronger military. (2) More military spending will mean a stronger military. (Answers will vary).

29. We are looking for possible unstated motives that may be the unstated "real reason" for opposition to the spending proposal. Among the possibilities is that the speaker may have a fundamental ideological opposition to paying taxes.

30. We are looking for possible unstated motives that may be the unstated "real reason" for support of eating meat. Among the possibilities is that the speaker may work for the meat industry.

31. a. Maria must file a return since her earned income is greater than $5450.
b. Van must file a return since his gross income of $3500 is greater than his earned income plus $300 ($3500 > $3000 + $300).
c. Walt need not file a return since his income does not meet any of the criteria.
d. Helena must to file a return since her gross income of $5500 is greater than her earned income (up to $5150) plus $300 ($5500 > $5150 + $300).

32. a. You cannot claim your stepdaughter as a dependent since she has lived with you for more than half the year.
b. You cannot claim your son as a dependent since he supports himself.
c. You can claim your nephew as a dependent as all criteria are met.
d. You can claim your half-brother as a dependent as all criteria are met.

33. a. The landlord has one month after June 5 to return the deposit, so the terms have been met.
b. The landlord has one month after June 5 to return the deposit, so the terms have been met.
c. The landlord has one month after June 5 to return the deposit, so the terms have not been met.

34. Plan A costs $2200 if you go and $0 if you cancel. Plan B costs $1200 if you go and $400 if you cancel. Plan A costs $1000 more if you go. Plan B costs $300 more if you cancel.

35. a. Since you will probably pay for service and insurance with either plan, those costs should not determine which option you choose.
b. Yes; the total cost of the car at the end of the lease is $1000 + $240 × 36 + $9000 = $18,640, which is greater than the purchase price of $18,000.
c. If you lease the care, you have years to decide if you want to buy it, don't need to worry about selling the car, and the dealer may offer special servicing prices with a lease. Leasing may also be better if you do not plan to keep the car for a long period of time.

36. A legitimate sweepstakes would not ask you to pay a processing fee in order to claim your prize. Note also that the notice never says your vacation will be fully paid for. In addition, the notice is asking for your credit card number, which should raise a "red flag" that should cause you to delete the message as spam.

FURTHER APPLICATIONS

37. Were there more than 350 people on each jet, or both jets combined? Was there any damage or injuries?

38. Who was fed the red meat?

39. Is $83 billion the gross domestic product, or 6% of the gross domestic product?

40. Who or what was arrested?.

41. a. They could be consistent, because Alice does not specify the time period for her 253 cases, and it's possible Zack is being selective about the cases he chooses to discuss (that is, he may not be talking about all the cases Alice tried).
b. They could be consistent if Alice obtained many convictions through plea agreements without going to trial.

42. a. The minimum payment will be $45, the total of the $35 in unpaid late fees and $10, since it is greater than 5% of your new balance.
b. Yes, to avoid a finance charge, you must pay within 25 days of the statement closing date.
c. You will be assessed a finance charge since you still have an unpaid balance more than 25 days after the statement closing date

43. a. The hire of a non-blood relative conforms with the law.
b. Is it legal to hire a former spouse? Is it legal to hire an adopted child?

44. a. Accepting a contribution from someone you have never met conforms with the law.
b. Accepting a contribution from a government campaign fund would conform with the law. Accepting money from a CEO who will benefit from a bill you are sponsoring would violate the law.

45. Under your current policy (and over the span of a nine-month pregnancy), you'll spend $115 per month, plus $4000 for prenatal care and delivery, for a total of $5035. Under the upgraded policy, you'll spend $275 per month, for a total of $2475. Thus, considering only these costs (we aren't told, for example, what happens if the mother requires an extensive hospital stay due to a C-section or other complications arising from delivery, or what happens if the baby is born prematurely and requires neo-natal care), the upgraded policy is best.

46. If you go and return on Monday, you'll spend $750 plus $55 on meals, for a total of $805. If you fly out Saturday evening (with no cost in meals for that day), stay in a hotel both Saturday and Sunday night, and eat out on Sunday and Monday, you'll spend $335 + $210 + $110 = $655. As long as you don't mind being away from home a little longer, the weekend trip is the better deal.

47. If you fly nine times with Airline A, at a cost of $3150, your tenth flight will be free (because you will have flown 27,000 miles at that point). If you fly ten times with Airline B, your cost will be $3250. Thus if you plan to fly ten times (or a multiple of ten times), Airline A is cheaper than Airline B.

48. Assuming your accident rate (and the costs of those accidents) remains the same for the next ten years, you should choose the policy with the lower premium of $200 per year. Under that plan, you'll spend $2900 over the next decade ($2000 for the premiums, and $900 for claims, as your $1000 deductible will not come into effect for any of the claims). Under the other plan, you'll spend $5000 ($4500 for premiums, and $500 for claims -- the

$200 deductible would save you $400 on a $600 claim).

49. The AFC has stronger teams or a streak of five games is not unexpected.

50. The parrot is extinct in the wild.

51. Sentencing by judges and juries became stricter.

52. Watching TV and playing video games increased independently because of lifestyle changes.

53. If the population increases quickly enough, then the death *rate* can decrease even though the number of deaths increases.

54. Fewer assaults are reported than in the past.

55. Country Y has a high gun suicide rate.

56. The population can be decreasing if the death rate remains higher than the birth rate.

57–65. Answers will vary.

66. One interpretation of the poem is that the poet was 20 years old when he wrote the poem, and he expects to live to age 70.

UNIT 2A

TIME OUT TO THINK

Pg. 83. Answers will vary. This question should help the student think about the units associated with everyday numbers. Even if they pick a page number from the newspaper or magazine, note that this has units of "pages." This would be a good topic for a discussion either during or outside of class.

Pg. 88(1st). The values in the two columns are reciprocals of one another (at least approximately). For example, the conversion factor used to convert from euros to U.S. dollars is $\dfrac{\$1}{1.256 \text{ euro}}$ and the conversion factor to change from U.S. dollars to euros is $\dfrac{1.256 \text{ euro}}{\$1}$. These numbers are reciprocals.

Pg. 88(2nd). Answers will vary depending on which currency is selected. Reasons could include political, environmental, or economic changes in the country. This would be a good topic for a discussion either during or outside of class.

Pg. 91. Answers will vary. Possible topics include problems involving density, rates of change, or area and volume of objects with differing units of measure. This would be a good topic for a discussion either during or outside of class.

QUICK QUIZ

1. **a.** Think of the unit *miles per hour*; the unit of *mile* is divided by the unit of *hour*.

2. **b.** The area of a square is its length multiplied by its width (these are, of course, equal for squares), and thus a square of side length 2 mi has area of $2 \text{ mi} \times 2 \text{ mi} = 4 \text{ mi}^2$.

3. **c.** When multiplying quantities that have units, the units are also multiplied, so $\text{ft}^2 \times \text{ft} = \text{ft}^3$.

4. **b.** $1 \text{ mi}^3 = (1760 \text{ yd})^3 = 1760^3 \text{ yd}^3$.

5. **a.** Divide both sides of $1 \text{ L} = 1.06 \text{ qt}$ by 1 L.

6. **b.** Speed is described by distance per unit of time, so dividing a distance by a time is the correct choice.

7. **b.** $1.20 per euro means 1 euro = $1.20, which is more than $1.

8. **c.** $1 \text{ ft}^2 = 12 \text{ in} \times 12 \text{ in} = 144 \text{ in}^2$.

9. **b.** Intuitively, it makes sense to divide a volume (with units of, say, ft^3) by a depth (with units of ft) to arrive at surface area (which has units of ft^2).

10. **a.** Take dollars per gallon and divide it by miles per gallon, and you get
$$\frac{\$}{\text{gal}} \div \frac{\text{mi}}{\text{gal}} = \frac{\$}{\text{gal}} \times \frac{\text{gal}}{\text{mi}} = \frac{\$}{\text{mi}}.$$

DOES IT MAKE SENSE?

7. Does not make sense. 35 miles is a distance, not a speed.

8. Makes sense. Area is often measured in ft^2.

9. Does not make sense. Two ft^2 describes an area, not a volume.

10. Does not make sense. Two acres describes an area, not a volume.

11. Does not make sense. Using the familiar formula *distance = rate × time*, one can see that it would be necessary to divide the distance by the rate (or speed) in order to compute the time, not the other way around.

12. Makes sense. Using the familiar formula *distance = rate × time*, one can see that dividing the distance by the rate (or speed) will result in time.

BASIC SKILLS & CONCEPTS

13. a. $\dfrac{3}{4} \times \dfrac{1}{2} = \dfrac{3 \cdot 1}{4 \cdot 2} = \dfrac{3}{8}$.

b. $\dfrac{2}{3} \times \dfrac{3}{5} = \dfrac{2 \cdot 3}{3 \cdot 5} = \dfrac{2}{5}$.

c. $\dfrac{1}{2} + \dfrac{3}{2} = \dfrac{1+3}{2} = \dfrac{4}{2} = 2$.

d. $\dfrac{2}{3} + \dfrac{1}{6} = \dfrac{4}{6} + \dfrac{1}{6} = \dfrac{4+1}{6} = \dfrac{5}{6}$.

e. $\dfrac{2}{3} \times \dfrac{1}{4} = \dfrac{2 \cdot 1}{3 \cdot 4} = \dfrac{2}{12} = \dfrac{1}{6}$.

f. $\dfrac{1}{4} + \dfrac{3}{8} = \dfrac{2}{8} + \dfrac{3}{8} = \dfrac{2+3}{8} = \dfrac{5}{8}$.

g. $\dfrac{5}{8} - \dfrac{1}{4} = \dfrac{5}{8} - \dfrac{2}{8} = \dfrac{5-2}{8} = \dfrac{3}{8}$.

h. $\dfrac{3}{2} \times \dfrac{2}{3} = \dfrac{3 \cdot 2}{3 \cdot 2} = 1$.

14. a. $\dfrac{1}{3} + \dfrac{1}{5} = \dfrac{5}{15} + \dfrac{3}{15} = \dfrac{8}{15}$.

b. $\dfrac{10}{3} \times \dfrac{3}{7} = \dfrac{10 \cdot 3}{3 \cdot 7} = \dfrac{10}{7} = 1\dfrac{3}{7}$.

c. $\dfrac{3}{4} - \dfrac{1}{8} = \dfrac{6}{8} - \dfrac{1}{8} = \dfrac{5}{8}$.

d. $\dfrac{1}{2}+\dfrac{2}{3}+\dfrac{3}{4}=\dfrac{6}{12}+\dfrac{8}{12}+\dfrac{9}{12}=\dfrac{23}{12}=1\dfrac{11}{12}$.

e. $\dfrac{6}{5}+\dfrac{4}{15}=\dfrac{18}{15}+\dfrac{4}{15}=\dfrac{22}{15}$.

f. $\dfrac{3}{5}\times\dfrac{2}{7}=\dfrac{3\cdot 2}{5\cdot 7}=\dfrac{6}{35}$.

g. $\dfrac{1}{3}+\dfrac{13}{6}=\dfrac{2}{6}+\dfrac{13}{6}=\dfrac{15}{6}=\dfrac{5}{2}=2\dfrac{1}{2}$.

h. $\dfrac{3}{5}\times\dfrac{10}{3}\times\dfrac{3}{2}=\dfrac{3\cdot 10\cdot 3}{5\cdot 3\cdot 2}=3$.

15. Answers may vary depending on whether fractions are reduced.

a. $3.5=\dfrac{35}{10}=\dfrac{7}{2}$. b. $0.3=\dfrac{3}{10}$.

c. $0.05=\dfrac{5}{100}=\dfrac{1}{20}$. d. $4.1=\dfrac{41}{10}$.

e. $2.15=\dfrac{215}{100}=\dfrac{43}{20}$. f. $0.35=\dfrac{35}{100}=\dfrac{7}{20}$.

g. $0.98=\dfrac{98}{100}=\dfrac{49}{50}$. h. $4.01=\dfrac{401}{100}$.

16. Answers may vary depending on whether fractions are reduced.

a. $2.75=\dfrac{275}{100}=\dfrac{11}{4}$. b. $0.45=\dfrac{45}{100}=\dfrac{9}{20}$.

c. $0.005=\dfrac{5}{1000}=\dfrac{1}{200}$. d. $1.16=\dfrac{116}{100}=\dfrac{29}{25}$.

e. $6.5=\dfrac{65}{10}=\dfrac{13}{2}$. f. $4.123=\dfrac{4123}{1000}$.

g. $0.0003=\dfrac{3}{10,000}$. h. $0.034=\dfrac{34}{1000}=\dfrac{17}{500}$.

17. a. 1/4 = 0.25. b. 3/8 = 0.375.
c. 2/3 = 0.667. d. 3/5 = 0.6.
e. 13/2 = 6.5. f. 23/6 = 3.833.
g. 103/50 = 2.06. h. 42/26 = 1.615.

18. a. 1/5 = 0.2. b. 4/9 = 0.444.
c. 4/11 = 0.364. d. 12/7 = 1.714.
e. 28/9 = 3.111. f. 56/11 = 5.091.
g. 102/49 = 2.082. h. 15/4 = 3.75.

19. Speed has units of miles per hour, or mi/hr.

20. The price of oranges has units of dollars per pound, or $/lb.

21. The cost of carpet has units of dollars per square yard, or $/ yd^2.

22. The flow rate has units of 5000 cubic feet per second, or 5000 cfs (or ft^3/s).

23. The price of rice has units of yen per kilogram, or yen/kg.

24. The production rate has units of bagels per hour, or bagels/hr.

25. The daily consumption has units of gallons per person, or gal/person.

26. The density of rock has units of grams per cubic centimeter, or g/cm^3.

27. $24\text{ ft}\times\dfrac{12\text{ in.}}{1\text{ ft}}=288\text{ in}$.

28. $24\text{ ft}\times\dfrac{1\text{ yd}}{3\text{ ft}}=8\text{ yd}$.

29. $25\text{ min}\times\dfrac{60\text{ s}}{1\text{ min}}=1{,}500\text{ s}$.

30. $2.5\text{ hr}\times\dfrac{60\text{ min}}{1\text{ hr}}\times\dfrac{60\text{ s}}{1\text{ min}}=9{,}000\text{ s}$.

31. $15\text{ gal}\times\dfrac{4\text{ qt}}{1\text{ gal}}=60\text{ qt}$.

32. $4\text{ acre}\times\dfrac{43{,}560\text{ ft}^2}{1\text{ acre}}=174{,}240\text{ ft}^2$.

33. $140\text{ wk}\times\dfrac{7\text{ day}}{1\text{wk}}=980\text{ day}$.

34. $60\dfrac{\text{mi}}{\text{hr}}\times\dfrac{1\text{ hr}}{60\text{ min}}=1\dfrac{\text{mi}}{\text{min}}$.

35. $3\text{ yr}\times\dfrac{365\text{ day}}{1\text{ yr}}\times\dfrac{24\text{ hr}}{1\text{ day}}=26{,}280\text{ hr}$.

36. $1\text{ ton}\times\dfrac{2000\text{ lb}}{1\text{ ton}}\times\dfrac{16\text{ oz}}{1\text{ lb}}=32{,}000\text{ oz}$.

37. a. The area of the arena's floor is 200 ft × 150 ft = 30,000 ft^2, and the volume of the arena is 200 ft × 150 ft × 35 ft = 1,050,000 ft^3.
b. The surface area of the pool is 30 yd × 10 yd = 300 yd^2, and the volume of the snow is 30 yd × 10 yd × 0.3 yd = 90 yd^3.
c. The area of the bed is 25 ft × 8 ft = 200 ft^2, and the volume of soil it holds is 25 ft × 8 ft × 1.5 ft = 300 ft^3.

38. a. The area of the warehouse floor is 40 yd × 25 yd = 1000 yd^2, and the volume of the cartons is 40 yd × 25 yd × 3 yd = 3000 yd^3.
b. The area of the bed's floor is 12 ft × 5 ft = 60 ft^2, and the volume of the bed is 12 ft × 5 ft × 3.5 ft = 210 ft^3.
c. The volume of the can is the area of its base multiplied by its height, which is 6 in.^{2} × 4 in. = 24 in.^{3}.

39. Note that 1 ft = 12 in., and thus $(1 \text{ ft})^2 = (12 \text{ in.})^2$, which means $1 \text{ ft}^2 = 144 \text{ in.}^2$. This can also be written as $\dfrac{1 \text{ ft}^3}{1728 \text{ in.}^3} = 1$, or $\dfrac{144 \text{ in}^3}{1 \text{ ft}^3} = 1$.

40. Note that 1 ft = 12 in, and thus $(1 \text{ ft})^3 = (12 \text{ in.})^3$, which means $1 \text{ ft}^3 = 1728 \text{ in.}^3$. This can also be written as $\dfrac{1 \text{ ft}^3}{1728 \text{ in.}^3} = 1$, or $\dfrac{1728 \text{ in}^3}{1 \text{ ft}^3} = 1$.

41. Since 1 m = 100 cm, we have $(1 \text{ m})^2 = (100 \text{ cm})^2$, which means $1 \text{ m}^2 = 10{,}000 \text{ cm}^2$. This can also be written as $\dfrac{1 \text{ m}^2}{10{,}000 \text{ cm}^2} = 1$, or $\dfrac{10{,}000 \text{ cm}^2}{1 \text{ m}^2} = 1$.

42. The area of the yard is 20 yd × 12 yd = 240 yd^2. Since 1 yd = 3 ft, we know $1 \text{ yd}^2 = 9 \text{ ft}^2$, and this can be used to convert to square feet.
$$240 \text{ yd}^2 \times \dfrac{9 \text{ ft}^2}{1 \text{ yd}^2} = 2160 \text{ ft}^2 .$$

43. The volume of the sidewalk is 4 ft × 200 ft × 0.5 ft = 400 ft^3. Since 1 yd = 3 ft, we know $1 \text{ yd}^3 = 27 \text{ ft}^3$, and this can be used to convert to cubic yards.
$$400 \text{ ft}^3 \times \dfrac{1 \text{ yd}^3}{27 \text{ ft}^3} = 14.8 \text{ yd}^3 .$$

44. Use the fact that $1 \text{ ft}^3 = 1728 \text{ in.}^3$ and $1 \text{ yd}^3 = 27 \text{ ft}^3$ (see exercises 40 and 43)
$$2.3 \text{ yd}^3 \times \dfrac{27 \text{ ft}^3}{1 \text{ yd}^3} \times \dfrac{1728 \text{ in.}^3}{1 \text{ ft}^3} = 1{,}073{,}308.8 \text{ in.}^3 .$$

45. Use the fact that $1 \text{ yd}^3 = 27 \text{ ft}^3$ (see exercise 43).
$$320 \text{ ft}^3 \times \dfrac{1 \text{ yd}^3}{27 \text{ ft}^3} = 11.9 \text{ yd}^3 .$$

46. Use the fact that $1 \text{ ft}^3 = 1728 \text{ in.}^3$ (exercise 40).
$$4 \text{ ft}^3 \times \dfrac{1728 \text{ in.}^3}{1 \text{ ft}^3} = 6912 \text{ in.}^3 .$$

47. $\$400 \times \dfrac{0.7072 \text{ lb}}{\$1} = 282.80 \text{ lb}$, so $400 U.S. is worth 282.80 lb. Note that if you use the conversion 1 lb = $1.414, you'll get an answer of 282.89 lb (this is due to errors in rounding).

48. $4500 \text{ euro} \times \dfrac{\$1.256}{1 \text{ euro}} = \$5{,}652$, so you can convert 4,500 euros to $5,652 U.S.

49. $3000 \text{ peso} \times \dfrac{\$1}{15.19 \text{ peso}} = \$197.50$, so 3,000 pesos is worth $197.50 U.S. Note that if you use the conversion 1 peso = $0.06584, you'll get an answer of $197.52 U.S. (this is due to errors in rounding).

50. Since $1 U.S. is worth $1.772 Canadian, the U.S dollar is worth more than the Canadian dollar (which is about 78¢).

51. One peso is worth $0.06584 U.S., whereas one yen is worth only $0.01007 U.S., so the peso is worth more.

52. $\dfrac{0.75 \text{ euro}}{1 \text{ L}} \times \dfrac{\$1.256}{1 \text{ euro}} \times \dfrac{0.9464 \text{ L}}{1 \text{ qt}} = \dfrac{\$0.89}{\text{qt}}$, so the price is about 89¢ per quart.

53. $\dfrac{1.2 \text{ euro}}{1 \text{ L}} \times \dfrac{\$1.256}{1 \text{ euro}} \times \dfrac{3.785 \text{ L}}{1 \text{ gal}} = \dfrac{\$5.70}{\text{gal}}$, so the price is $5.70 per gallon.

54. $\dfrac{1.80 \text{ euro}}{1 \text{ kg}} \times \dfrac{\$1.256}{1 \text{ euro}} \times \dfrac{1 \text{ kg}}{2.205 \text{ lb}} = \dfrac{\$1.03}{\text{lb}}$, so the price is $1.03 per pound.

55. The car is traveling with speed $\dfrac{45 \text{ mi}}{5 \text{ min}}$, and this needs to be converted to mi/hr.
$$\dfrac{45 \text{ mi}}{5 \text{ min}} \times \dfrac{60 \text{ min}}{1 \text{ hr}} = 540 \ \dfrac{\text{mi}}{\text{hr}} .$$

56. Convert 1.2 cubic yards to dollars by using the conversion 1 cubic yard = $24.
$$1.2 \text{ yd}^3 \times \dfrac{\$24}{\text{yd}^3} = \$28.80 .$$

57. Convert 300 gallons to hours by using the conversion 3.2 gallons = 1 minute.
$$300 \text{ gal} \times \dfrac{1 \text{ min}}{3.2 \text{ gal}} \times \dfrac{1 \text{ hr}}{60 \text{ min}} = 1.56 \text{ hr} .$$

58. The skydiver is traveling with speed 614 mi/hr, and this needs to be converted to ft/s.
$$\dfrac{614 \text{ mi}}{1 \text{ hr}} \times \dfrac{1 \text{ hr}}{60 \text{ min}} \times \dfrac{1 \text{ min}}{60 \text{ s}} \times \dfrac{5280 \text{ ft}}{1 \text{ mi}} = 901 \ \dfrac{\text{ft}}{\text{s}} .$$

59. Convert 2.5 ounces to dollars by using the conversion 1 oz = $920.
$$2.5 \text{ oz} \times \dfrac{\$920}{\text{oz}} = \$2{,}300 .$$

60. You would earn $24 \text{ days} \times \dfrac{8 \text{ hr}}{1 \text{ day}} \times \dfrac{\$8.50}{\text{hr}} = \$1632$ in that month.

61. First, note that 305 million people is 3050 groups of 100,000 people each. The mortality rate is
$$\frac{565,650 \text{ deaths}}{305,000,000 \text{ people}} \times \frac{305,000,000 \text{ people}}{3050 \text{ groups of } 100,000} =$$
185 deaths/100,000 people .

62. First, note that 305 million people is 3050 groups of 100,000 people each. The mortality rate is
$$\frac{310,000 \text{ deaths}}{305,000,000 \text{ people}} \times \frac{305,000,000 \text{ people}}{3050 \text{ groups of } 100,000} =$$
102 deaths/100,000 people .

63. Convert 3 million births per year into births per minute.
$$\frac{3,000,000 \text{ births}}{\text{yr}} \times \frac{1 \text{ yr}}{365 \text{ d}} \times \frac{1 \text{ d}}{24 \text{ hr}} \times \frac{1 \text{ hr}}{60 \text{ min}} =$$
$5.7 \dfrac{\text{births}}{\text{deaths}}$.

64. Divide the total miles travelled by the number of gallons to find the miles per gallon.
$$\frac{420 \text{ mi}}{12 \text{ gal}} = 35 \frac{\text{mi}}{\text{gal}}.$$

65. The cost to drive 250 miles is
$$250 \text{ mi} \times \frac{1 \text{ gal}}{28 \text{ mi}} \times \frac{\$2.90}{1 \text{ gal}} = \$25.89.$$

66. The salary in dollars per game is:
$$\frac{\$1,875,000}{160 \text{ days}} = \$11,719/\text{day}.$$

67. Convert one year into hours of sleep.
$$1 \text{ yr} \times \frac{365 \text{ d}}{\text{yr}} \times \frac{8 \text{ hr (of sleep)}}{\text{d}} = 2,920 \text{ hr}.$$

68. Convert one lifetime into heart beats.
$$1 \text{ lifetime} \times \frac{80 \text{ yr}}{\text{lifetime}} \times \frac{365 \text{ d}}{\text{yr}} \times \frac{24 \text{ hr}}{1 \text{ d}} \times \frac{60 \text{ min}}{1 \text{ hr}} \times$$
$$\frac{70 \text{ beats}}{1 \text{ min}} = 2,943,360,000 \text{ beats}.$$

69. The solution is wrong. It's helpful to include units on your numerical values. This would have signaled your error, as witness:
$$(\textit{incorrect}) \ 0.11 \text{ lb} \div \frac{\$7.70}{\text{lb}} = \frac{0.11 \text{ lb}^2}{\$7.70} =$$
$0.014 \ \dfrac{\text{lb}^2}{\$}$.

Notice that your solution, when the correct units are added, produces units of square pounds per dollar, which isn't very helpful, and doesn't answer the question. The correct solution is
$$0.11 \text{ lb} \times \frac{\$7.70}{\text{lb}} = \$0.85.$$

70. The solution is wrong. Attach units to your numerical quantities so that you can determine whether the answer has correct units. When it doesn't, this is an indication there's an error. Here's your incorrect solution with units attached:
$$\frac{5 \text{ mi}}{\text{hr}} \div 3 \text{ hr} = \frac{5 \text{ mi}}{\text{hr}} \times \frac{1}{3 \text{ hr}} = 1.7 \frac{\text{mi}}{\text{hr}^2}.$$
It's clear this is incorrect as the question asked how far did you go, and thus you should expect an answer with units of miles. The correct solution is
$$3 \text{ hr} \times \frac{5 \text{ mi}}{\text{hr}} = 15 \text{ mi}.$$

71. The solution is wrong. Units should be included with all quantities. When dividing by $11, the unit of dollars goes with the 11 into the denominator (as shown below). Also, while it's reasonable to round an answer to the nearest tenth, it's more useful to round to the nearest hundredth in a problem like this, as you'll be comparing the price per pound of the large bag to the price per pound of the small bag, which is 39¢ per pound. Here's your solution with all units attached, division treated as it should be, and rounded to the hundredth-place:
$$50 \text{ lb} \div \$11 = \frac{50 \text{ lb}}{\$11} = 4.55 \frac{\text{lb}}{\$}.$$
This actually produces some useful information, as you can see a dollar buys 4.55 pounds of potatoes. If you're good with numbers, you can already see this is a better buy than 39¢ per pound, which is roughly 3 pounds for a dollar. But it's better to find the price per pound for the large bag:
$$\$11 \div 50 \text{ lb} = \frac{\$11}{50 \text{ lb}} = 0.22 \frac{\$}{\text{lb}} = 22¢ \text{ per pound}.$$
Now you can compare it to the price per pound of the small bag (39¢/lb) and tell which is the better buy.

72. The solution is wrong. Always include units with numerical quantities; this helps in deciding whether the correct procedure was followed. Here's your solution with units attached:
$$\frac{1500 \text{ Cal}}{\text{d}} \times \frac{140 \text{ Cal}}{\text{Coke}} = 210,000 \frac{\text{Cal}^2}{\text{d-Coke}}.$$
It's clear this calculation won't answer the question (note that as shown, there's nothing mathematically incorrect about the above calculation – it just doesn't provide useful information). The correct solution looks like this:
$$\frac{1500 \text{ Cal}}{\text{d}} \times \frac{1 \text{ Coke}}{140 \text{ Cal}} = 10.7 \frac{\text{Cokes}}{\text{d}}.$$
Thus you would need about 11 Cokes per day to meet your caloric needs.

73. Convert 2000 miles into gallons by using the conversion 32 miles = 1 gallon.

$$2000 \text{ mi} \times \frac{1 \text{ gal}}{32 \text{ mi}} = 62.5 \text{ gal}.$$

Yes; a car that has half the gas mileage would need twice as much gas. Halving the value of the denominator has the same effect as doubling the value of the fraction.

74. a. One full tank of gas for Car A costs $12 \text{ gal} \times \frac{\$2.90}{1 \text{ gal}} = \$34.80$ and one full tank of gas for Car B costs $20 \text{ gal} \times \frac{\$2.90}{1 \text{ gal}} = \$58.00$.

b. Car A will use $3000 \text{ mi} \times \frac{1 \text{ gal}}{40 \text{ mi}} \times \frac{1 \text{ tank}}{12 \text{ gal}} = 6.25$ tanks of gas and Car B will use $3000 \text{ mi} \times \frac{1 \text{ gal}}{30 \text{ mi}} \times \frac{1 \text{ tank}}{20 \text{ gal}} = 5$ tanks of gas.

c. The driver of Car A will spend $6.25 \text{ tank} \times \frac{\$34.80}{1 \text{ tank}} = \$217.50$ and the driver of Car B will spend $5 \text{ tank} \times \frac{\$58.00}{1 \text{ tank}} = \$290.00$.

75. a. The driving time when traveling at 55 miles per hour is $2000 \text{ mi} \times \frac{1 \text{ hr}}{55 \text{ mi}} = 36.36 \text{ hr}$, while the time at 70 miles per hour is $2000 \text{ mi} \times \frac{1 \text{ hr}}{70 \text{ mi}} = 28.57 \text{ hr}$.

b. Your car gets 38 miles to the gallon when driving at 55 mph, so the cost is

$$2000 \text{ mi} \times \frac{1 \text{ gal}}{38 \text{ mi}} \times \frac{\$2.90}{\text{gal}} = \$152.63.$$

Your car gets 32 miles to the gallon when driving at 70 mph, so the cost is

$$2000 \text{ mi} \times \frac{1 \text{ gal}}{32 \text{ mi}} \times \frac{\$2.90}{\text{gal}} = \$181.25.$$

76. a. The driving time when traveling at 60 miles per hour is $1500 \text{ mi} \times \frac{1 \text{ hr}}{60 \text{ mi}} = 25 \text{ hr}$, while the time at 75 miles per hour is $1500 \text{ mi} \times \frac{1 \text{ hr}}{75 \text{ mi}} = 20 \text{ hr}$.

b. Your car gets 32 miles to the gallon when driving at 60 mph, so the cost is

$$1500 \text{ mi} \times \frac{1 \text{ gal}}{32 \text{ mi}} \times \frac{\$2.90}{\text{gal}} = \$135.94.$$

Your car gets 25 miles to the gallon when driving at 75 mph, so the cost is

$$1500 \text{ mi} \times \frac{1 \text{ gal}}{25 \text{ mi}} \times \frac{\$2.90}{\text{gal}} = \$174.00.$$

77. a. The rise in sea level is found by dividing the volume of water by the Earth's surface area, so

$$\text{sea level rise} = \frac{2.5 \times 10^6 \text{ km}^3}{340 \times 10^6 \text{ km}^2} = 0.007 \text{ km} \quad \text{or}$$

about 7 meters.

78. Buy 36 feet of the 12-ft wide roll, and cut off an 18-ft long piece to be laid along the edge with that dimension. Take the remaining piece (also 18 feet long) and cut off a 2-ft wide strip (which will be waste) – this will cover the remaining portion of the room. The cost is

$$36 \text{ ft} \times 12 \text{ ft} \times \frac{1 \text{ yd}^2}{9 \text{ ft}^2} \times \frac{\$28.50}{\text{yd}^2} = \$1368.$$

A cheaper method ($1254) can be found with two seams.

FURTHER APPLICATIONS

79. a. Convert $24,750,000 into dollars per game.

$$\frac{\$24,750,000}{80 \text{ games}} = \$309,375/\text{game}.$$

b. Convert $309,375 per game into dollars per minute.

$$\frac{\$309,375}{1 \text{ game}} \times \frac{1 \text{ game}}{48 \text{ min}} = \$6,445/\text{min}.$$

c. Convert $309,375 per game into dollars per minute, using $\frac{2}{3} \times 48 \text{ min} = 32 \text{ minutes}$.

$$\frac{\$309,375}{1 \text{ game}} \times \frac{1 \text{ game}}{32 \text{ min}} = \$9,668/\text{min}.$$

d. His total hours spent training were $\frac{40 \text{ hrs}}{1 \text{ game}} \times 80 \text{ games} = 3200 \text{ hours}$ His total time playing was $\frac{48 \text{ min}}{1 \text{ game}} \times \frac{1 \text{ hr}}{48 \text{ min}} \times 80 \text{ games} = 64 \text{ hr}.$ The total time related to basketball was 3200 hr + 64 hr = 3264 hr. Convert $24,750,000 into dollars per hour.

$$\frac{\$24,750,000}{3264 \text{ hr}} = \$7,583/\text{hr}.$$

80. Convert one day into liters of warmed air using 1 minute = 6 breaths, and 1 breath = 0.5 L.

$$1 \text{ d} \times \frac{24 \text{ hr}}{1 \text{ d}} \times \frac{60 \text{ min}}{1 \text{ hr}} \times \frac{6 \text{ breaths}}{1 \text{ min}} \times \frac{0.5 \text{ L}}{1 \text{ breath}} =$$

4320 L.

81. Convert 1.4 gigabytes into pages, using 2000 bytes = 1 page.

$$1.4 \text{ Gbyte} \times \frac{1.4 \text{ billion bytes}}{\text{Gbyte}} \times \frac{1 \text{ page}}{2000 \text{ bytes}} =$$

700,000 pages.

82. If the volume of ash is divided by the area it covers, you'll get the average depth of the ash (see exercise 9):

$$\text{average depth} = \frac{\text{volume}}{\text{area}} = \frac{100 \text{ km}^3}{600 \text{ km}^2}.$$

$$= 0.167 \text{ km} = 167 \text{ km}$$

83. a. The volume of the bath is 6 ft $\times$ 3 ft $\times$ 2.5 ft = 45 ft^3. Fill it to the halfway point, and you'll use 22.5 ft^3 of water (half of 45 is 22.5). (Interesting side note: it doesn't matter which of the bathtub's three dimensions you regard as the height – fill it halfway, and it's always 22.5 ft^3 of water). When you take a shower, you use

$$1 \text{ shower} \times \frac{10 \text{ min}}{\text{shower}} \times \frac{1.75 \text{ gal}}{\text{min}} \times \frac{1 \text{ ft}^3}{7.5 \text{ gal}} = 2.33 \text{ ft}^3$$

of water, and thus you use considerably more water when taking a bath.

b. Convert 22.5 ft^3 of water (the water used in a bath) into minutes.

$$22.5 \text{ ft}^3 \times \frac{7.5 \text{ gal}}{1 \text{ ft}^3} \times \frac{1 \text{ min}}{1.75 \text{ gal}} = 96 \text{ min}.$$

c. Plug the drain in the bathtub, and mark the depth to which you would normally fill the tub when taking a bath. Take a shower, and note how long your shower lasts. Step out and towel off, but keep the shower running. When the water reaches your mark (you used a crayon, and not a pencil, right?), note the time it took to get there. You now have a sense of how many showers it takes to use the same amount of water as a bath. For example, suppose your shower took 12 minutes, and it takes a full hour (60 minutes) for the water to reach your mark. That would mean every bath uses as much water as five showers.

84. a. Convert 9 billion gallons per day into cfs.

$$\frac{9,000,000,000 \text{ gal}}{\text{d}} \times \frac{1 \text{ ft}^3}{7.5 \text{ gal}} \times \frac{1 \text{ d}}{24 \text{ hr}} \times \frac{1 \text{ hr}}{60 \text{ min}}$$

$$\times \frac{1 \text{ min}}{60 \text{ s}} = 13,889 \frac{\text{ft}^3}{\text{s}}, \text{ or } 13,889 \text{ cfs},$$

which is about 46% of the flow rate of the Colorado River.

b. The volume of water entering the city over the course of a day, in cubic feet, was

$$9,000,000,000 \text{ gal} \times \frac{1 \text{ ft}^3}{7.5 \text{ gal}} = 1,200,000,000 \text{ ft}^3.$$

The area of the flooded portion of the city, in square feet, was

$$6 \text{ mi}^2 \times \left(\frac{5280 \text{ ft}}{1 \text{ mi}} \right)^2 = 167,270,400 \text{ ft}^2.$$

If the volume of water is divided by the area it covers, you'll get the average depth of the water (see exercise 9):

$$\text{average depth} = \frac{\text{volume}}{\text{area}} = \frac{1,200,000,000 \text{ ft}^3}{167,270,400 \text{ ft}^2} = 7.2 \text{ ft}$$

Thus the water level rose about 7 feet in one day, assuming the entire 6 square miles was covered in that day.

85. Convert 1 week into cubic feet of water.

$$1 \text{ wk} \times \frac{7 \text{ d}}{1 \text{ wk}} \times \frac{24 \text{ hr}}{1 \text{ d}} \times \frac{60 \text{ min}}{1 \text{ hr}} \times \frac{60 \text{ s}}{1 \text{ min}} \times$$

$$\frac{25,800 \text{ ft}^3}{\text{s}} = 15,603,840,000 \text{ ft}^3,$$

which is about 15.6 billion cubic feet. Since

$$\frac{15,603,840,000}{1,200,000,000,000} = 0.013, \text{ about } 1.3\% \text{ of the}$$

water in the reservoir was released.

UNIT 2B

TIME OUT TO THINK

Pg. 96. Answers will vary, but this question should help the student make the connection between abstract ideas of measurement and the ancient origin of units as body measures. This would be a good topic for a discussion either during or outside of class.

Pg. 99. Literally, a megabuck is a million dollars. But it is used colloquially to mean "a lot of money." Another example of the use of metric prefixes is "nanotechnology" for very small machines. This would be a good topic for a discussion either during or outside of class.

Pg. 103. Even without carrying out the conversions, it should be obvious that this is a Fahrenheit temperature; 59°C is more than halfway between the freezing and boiling points of water, which means it is well over 100°F (a precise conversion shows it is 138.2°F). No populated place on Earth gets this hot, so the forecast of 59° must refer to a Fahrenheit temperature.

Pg. 105. Answers will vary. Note: many utility bills do not give the price per kilowatt-hour explicitly, but it can be calculated by dividing the total price charged for electricity by the metered usage in kilowatt-hours, both of which are almost always shown clearly.

Pg. 106. You have a greater total volume but essentially the same mass (except for the weight of air) when your lungs are filled with air, so your density is lower and you float better.

Pg. 107. The two beers contain enough alcohol to put you at 12 times the legal limit if it were all in your bloodstream at once. Given the metabolic absorption rate, you should wait at least 3 hours before driving.

QUICK QUIZ

1. **c**. The metric prefix *kilo* means 1000, so a kilometer is 1000 meters.
2. **c**. The metric prefix *mega* means 1,000,000, so a megaton is one million tons.
3. **a**. A millimeter is one-thousandth of a meter (or 0.001 meter), which is about the size of the point on a pen.
4. **a**. Apples are most likely to be sold by units of weight (or more accurately, mass), and thus euros per kilogram is the best answer.
5. **c**. One liter is equal to 1.057 quart, which is about one quart.
6. **c**. Water boils at 100°C (at sea level), so 105°C is boiling hot.
7. **b**. A watt is defined to be one joule per second, which is a unit of power, not energy.
8. **c**. Energy used by an appliance is computed by multiplying the power rating by the amount of time the appliance is used, so you need to know how long the light bulb is on in order to compute the energy it uses in that time span.
9. **a**. Multiplying the population density, which has units of $\frac{\text{people}}{\text{mi}^2}$, by the area, which has units of mi^2, will result in an answer with units of people.
10. **b**. Concentrations of gases are often stated in parts per million (and the other two answers make no sense).

DOES IT MAKE SENSE?

8. Makes sense. Liquids are measured in liters, and since one liter is about a quart, drinking two liters is a reasonable amount.
9. Does not make sense. First of all, we use the unit of kilogram to measure mass, not weight, though mass and weight are often used interchangeably in everyday conversation. Even so, a bicyclist with mass of 300 kg would weigh more than 650 pounds (on the surface of the earth), which is an unheard of weight for a professional cyclist.
10. Makes sense. 100 km/hr is roughly 60 mi/hr, which is a reasonable speed on an interstate.

11. Does not make sense. The units of liters per second might be used to measure the flow rate of a faucet, but not the speed at which someone runs (meters per second would make more sense for that).
12. Does not make sense. The world record for the high jump is around 8 feet (about 2.4 meters), and no one can high jump 7 meters.
13. Makes sense. 10,000 meters is 10 kilometers, which is about 6.2 miles, a common length for foot races. Anyone who can run six back-to-back 9-minute miles has no trouble running 10,000 meters in less than an hour.
14. Does not make sense. A milligram is a thousandth of a gram, and there are about 450 grams in a pound. Thus 3 milligrams is a very small weight compared to the weight of a book.
15. Does not make sense. The unit of meter measures length, not volume.
16. Makes sense. There are 4184 joules in a Calorie, and when 10,000,000 joules is converted into Calories, the result is about 2400 Calories, which is a typical caloric intake for an active person.
17. Does not make sense. Utility companies bill you for energy use (typically in units of kW-hr), not power ratings (recall that the watt is a unit of power).
18. Does not make sense. The volume of a sphere is $V = \frac{4}{3}\pi r^3$, so the volume of a beach ball with a radius of 20 cm (about 8 inches) would be more than $32{,}000\,\text{cm}^3$. This translates into a mass of 320,000 grams if the density is 10 grams per cm^3, which is 320 kg. The mass of a beach ball isn't anywhere near that large.

BASIC SKILLS & CONCEPTS

19. a. $10^4 \times 10^7 = 10^{4+7} = 10^{11}$.
    b. $10^5 \times 10^{-3} = 10^{5-3} = 10^2$.
    c. $10^6 \div 10^2 = 10^{6-2} = 10^4$.
    d. $10^8 \div 10^{-4} = 10^{8-(-4)} = 10^{12}$.
20. a. $10^{-2} \times 10^{-6} = 10^{-2+(-6)} = 10^{-8}$.
    b. $10^{-6} \div 10^{-8} = 10^{-6-(-8)} = 10^2$.
    c. $10^{12} \times 10^{23} = 10^{12+23} = 10^{35}$.
    d. $10^{-4} \div 10^5 = 10^{-4-5} = 10^{-9}$.
21. a. $10^{25} \div 10^{15} = 10^{25-15} = 10^{10}$.
    b. $10^1 + 10^0 = 10 + 1 = 11$.
    c. $10^2 + 10^{-1} = 100 + 0.1 = 100.1$
    d. $10^2 - 10^1 = 100 - 10 = 90$.

22. a. $10^{12} \div 10^{-4} = 10^{12-(-4)} = 10^{16}$.

    b. $10^{23} \times 10^{-23} = 10^{23-23} = 10^0 = 1$.

    c. $10^4 + 10^2 = 10,000 + 100 = 10,100$.

    d. $10^{15} \div 10^{-5} = 10^{15-(-5)} = 10^{20}$.

23. Since $6 \text{ ft} = 6 \text{ ft} \times \dfrac{12 \text{ in.}}{1 \text{ ft}} = 72 \text{ in.}$, that person is 72 in. + 10 in. = 82 in. tall.

24. Convert 345 pounds to tons by using the conversion 1 ton = 2000 lb.

    $$345 \text{ lb} \times \frac{1 \text{ ton}}{2000 \text{ lb}} = 0.1725 \text{ tons}.$$

25. Convert a cubic foot of water into pounds.

    $$1 \text{ ft}^3 \text{ (of water)} \times \frac{7.48 \text{ gal}}{1 \text{ ft}^3} \times \frac{8.33 \text{ lb}}{1 \text{ gal}} = 62.3 \text{ lb}.$$

    Now convert that answer into ounces.

    $$62.3 \text{ lb} \times \frac{16 \text{ oz}}{1 \text{ lb}} = 997 \text{ oz}.$$

26. Convert six-packs to gallons.

    $$10 \text{ six-packs} \times \frac{6 \text{ cans}}{1 \text{ six-pack}} \times \frac{12 \text{ oz}}{1 \text{ can}} \times \frac{1 \text{ pint}}{16 \text{ oz}} \times$$

    $$\frac{1 \text{ qt}}{2 \text{ pint}} \times \frac{1 \text{ gal}}{4 \text{ qt}} = 5.625 \text{ gal}.$$

27. Use the fact that 1 nautical mile = 6076.1 feet to convert knots into mph.

    $$46 \text{ knots} = \frac{46 \text{ naut. mi}}{\text{hr}} \times \frac{6076.1 \text{ ft}}{1 \text{ naut. mi}} \times \frac{1 \text{ mi}}{5280 \text{ ft}} =$$

    $$52.94 \frac{\text{mi}}{\text{hr}}.$$

28. Convert 18 gallons to pints, cubic inches, and then into ounces.

    $$18 \text{ gal} \times \frac{4 \text{ qt}}{1 \text{ gal}} = 72 \text{ qt};$$

    $$72 \text{ qt} \times \frac{2 \text{ pt}}{1 \text{ qt}} = 144 \text{ pt};$$

    $$144 \text{ pt} \times \frac{16 \text{ oz}}{1 \text{ pt}} = 2,304 \text{ oz}.$$

29. The volume of the room is $4 \text{ yd} \times 4 \text{ yd} \times 2 \text{ yd} = 32 \text{ yd}^3$.

    Convert cubic yards into cords.

    $$32 \text{ yd}^3 \times \left(\frac{3 \text{ ft}}{1 \text{ yd}}\right)^3 \times \frac{1 \text{ cord}}{128 \text{ ft}^3} = 6.75 \text{ cords}.$$

30. Divide the volume by the area it covers to find the depth of the garbage pile. Since the volume is reported in cubic feet, and the dimensions of the football field are given in yards, it is best to convert the football field's dimensions into feet before finding its area.

    $$100 \text{ yd} \times \frac{3 \text{ ft}}{1 \text{ yd}} = 300 \text{ ft}; \quad 60 \text{ yd} \times \frac{3 \text{ ft}}{1 \text{ yd}} = 180 \text{ ft}$$

    So the area is $300 \text{ ft} \times 180 \text{ ft} = 54,000 \text{ ft}^2$, and the depth is $\dfrac{500,000 \text{ ft}^3}{54,000 \text{ ft}^2} = 9.26 \text{ ft}$.

31. You can tell the factor by which the first unit is larger than the second by dividing the second into the first. Rewrite metric prefixes as powers of 10, and then simplify, as shown below.

    $\dfrac{1 \text{ m}}{1 \text{ mm}} = \dfrac{10^0 \text{ m}}{10^{-3} \text{ m}} = \dfrac{10^0}{10^{-3}} = 10^{0-(-3)} = 10^3$. This means a meter is 1,000 times as large as a millimeter.

32. See exercise 31.

    $\dfrac{1 \text{ kg}}{1 \text{ mg}} = \dfrac{10^3 \text{ g}}{10^{-3} \text{ g}} = 10^{3-3} = 10^6$, so a kilogram is 1,000,000 times as large as a milligram.

33. See exercise 31.

    $\dfrac{1 \text{ L}}{1 \text{ mL}} = \dfrac{1 \text{ L}}{10^{-3} \text{ L}} = \dfrac{1}{10^{-3}} = 10^3 = 1000$, so a liter is 1000 times larger than a milliliter.

34. See exercise 31.

    $\dfrac{1 \text{ km}}{1 \text{ } \mu\text{m}} = \dfrac{10^3 \text{ m}}{10^{-6} \text{ m}} = 10^{3-(-6)} = 10^9$, so a kilometer is 1,000,000,000 times as large as a micrometer.

35. See exercise 31.

    $\dfrac{1 \text{ m}^2}{1 \text{ cm}^2} = \dfrac{1 \text{ m}^2}{(10^{-2} \text{ m})^2} = \dfrac{1 \text{ m}^2}{10^{-4} \text{ m}^2} = \dfrac{1}{10^{-4}} = 10^4$, so a square meter is 10,000 times as large as a square centimeter.

36. See exercise 31.

    $\dfrac{1 \text{ m}^3}{1 \text{ mm}^3} = \dfrac{1 \text{ m}^3}{(10^{-3} \text{ m})^3} = \dfrac{1 \text{ m}^3}{10^{-9} \text{ m}^3} = 10^9$, so a cubic meter is 1,000,000,000 times as large as a cubic millimeter.

37. $22 \text{ lb} \times \dfrac{2.205 \text{ lb}}{1 \text{ kg}} = 48.51 \text{ lb}$. (Note: you'll get an answer of 48.50 lb if you use the conversion 0.4536 kg = 1 lb).

38. $160 \text{ cm} \times \dfrac{1 \text{ in.}}{2.54 \text{ cm}} = 62.99 \text{ in.}$

39. $16 \text{ qt} \times \dfrac{1 \text{ L}}{1.057 \text{ qt}} = 15.14 \text{ L}$.

40. Square both sides of the conversion 1 km = 0.6214 mi to find the conversion between square miles and square kilometers.

$$(1 \text{ km})^2 = (0.6214 \text{ mi})^2 \Rightarrow 1 \text{ km}^2 = 0.38614 \text{ mi}^2.$$

Now use this to complete the problem.

$$2 \text{ km}^2 \times \frac{0.38614 \text{ mi}^2}{1 \text{ km}^2} = 0.77 \text{ mi}^2.$$

41. $$\frac{55 \text{ mi}}{\text{hr}} \times \frac{1.6093 \text{ km}}{1 \text{ mi}} = 88.51 \frac{\text{km}}{\text{hr}}.$$

42. $$\frac{120 \text{ km}}{\text{hr}} \times \frac{0.6214 \text{ mi}}{1 \text{ km}} = 74.57 \frac{\text{mi}}{\text{hr}}.$$

43. $$\frac{18 \text{ m}}{\text{s}} \times \frac{1 \text{ km}}{1000 \text{ m}} \times \frac{1 \text{ mi}}{1.6093 \text{ km}} \times \frac{60 \text{ s}}{1 \text{ min}} \times \frac{60 \text{ min}}{1 \text{ hr}} = \frac{40.27 \text{ mi}}{\text{hr}}.$$

44. Square both sides of the conversion 1 m = 3.28 ft to find the conversion between square meters and square feet.

$$(1 \text{ m})^2 = (3.28 \text{ ft})^2 \Rightarrow 1 \text{ m}^2 = 10.7584 \text{ ft}^2.$$

Now use this to complete the problem.

$$20 \text{ m}^2 \times \frac{10.7584 \text{ ft}^2}{1 \text{ m}^2} = 215.16 \text{ ft}^2.$$

45. Cube both sides of the conversion 2.54 cm = 1 in. to find the conversion between cubic centimeters and cubic inches.

$$(2.54 \text{ cm})^3 = (1 \text{ in.})^3 \Rightarrow 16.387 \text{ cm}^3 = 1 \text{ in.}^3.$$

Now use this to complete the problem.

$$300 \text{ in.}^3 \times \frac{16.387 \text{ cm}^3}{1 \text{ in.}^3} = 4916.12 \text{ cm}^3.$$

46. $$\frac{18 \text{ g}}{1 \text{ cm}^3} \times \frac{1 \text{ kg}}{1000 \text{ g}} \times \frac{2.205 \text{ lb}}{1 \text{ kg}} \times \left(\frac{2.54 \text{ cm}}{1 \text{ in.}}\right)^3 = 0.650 \frac{\text{lb}}{\text{in}^3}.$$

47. a. Use C = (F − 32)/1.8. C = (45 − 32)/1.8 = 7.2°C.
    b. Use F = 1.8C + 32. F = 1.8(20) + 32 = 68°F.
    c. F = 1.8(−15) + 32 = 5°F.
    d. F = 1.8(−30) + 32 = −22°F.
    e. C = (70 − 32)/1.8 = 21.1°C.

48. a. Use F = 1.8C + 32. F = 1.8(−8) +32 = 17.6°F.
    b. Use C = (F − 32)/1.8. C = (15 − 32)/1.8 = −9.4°C.
    c. F = 1.8(15) + 32 = 59°F.
    d. C = (75 − 32)/1.8 = 23.9°C.
    e. C = (20 − 32)/1.8 = −6.7°C.

49. a. Use C = K − 273.15. C = 50 − 273.15 = −223.15°C.
    b. C = 240 − 273.15 = −33.15°C.
    c. Use K = C + 273.15. K = 10 + 273.15 = 283.15 K.

50. a. Use K = C + 273.15. K = −40 + 273.15 = 233.15 K.
    b. Use C = K − 273.15. C = 400 − 273.15 = 126.85°C.
    c. K = 125 + 273.15 = 398.15 K.

51. Power is the rate at which energy is used, so the power is 100 Calories per mile. Convert this to joules per second, or watts.

$$\frac{100 \text{ Cal}}{1 \text{ mi}} \times \frac{1 \text{ mi}}{10 \text{ min}} \times \frac{1 \text{ min}}{60 \text{ s}} \times \frac{4184 \text{ j}}{1 \text{ Cal}} = \frac{418{,}400 \text{ j}}{600 \text{ s}} = 697 \text{ W}$$

52. Power is the rate at which energy is used, so the power is 750 Calories per hour. Convert this to joules per second, or watts, adjusting for the 45-minute ride.

$$\frac{750 \text{ Cal}}{1 \text{ hr}} \times \frac{60 \text{ min}}{45 \text{ min}} \times \frac{1 \text{ hr}}{60 \text{ min}} \times \frac{1 \text{ min}}{60 \text{ s}} \times \frac{4184 \text{ j}}{1 \text{ Cal}} = 1662 \text{ W}.$$

53. a. Convert kilowatt-hours into joules.

$$900 \text{ kW-hr} \times \frac{3{,}600{,}000 \text{ j}}{1 \text{ kW-hr}} = 3{,}240{,}000{,}000 \text{ j}.$$

b. May has 31 days, so the average power is

$$\frac{3{,}240{,}000{,}000 \text{ j}}{31 \text{ d}} \times \frac{1 \text{ d}}{24 \text{ hr}} \times \frac{1 \text{ hr}}{60 \text{ min}} \times \frac{1 \text{ min}}{60 \text{ s}} = \frac{1210 \text{ j}}{\text{s}} = 1210 \text{ W}.$$

One could also begin with 900 kW-hr per 31 days, and convert that into watts, using 1 watt = 1 joule per second.

c. First, convert joules into liters.

$$3{,}240{,}000{,}000 \text{ j} \times \frac{1 \text{ L}}{12{,}000{,}000 \text{ j}} = 270 \text{ L}.$$

Now convert liters into gallons.

$$270 \text{ L} \times \frac{1 \text{ gal}}{3.785 \text{ L}} = 71.33 \text{ gal}.$$

Thus it would take 270 liters = 71.33 gallons of oil to provide the energy shown on the bill (assuming all the energy released by the burning oil could be captured and delivered to your home with no loss).

54. a. Convert kilowatt-hours into joules.

$$1050 \text{ kW-hr} \times \frac{3{,}600{,}000 \text{ j}}{1 \text{ kW-hr}} = 3{,}780{,}000{,}000 \text{ j}.$$

b. September has 31 days, so the average power is

$$\frac{3,780,000,000 \text{ j}}{31 \text{ d}} \times \frac{1 \text{ d}}{24 \text{ hr}} \times \frac{1 \text{ hr}}{60 \text{ min}} \times \frac{1 \text{ min}}{60 \text{ s}} =$$

$$\frac{1411 \text{ j}}{\text{s}} = 1411 \text{ W}.$$

One could also begin with 1050 kW-hr per 31 days, and convert that into watts, using 1 watt = 1 joule per second.

c. First, convert joules into liters.

$$3,780,000,000 \text{ j} \times \frac{1 \text{ L}}{12,000,000 \text{ j}} = 315 \text{ L}.$$

Now convert liters into gallons.

$$315 \text{ L} \times \frac{1 \text{ gal}}{3.785 \text{ L}} = 83.22 \text{ gal}.$$

Thus it would take 315 liters = 83.22 gallons of oil to provide the energy shown on the bill (assuming all the energy released by the burning oil could be captured and delivered to your home with no loss).

55. The volume of the block is $(3 \text{ cm})^3 = 27 \text{ cm}^3$. Density is mass per unit volume, so the density of the block is $\frac{20 \text{ g}}{27 \text{ cm}^3} = 0.74 \frac{\text{g}}{\text{cm}^3}$. It will float in water because the density of water is $1 \frac{\text{g}}{\text{cm}^3}$.

56. Density is mass per unit volume, so the density of the sample of plutonium is $\frac{1.98 \text{ g}}{0.1 \text{ cm}^3} = 19.8 \frac{\text{g}}{\text{cm}^3}$. It will sink in water because the density of water is $1 \frac{\text{g}}{\text{cm}^3}$.

57. Population density is people per unit area, so the average population density of the U.S. is

$$\frac{306,000,000 \text{ people}}{3,500,000 \text{ mi}^2} = 87 \frac{\text{people}}{\text{mi}^2}.$$

58. The population density for Monaco is

$$\frac{32,500 \text{ people}}{1.95 \text{ km}^2} = 16,667 \frac{\text{people}}{\text{km}^2}.$$

Monaco's population density is $\dfrac{16,667 \frac{\text{people}}{\text{km}^2}}{\frac{31 \text{ people}}{1 \text{ km}^2}}$

= 538 , or over 500 times greater than that of the Unites States.

59. The population density for New Jersey is

$$\frac{8,700,000 \text{ people}}{7417 \text{ mi}^2} = 1173 \frac{\text{people}}{\text{mi}^2}.$$

The population density for Alaska is

$$\frac{680,000 \text{ people}}{571,951 \text{ mi}^2} = 1.19 \frac{\text{people}}{\text{mi}^2},$$

which is smaller than New Jersey's population density.

60. Information density is bytes per unit area, so, depending on the formatting, the DVD's information density is either

$$\frac{4.7 \text{ Gbyte}}{134 \text{ cm}^2} \times \frac{10^9 \text{ byte}}{1 \text{ Gbyte}} = 35,000,000 \frac{\text{byte}}{\text{cm}^2} \text{ or}$$

$$\frac{8.5 \text{ Gbyte}}{134 \text{ cm}^2} \times \frac{10^9 \text{ byte}}{1 \text{ Gbyte}} = 63,000,000 \frac{\text{byte}}{\text{cm}^2}.$$

61. a. BAC is usually measured in units of grams of alcohol per 100 milliliters of blood. A woman who drinks two glasses of wine, each with 20 grams of alcohol, has consumed 40 grams of alcohol. If she has 4000 milliliters of blood, her BAC is

$$\frac{40 \text{ g}}{4000 \text{ mL}} = \frac{0.01 \text{ g}}{\text{mL}} \times \frac{100}{100} = \frac{1 \text{ g}}{100 \text{ mL}}.$$

It is fortunate that alcohol is not absorbed immediately, because if it were, the woman would most likely die – a BAC above 0.4 g/mL is typically enough to induce coma or death.

b. If alcohol is eliminated from the body at a rate of 10 grams per hour, then after 3 hours, 30 grams would have been eliminated. This leaves 10 grams in the woman's system, which means her BAC is $\frac{10 \text{ g}}{4000 \text{ mL}} = \frac{0.0025 \text{ g}}{\text{mL}} \times \frac{100}{100} = \frac{0.25 \text{ g}}{100 \text{ mL}}$. This is well above the legal limit for driving, so it is not safe to drive. Of course this solution assumes the woman survives 3 hours of lethal levels of alcohol in her body, because we have assumed all the alcohol is absorbed immediately. In reality, the situation is somewhat more complicated.

62. a. BAC is usually measured in units of grams of alcohol per 100 milliliters of blood. A man who drinks 8 ounces of hard liquor has consumed 70 grams of alcohol, and with 6000 milliliters of blood, his BAC is

$$\frac{70 \text{ g}}{6000 \text{ mL}} = \frac{0.0117 \text{ g}}{\text{mL}} \times \frac{100}{100} = \frac{1.17 \text{ g}}{100 \text{ mL}}.$$

It is fortunate that alcohol is not absorbed immediately, because if it were, the man would be dead – a BAC above 0.4g/mL is typically enough to induce coma or death.

b. If alcohol is eliminated from the body at a rate of 15 grams per hour, then after 4 hours, 60 grams would have been eliminated. This leaves 10 grams of alcohol in the man's system, which means his

BAC is $\dfrac{10\ g}{6000\ mL} = \dfrac{0.0017\ g}{mL} \times \dfrac{100}{100} = \dfrac{0.17\ g}{100\ mL}$.

This is well above the legal limit for driving, so it is not safe to drive. Of course this solution assumes the man survives 4 hours of lethal levels of alcohol in his body, because we have assumed all the alcohol is absorbed immediately. In reality, the situation is somewhat more complicated.

63. $\dfrac{2.50\ euro}{1\ kg} \times \dfrac{1\ kg}{2.205\ lb} \times \dfrac{\$1.256}{1\ euro} = \$1.42$

64. $\dfrac{1.40\ euro}{1\ L} \times \dfrac{3.785\ L}{1\ gal} \times \dfrac{\$1.256}{1\ euro} = \$6.66/gal$

65. $300\ km \times \dfrac{1\ L}{26\ km} \times \dfrac{1.50\ euro}{1\ L} \times \dfrac{\$1.256}{1\ euro} = \$21.74$.

66. $\dfrac{16\ lb}{1\ m^2} \times \left(\dfrac{1\ m}{1.094\ yd}\right)^2 \times \dfrac{\$1.414}{1\ lb} = \$18.90/yd^2$

67. $\dfrac{100\ peso}{0.8\ L} \times \dfrac{\$1}{15.19\ peso} \times \dfrac{1\ L}{1.057\ qt} \times \dfrac{1\ qt}{2\ pt} \times \dfrac{1\ pt}{16\ oz}$
$= \$0.24/oz$

68. Nice:
$\dfrac{1040\ euro}{80\ m^2} \times \left(\dfrac{1\ m}{3.28\ ft}\right)^2 \times \dfrac{\$1.256}{1\ euro} = \$1.52/ft^2$

Santa Fe:
$\dfrac{\$800}{500\ ft^2} = \$1.60/ft^2$

So Santa Fe is more expensive.

69. a. A metric mile is $1500\ m \times \dfrac{3.28\ ft}{1\ m} = 4920$ ft. A USCS mile is 5280 ft. Since 4920/5280 = 0.932, the metric mile is 93.2% of the USCS mile.

b. Men's mile: Note: (3:43:13 = 223.13 seconds)
$\dfrac{1\ mi}{223.13\ s} \times \dfrac{3600\ s}{1\ hr} = 16.13\ mi/hr$

Men's metric mile: Note: (3:26:00 = 206 seconds)
$\dfrac{4920\ ft}{206\ s} \times \dfrac{1\ mi}{5280\ ft} \times \dfrac{3600\ s}{1\ hr} = 16.28\ mi/hr$

The record holder in the metric mile ran at a faster pace.

c. Women's mile: Note: (4:12:56 = 252.56 seconds)
$\dfrac{1\ mi}{252.56\ s} \times \dfrac{3600\ s}{1\ hr} = 14.25\ mi/hr$

Women's metric mile: Note: (3:50:46 = 230.46 seconds)
$\dfrac{4920\ ft}{230.46\ s} \times \dfrac{1\ mi}{5280\ ft} \times \dfrac{3600\ s}{1\ hr} = 14.56\ mi/hr$

The record holder in the metric mile ran at a faster pace.

d. This would be true in both cases since, for both men and women, the record holder in the metric mile ran at a faster pace.

70. A. Convert 300,000 long tons into kilograms.
$300,000\ long\ ton \times \dfrac{2240\ lb}{1\ long\ ton} \times \dfrac{1\ kg}{2.205\ lb}$
$= 305,000,000\ kg$

b. Convert 305,000,000 kilograms to cubic meters.
$305,000,000\ kg \times \dfrac{1\ m^3}{850\ kg} = 359,000\ m^3$

c. Convert 359,000 cubic meters to barrels of oil.
$359,000\ m^3 \times \dfrac{1000\ L}{1\ m^3} \times \dfrac{1\ gal}{3.785\ L} \times \dfrac{1\ barrel}{42\ gal}$
$= 2,260,000\ barrels$.

71. a. The depth of Lake Victoria is found by dividing the its volume by its surface area, so
$depth = \dfrac{2750\ km^3}{68700\ km^2} = 0.03997\ km$ or about 40 meters.

b. The lost volume is
$68700\ km^2 \times 10\ ft \times \dfrac{0.3048\ m}{1\ ft} \times \dfrac{1\ km}{1000\ m}$
$= 209.3976\ km^3$ or about 210 cubic kilometers.

c. The lost volume as a percentage is $\dfrac{210\ km^3}{2750\ km^3}$
$= 0.076$ or 7.6%.

72. The Cullinan diamond weighs 3106 carats, and:
$3106\ carats \times \dfrac{0.2\ g}{1\ carat} \times \dfrac{1000\ mg}{1\ g} = 621,200\ mg$

$3106\ carats \times \dfrac{0.2\ g}{1\ carat} \times \dfrac{1\ kg}{1000\ g} \times \dfrac{2.205\ lb}{1\ kg} = 1.37\ lb$

The Star of Africa weighs 530.2 carats, which is 106,040 mg, and 0.23 lb (the conversions being identical to those shown above).

73. The Hope diamond weighs 45.52 carats, so:
$45.52\ carats \times \dfrac{0.2\ g}{1\ carat} = 9.1\ g$ and
$9.1\ g \times \dfrac{1\ kg}{1000\ g} \times \dfrac{2.205\ lb}{1\ kg} \times \dfrac{16\ oz}{1\ lb} = 0.32\ oz$.

74. 14-karat gold is 58% of pure gold since $\dfrac{14}{24} = 0.58$.

75. 2.2 ounces of 16-karat gold is
$2.2\ oz \times \dfrac{16}{24} = 1.47\ oz$ of pure gold.

76. A 0.15 ounce diamond will weigh

$$0.15 \text{ oz} \times \frac{437.5 \text{ grain}}{1 \text{ oz}} \times \frac{0.0648 \text{ g}}{1 \text{ grain}} \times \frac{1 \text{ carat}}{0.2 \text{ g}}$$

$$= 21.26 \text{ carat.}$$

77. In order to compute the cost, we need to find the energy used by the outdoor spa in kW-hr, and then convert to dollars. This can be done in a single chain of unit conversions, beginning with the idea that energy = power × time (this is true because power is the rate at which energy is consumed; that is, power = energy/time and assuming a 30-day month).

$$1500 \text{ W} \times 4 \text{ months} \times \frac{1 \text{ kW}}{1000 \text{ W}} \times \frac{30 \text{ d}}{1 \text{ month}} \times$$

$$\frac{24 \text{ hr}}{1 \text{ d}} \times \frac{\$0.10}{1 \text{ kW-hr}} = \$432$$

78. In order to compute the cost, we need to find the energy used by the hair dryer in kW-hr, and then convert to cents. This can be done in a single chain of unit conversions, beginning with the idea that energy = power × time.

$$1800 \text{ W} \times 10 \text{ min} \times \frac{1 \text{ kW}}{1000 \text{ W}} \times \frac{1 \text{ hr}}{60 \text{ min}} \times \frac{\$0.12}{1 \text{ kW-hr}} =$$

$$\$0.036.$$

This is the cost to run the hair dryer each day, because you use it for only 10 minutes per day. To find the cost per year, multiply \$0.036 by 365 (1 year = 365 days) to get \$13.14 per year.

79. Compute the energy used by a 75-watt bulb in 10,000 hours. This will be the energy saved when replacing a 100-watt bulb with a 25-watt bulb.

$$75 \text{ W} \times 10,000 \text{ hr} \times \frac{1 \text{ kW}}{1000 \text{ W}} = 750 \text{ kW-hr}.$$

Convert 750 kW-hr into dollars to find out how much money is saved.

$$750 \text{ kW-hr} \times \frac{\$0.12}{1 \text{ kW-hr}} = \$90.$$

80. a. Your power is the rate at which you use energy, and thus your average power is 2500 Calories per day. Convert this to watts.

$$\frac{2500 \text{ Cal}}{\text{d}} \times \frac{1 \text{ d}}{24 \text{ hr}} \times \frac{1 \text{ hr}}{60 \text{ min}} \times \frac{1 \text{ min}}{60 \text{ s}} \times \frac{4184 \text{ j}}{1 \text{ Cal}} =$$

$$121 \frac{\text{j}}{\text{s}}.$$

Since 1 W = 1 j/s, this is 121 watts.

b. $$\frac{2500 \text{ Cal}}{\text{d}} \times \frac{365 \text{ d}}{\text{yr}} \times \frac{4184 \text{ j}}{1 \text{ Cal}} = 3,817,900,000 \text{ j},$$

so you need about 3.8 billion joules each year from food, which is very close to 1% of your total energy consumption (3.8 billion/400 billion = 0.0095).

81. Since energy = power × time, the power plant can produce (assuming a 30-day month)

$$1.5 \times 10^9 \text{ W} \times 1 \text{ month} \times \frac{30 \text{ d}}{\text{month}} \times \frac{24 \text{ hr}}{\text{d}} \times \frac{1 \text{ kW}}{1000 \text{ W}}$$

$$= 1.08 \times 10^9 \text{ kW-hr} = 1.08 \text{ billion kW-hr}$$

of energy every month. The plant needs

$$1.08 \times 10^9 \frac{\text{kW-hr}}{1 \text{ month}} \times \frac{1 \text{ kg}}{450 \text{ kW-hr}} =$$

$$2.4 \times 10^6 \frac{\text{kg}}{\text{month}}, \text{ or } 2.4 \text{ million kg of coal every}$$

month. Because 1.08×10^9 kW-hr ×

$$\frac{1 \text{ home}}{1000 \text{ kW-hr}} = 1.08 \times 10^6 \text{ homes}, \text{ the plant can}$$

serve 1.08 million homes.

82. Since energy = power × time, the power plant can produce (assuming a 30-day month)

$$740 \text{ MW} \times 1 \text{ month} \times \frac{30 \text{ d}}{1 \text{ month}} \times \frac{24 \text{ hr}}{1 \text{ d}} \times$$

$$\frac{1000 \text{ kW}}{1 \text{ MW}} = 5.328 \times 10^8 \text{ kW-hr of energy each}$$

month. The amount of uranium used each month is given by

$$5.328 \times 10^8 \frac{\text{kW-hr}}{\text{month}} \times \frac{1 \text{ kg}}{16 \times 10^6 \text{ kW-hr}} =$$

$$33.3 \frac{\text{kg}}{\text{month}}.$$

The plant can serve 532,800 homes, because

$$5.328 \times 10^8 \text{ kW-hr} \times \frac{1 \text{ home}}{1000 \text{ kW-hr}} =$$

$$532,800 \text{ homes}.$$

83. At 20% efficiency, this solar panel can generate 200 watts of power when exposed to direct sunlight. Since energy = power × time, and because the panel receives the equivalent of 6 hours of direct sunlight, the panel can produce

$$200 \text{ W} \times 6 \text{ hr} \times \frac{1 \text{ kW}}{1000 \text{ W}} \times \frac{3,600,000 \text{ j}}{\text{kW-hr}} =$$

$$4,320,000 \text{ j}.$$

This occurs over the span on one day, so the panel produces an average power of

$$\frac{4,320,000 \text{ j}}{\text{d}} \times \frac{1 \text{ d}}{24 \text{ hr}} \times \frac{1 \text{ hr}}{60 \text{ min}} \times \frac{1 \text{ min}}{60 \text{ s}} = 50 \frac{\text{j}}{\text{s}} =$$

50 W.

84. In exercise 83, each solar panel covers one square meter. You would need

$$1 \text{ kW} \times \frac{1000 \text{ W}}{1 \text{ kW}} \times \frac{1 \text{ panel}}{50 \text{ W}} = 20 \text{ panels},$$

which is 20 square meters of solar panels.

85. Energy = power × time, so the energy produced by a wind turbine over the course of a year is

$$200 \text{ kW} \times 1 \text{ yr} \times \frac{365 \text{ d}}{1 \text{ yr}} \times \frac{24 \text{ hr}}{1 \text{ d}} = 1,752,000 \text{ kW-hr}$$

This is enough energy to serve

$$1,752,000 \text{ kW-hr} \times \frac{1 \text{ home}}{10,000 \text{ kW-hr}} = 175 \text{ homes}.$$

86. a. Energy = power × time, so the energy capacity of the wind farms over the span of a year is

$$2.5 \times 10^9 \text{ W} \times 1 \text{ yr} \times \frac{365 \text{ d}}{1 \text{ yr}} \times \frac{24 \text{ hr}}{1 \text{ d}} \times \frac{1 \text{ kW}}{1000 \text{ W}} \times 0.30$$

$$= 2.19 \times 10^{10} \text{ kW-hr}$$

Since the wind farms produce 30% of their capacity, on average, the energy produced is

$$= 2.19 \times 10^{10} \text{ kW-hr} \times 0.30 = 6.57 \times 10^9 \text{ kW-hr or}$$
$$6,570,000,000 \text{ kW-hr}.$$

This is enough energy to serve

$$6.57 \times 10^{10} \text{ kW-hr} \times \frac{1 \text{ home}}{10,000 \text{ kW-hr}}$$

$$= 657,000 \text{ homes}.$$

b. If the 2.19×10^{10} kW-hr of energy produced by wind farms were instead produced from fossil fuels, there would be

$$6.57 \times 10^{10} \text{ kW-hr} \times \frac{1.5 \text{ lb}}{1 \text{ kw-hr}} = 9.855 \times 10^{10} \text{ lb},$$

or about 9,855,000 pounds of carbon dioxide entering the atmosphere each year.

UNIT 2C

TIME OUT TO THINK

Pg. 114(1st). Answers will vary. Recall that the four-step process is: Step 1: Understand the problem; Step 2: Devise a strategy for solving the problem; Step 3: Carry out your strategy, and revise it if necessary; Step 4: Look back to check, interpret, and explain your result.

Pg. 114(2nd). The combination of 5 child tickets and 4 adult tickets totals to $130 ($10 × 5 + $20 × 4 = $130). Similar calculations will verify the remained child/ticket combinations. There cannot be an even number of child tickets since the amount of money left for adult tickets would not be evenly divisible by $20. For example, if there were 4 child tickets, the adult tickets would have to be worth $130 − 4 × $10 = $90, which is not divisible by $20, so there could not be a whole number of tickets.

Pg. 118. Answers will vary. This would be a good topic for a discussion either during or outside of class.

Pg. 121(1st). This question simply checks that students followed Example 6. This is a subjective question designed to spur debate.

Pg. 121(2nd). Answers will vary. This would be a good topic for a discussion either during or outside of class.

QUICK QUIZ

1. **c.** Look at example 1 (*Box Office Receipts*) in this unit.

2. **a.** You must have done something wrong as gas mileage is reported in units of miles per gallon.

3. **b.** Common experience tells us that batteries can power a flashlight for many hours, not just a few minutes nor several years.

4. **b.** An elevator that carried only 10 kg couldn't accommodate even one person (a 150 lb person weighs about 75 kg), and hotel elevators aren't designed to carry hundreds of people (you'd need at least 100 people to reach 10,000 kg).

5. **b.** Refer to the discussion of Zeno's paradox in the text. There, it was shown that the sum of an infinite number of ever-smaller fraction is equal to 2, and thus we can eliminate answers **a** and **c**. This leaves **b**.

6. **a.** If you cut the cylinder along its length, and lay it flat, it will form a rectangle with width equal to the circumference of the cylinder (i.e. 10 in.), and with length equal to the length of the cylinder.

7. **c.** A widow is a woman who survives the death of her husband, and thus the man is dead, making it impossible for him to marry anyone.

8. **c.** It could happen that the first 20 balls selected are odd, in which case the next two would have to be even, and this is the first time one can be certain of selecting two even balls.

9. **b.** The most likely explanation is that the A train always arrives 10 minutes after the B train. Suppose the A train arrives on the hour (12:00, 1:00, 2:00,...), while the B train arrives ten minutes before the hour (11:50, 12:50, 1:50,...). If Karen gets to the station in the first 50 minutes of the hour, she'll take the B train; otherwise she'll take the A train. Since an hour is 60 minutes long, 5/6 of the time, Karen will take the B train to the

beach. Note that 5/6 of 30 days is 25 days, which is the number of times Karen went to the beach. The other scenarios *could* happen, but they aren't nearly as likely as the scenario in answer **b**.

10. **b**. Label the hamburgers as A, B, and C. Put burgers A and B on the grill. After 5 minutes, turn burger A, take burger B and put it on a plate, and put burger C on the grill. After 10 minutes, burger A is cooked, while burgers B and C are half-cooked. Finish off burgers B and C in the final 5 minutes, and you've cooked all three in 15 minutes.

DOES IT MAKE SENSE?

3. Does not make sense. There is no problem-solving recipe that can be applied to all problems.

4. Makes sense. It's generally a waste of time to blindly dive into the solution of a problem if you don't take the time to understand its nature.

5. Does not make sense. The four-step method is applicable to a wide variety of problems, and is not limited to mathematical problems. (It's not a cure-all, either, but it's quite useful, and worth learning).

6. Does not make sense. Pictures can be extremely beneficial in the problem solving process as they allow young and old alike to visualize the problem.

BASIC SKILLS & CONCEPTS

7. You won't be able to determine the exact number of cars and buses that passed through the toll booth, but the method of trial-and-error leads to the following possible solutions: (16 cars, 0 buses), (13 cars, 2 buses), (10 cars, 4 buses), (7 cars, 6 buses), (4 cars, 8 buses), (1 car, 10 buses). Along the way, you may have noticed that the number of buses must be an even number, because when it is odd, the remaining money cannot be divided evenly into $2 (car) tolls.

8. The method of trial-and-error produces the following possible recipes, the ordered pairs are (Level 1, Level 2): (14, 0), (12, 1), (10, 2), (8, 3), (6, 4), (4, 5), (2, 6), (0, 7).

9. a. Based on the first race data, Jordan runs 200 meters in the time it takes Amari to run 190 meters. In the second race, Jordan will catch up to Amari 10 meters from the finish line (because Jordan has covered 200 meters at that point, and Amari has covered 190 meters). Jordan will win the race in the last ten meters, because Jordan runs faster than Amari.

b. Jordan will be 5 meters from the finish line when Amari is 10 meters from the finish line (because Jordan has covered 200 meters at that point, and Amari has covered 190 meters). Jordan will win the race in the because Jordan runs faster than Amari and is in the lead.

c. Jordan will be 15 meters from the finish line when Amari is 10 meters from the finish line (because Jordan has covered 200 meters at that point, and Amari has covered 190 meters). In the time Amari runs 10 meters, Jordan will only run

$$10 \text{ m}_{Amari} \times \frac{200 \text{ m}_{Jordan}}{190 \text{ m}_{Amari}} = 10.53 \text{ m}_{Jordan}, \qquad \text{so}$$

Amari wins the race.

d. From part **c**, Jordan must start 10.53 meters behind the starting line, since that is how far she would run in the same time Amari finishes the last 10 meters of the race.

10. Note that after two hours, the cars collide, because the first travels at 80 km/hr, and thus covers 160 km, while the second travels at 100 km/hr, and covers 200 km. The canary is flying at 120 km/hr for the entire 2 hours, so it has flown 240 km.

11. On the second transfer, there are four possibilities to consider. A) All three marbles are black. B) Two are black, one is white. C) One is black, two are white. D) All three are white. In case A), after the transfer, there are no black marbles in the white pile, and no white marbles in the black pile. In case B), one white marble is transferred to the black pile, and one black marble is left in the white pile. In case C), two white marbles are transferred to the black pile, and two black marbles are left in the white pile. In case D), three white marbles are transferred to the black pile, and three black marbles are left in the white pile. In all four cases, there are as many white marbles in the black pile as there are black marbles in the white pile after the second transfer.

12. Cut the pipe along its length, and press it flat – this results in a rectangle with height = 20 cm, and width = circumference of pipe = 6 cm. As shown in example 5, a wrap of wire becomes the hypotenuse of a right triangle, whose base is 6 cm, and whose height, because there are 8 turns of wire, is 1/8 of 20 cm = 2.5 cm. By the Pythagorean theorem, the length of one turn of the wire is $h = \sqrt{6^2 + 2.5^2} = 6.5 \text{ cm}$, and thus the total length of wire required is 52 cm (8 turns of wire, each 6.5 cm long).

13. Proceeding as in example 6, the circular arc formed by the bowed track can be approximated by two congruent right triangles. Since 1 km is 100,000 cm, the base of one of the triangles is 50,000 cm, and its hypotenuse is 50,005 cm. The height of the triangle can be computed as

$$h = \sqrt{50{,}005^2 - 50{,}000^2} = 707 \text{ cm},$$

which is about 7.1 meters.

14. Answers will vary.

15. For every 220 people, 120 are male, and 100 are female. Thus 120/220 = 54.55% of the population is male, and 100/220 = 45.45% of the population is female. The difference in these percents (9.1%) represents the percent of men who will not be able to find a spouse. 9.1% of 450 million is 0.091×450 million = 40,950,000, or about 41 million. This of course assumes one female for every male – the reality is somewhat different when things like divorce and second marriages are factored into the equation.

FURTHER APPLICATIONS

16. a. Yes; $P = 2(7) + 2(3) = 20$; $A = 7 \times 3 = 21$

    b. Yes; $P = 2(8) + 2(2) = 20$; $A = 8 \times 2 = 16$

    c. By trial and error, possible dimensions (l, w) are:

    $(9,1)$; $P = 2(9) + 2(1) = 20$; $A = 9 \times 1 = 9$

    $(6,4)$; $P = 2(6) + 2(4) = 20$; $A = 6 \times 4 = 24$

    $(5,5)$; $P = 2(5) + 2(5) = 20$; $A = 5 \times 5 = 25$

    Note that reversing the length and width will result in the same areas, so the maximum area is when the yard is a square with sides of length 5 meters.

17. Note that at least one truck must have passed over the counter as there are an odd number of counts, and we must have an odd number of trucks for the same reason. Beginning with one truck, followed by 3, 5, 7, etc. trucks, and computing the number of cars that go along with these possible truck solutions, we arrive at the following answers: (1 truck, 16 cars), (3 t, 13 c), (5 t, 10 c), (7 t, 7 c), (9 t, 4 c), and (11 t, 1 c).

18. Following the hint given in the problem, the best place to start is with a drawing that shows the room cut along its vertical corners and laid flat. Figure 18a shows the room and the configuration of the amplifier and speaker before the cuts are made, and Figure 18b shows the room in "flat mode." Note that there are at least two solutions to consider (a third will be presented in Figure 18c).

FIGURE 18a

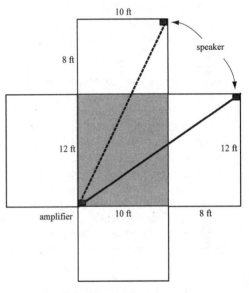

FIGURE 18b

In flat mode, it is clear that the shortest distance between the amplifier and the speaker is a straight line, though there are two possible paths (the upper right hand corner of the room, where the speaker is situated, must be represented twice, as shown in Figure 18b). In both cases, the distance from the amplifier to the speaker can be computed using the Pythagorean theorem.

Case 1 (lower triangle): the length of the wire is

$$\sqrt{18^2 + 12^2} = \sqrt{468} = 21.6 \text{ ft}.$$

Case 2 (upper triangle): the length of the wire is

$$\sqrt{20^2 + 10^2} = \sqrt{500} = 22.4 \text{ ft}.$$

Based on these calculations, the shortest length of wire needed to connect the amplifier to the speaker is 21.6 ft. However, there's a third possibility that is not evident when looking at

Figure 18b. In order to see it, the room must be cut and laid flat in a different configuration, shown here.

FIGURE 18c

This solution has the wire traveling along the walls of the room for its entire length, which is

$$\sqrt{22^2 + 8^2} = \sqrt{548} = 23.4 \text{ ft}.$$

Since this does not produce a shorter length of wire than the previous solution, the answer remains 21.6 ft (different room dimensions might reveal that Figure 18c is the best choice). There are other ways to run the wire not shown here, such as rotating the back wall in a manner similar to Figure 18c (this gives an equivalent solution of 23.4 ft), or running the wire along the ceiling. However, the problem states the wire is to run along the floor and walls, so the ceiling solutions need not be considered. Try some solutions along the ceiling if you're curious – you'll find they are equivalent to running the wire along the floor.

19. a. The time spent running is $2 \text{ mi} \div 4 \dfrac{\text{mi}}{\text{hr}}$

$= 2 \text{ mi} \times \dfrac{1 \text{ hr}}{4 \text{ mi}} = \dfrac{1}{2} \text{ hr}.$

b. The time spent walking is $2 \text{ mi} \div 2 \dfrac{\text{mi}}{\text{hr}}$

$= 2 \text{ mi} \times \dfrac{1 \text{ hr}}{2 \text{ mi}} = 1 \text{ hr}.$

c. Not true; more time is spent walking than running.

d. The average speed for the trip is $4 \text{ mi} \div \dfrac{3}{2} \text{hr}$

$4 \text{ mi} \times \dfrac{2}{3 \text{ hr}} = \dfrac{8}{3} \text{ mi/hr or 2.7 mi/hr.}$

20. In going from the first floor to the third floor, you have gone up two floors. Since it takes 30 seconds to do that, your pace is 15 seconds per floor. Walking from the first floor to the sixth floor means walking up five floors, and at 15 seconds per floor, this will take 75 seconds.

21. Reuben's birthday is December 31, and he's talking to you on January 1. Thus two days ago, he was 20 years old on December 30. He turned 21 the next day. "Later *next* year," refers to almost two years later, when he will turn 23 (*this* year on December 31, he will turn 22).

22. You might pick one of each kind of apple on the first three draws. On the fourth draw, you are guaranteed to pick an apple that matches one of the first three, so four draws are required.

23. That man is the son of the person speaking (who, in turn, is the son of his father, and an only child).

24. The blind fiddler is a woman.

25. The woman gained $100 in each transaction, so she gained $200 overall.

26. Select a fruit from the box labeled *Apples and Oranges*. If it's an apple, that box must be the *Apple* box (because its original label is incorrect, leaving only *Apples* or *Oranges* as its correct label). The correct label for the box labeled *Oranges* is either *Apples* or *Apples and Oranges*, but we just determined the box containing apples, so the correct label for this box is *Apples and Oranges*. There's only one choice left for the box labeled *Apples*, and that's *Oranges*. A similar argument allows one to determine the correct labeling for each box if an orange is selected first.

27. Select one ball from the first barrel, two balls from the second barrel, three from the third, and so on, ending with ten balls chosen from the tenth barrel. Find the weight of all 55 balls thus chosen. If all the balls weighed one ounce, the weight would be 55 ounces. But we know one of the barrels contains two-ounce balls. Suppose the first barrel contained the two-ounce balls – then the weighing would reveal a result of 56 ounces, and we'd know the first barrel was the one that contains two-ounce balls. If, in fact, the second barrel contained the two-ounce balls, the combined weight would be 57 ounces. A combined weight of 58 ounces means the third barrel contained the heavy balls. Continuing in this fashion, we see that a combined weight of n ounces more than 55 ounces corresponds to the nth barrel containing the two-ounce balls.

28. Seven crossings are required. Trip 1: the woman crosses with the goose. Trip 2: the woman returns to the other shore by herself. Trip 3: the woman takes the mouse across. Trip 4: the woman returns with the goose. Trip 5: the woman brings the wolf across. Trip 6: the woman returns to the other shore by herself. Trip 7: the woman brings the goose over. In this way, the goose is never left

alone with the wolf, nor the mouse with the goose. The foursome could get to the other side of the river in five crossings if you give rowing abilities to the animals, but the statement of the problem (and common sense) probably forbids it (the boat "...will hold only herself and one other animal"). Try it anyway for an interesting twist to the problem.

29. Turn both the 7-minute and 4-minute hourglasses over to begin timing. At 4 minutes, turn the 4-minute hourglass over again. At 7 minutes, turn the 7-minute hourglass over; there will be one minute of sand left in the 4-minute hourglass. At 8 minutes, the upper chamber of the 4-minute hourglass will be empty, and one minute of sand will have drained into the lower chamber of the 7-minute hourglass. Turn the 7-minute hourglass over to time the last minute. This is only one solution of many. Another: Turn both hourglasses over whenever their upper chambers are empty. After 12 minutes (three cycles of the 4-minute hourglass), there will be 5 minutes of sand in the bottom chamber of the 7-minute hourglass. Turn that hourglass on its side. Now you are prepared to measure a 9-minute interval whenever you please (use the 5 minutes of sand in the 7-minute hourglass, followed by one cycle of the 4-minute hourglass).

30. Ten rungs will be showing – the boat rises with the tide.

31. A balance scale is one that displays a needle in the middle when both sides of the scale are loaded with equal weights. Put six coins on each side of the scale. The side with the heavy coin will be lower, so discard the other six. Now put three coins of the remaining six on each side of the scale, and as before, discard the three that are in the light group. Finally, select two of the remaining three coins, and put one on each side of the scale. The scale will be even if the heavy coin is not on the scale. The scale will tip to one side if the heavy coin was in the final selection. This is just one solution – another begins by dividing the 12 coins into three groups of four coins. See if you can supply the logic necessary to find the heavy coin in that scenario.

32. It's possible you'll pick a sock of each color on the first two draws, but on the third draw, you are assured of making a match.

33. Since the gray, orange, and pink books are consecutive and the pink book cannot be rightmost, the only possible orders are *gray, orange, pink, other, other* or *other, gray, orange, pink, other*. The only way to add the brown and gold books so that the gold book is not leftmost and there are two books between the brown and gold books is the order *brown, gray, orange, pink, gold*.

34. The first prisoner would know he had a white hat if he saw red hats on prisoners 2 and 3. Since he doesn't know the color of his hat, prisoners 2 and 3 are both wearing white hats, or one has a white hat while the other has a red hat. If prisoner 2 saw a red hat on prisoner 3, he would know that he must have a white hat (he can't have a red hat while seeing red on prisoner 3, because then prisoner 1 would know his color). But he doesn't know, which means prisoner 3 must have a white hat. Prisoner 3 doesn't need to see the hats of the other prisoners; he can deduce that his hat is white simply by hearing the other two prisoners confess they don't know what hats they are wearing.

35. The visitor should patronize the barber with unkempt hair, because he's the barber that cuts the hair of the other barber (who has a splendid hair cut). Of course we are assuming that these barbers don't travel out of town to get their hair done.

36. The coin has revolved twice (720° of revolution). The best way to see this is to duplicate the experiment. Another way to think about it: consider two circular clocks (instead of coins), nestled side by side, both in the same position, with 12-o'clock pointing straight ahead (see Figure 36). Roll the right clock around the left clock until the 12's are touching. The right clock has rotated 180°, but it's made only 1/4 of its journey around the left clock. By the time it makes the full journey around, it will have rotated 720°.

initial position of clocks

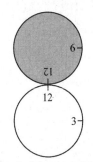

right clock has rotated 180° (it's upside down), yet it has made only 1/4 of its journey around the left clock

FIGURE 36

37. When a clock chimes five times, there are four pauses between the chimes. Since it takes five seconds to chime five times, each pause lasts 1.25 seconds. There are nine pauses that need to be accounted for when the clock chimes 10 times, and thus it takes $9 \times 1.25 = 11.25$ seconds to chime 10 times. This solution assumes it takes no time for the clock to chime once (we'd need to know the duration of the chime to solve it otherwise).

38. a. Assume the babies are named A, B, C, and D. If two babies are correctly tagged, the other two labels must be switched for their labels to be incorrect. Thus the problem boils down to counting the number of ways two of the babies can be correctly tagged. Listing all the options is the easiest way to count them. Babies AB could be correctly labeled (leaving babies C and D labeled incorrectly), and the other options for correct labels are AC, AD, BC, BD, and CD. This makes six different ways.

    b. If three of the babies have correct labels, the other baby must also have a correct label, which means there is no way to label three of the babies correctly while the fourth is labeled incorrectly.

39. Each guest has, in fact, spent $9. But not all of the $27 spent is resting in the cash register at the front desk. The front desk has $25, the bellhop has $2 (this adds up to the $27 spent), and each guest has $1, for a total of $30. The reason the problem is perplexing is that we think of the $2 held by the bellhop as a *positive* $2, and so it should be added to the $27 spent by the guests to somehow produce the original $30. But from the perspective of the desk clerk running the cash register, the $2 is a *negative* value – it represents money out of the till. $30 (*positive*) came into the till, $2 (*negative*) went to the bellhop, and $1 (*negative*) went to each of the guests. Thus the equation we should be looking at is 30 – 2 – 1 – 1 – 1 = $25 in the cash register (which is correct), or $27 – $2 = $25 (also correct), but *not* $27 + $2 (which is just silly).

UNIT 3A

TIME OUT TO THINK

Pg. 131. If you increase something by 100%, you have doubled its value. If a value A is doubled, its new value would be $2A$. The relative increase would be $\dfrac{2A - A}{A} = 2.00 = 200\%$. The same reasoning can be applied to an increase of 200%.

Pg. 134. Students simply need to recognize that 200 is the reference value and 600 is the new value. Substituting into the relative change formula then gives $[(600 - 200)/200] \times 100\% = 200\%$

Pg. 135. The "30% off" sale means that prices are $(100 - 30) = 70\%$ of their original values — not nearly as good as a sale where prices are 30% of their original values.

Pg. 139. For the first question, it depends on how we define "effort." If we mean an athlete's personal effort, it is impossible to give 110% because a 100% effort already means the athlete is giving it everything he or she has. But if we define it as past performance efforts, then athletes might well exceed their best previous effort by 10%. For the second question, the answer is clearly yes, since it just means 1.1 times the minimum requirement.

QUICK QUIZ

1. **b.** A quantity triples when it is increased by 200%.
2. **b.** The absolute change is $75,000 - 50,000 = 25,000$, and the relative change is $\dfrac{75,000 - 50,000}{50,000} = 0.5 = 50\%$.
3. **c.** A negative relative change corresponds to a decreasing quantity.
4. **c.** Suppose Joshua scored 1000 on the SAT. Then Emily would have scored 1500 (50% more than 1000), and Joshua's score is clearly two-thirds of Emily's score $(1000/1500 = 2/3)$.
5. **c.** 120% of $10 is $12.
6. **c.** Multiplying a pre-tax price by 1.09 is equivalent to adding 9% tax to the price, and thus dividing a post-tax price by 1.09 will result in the original price. To find out how much tax was paid, take the post-tax price, and subtract the original price: $\$47.96 - \dfrac{\$47.96}{1.09}$.
7. **a.** The relative change in interest rates that go from 6% to 9% is $\dfrac{9\% - 6\%}{6\%} = 0.5 = 50\%$.

8. **c.** When a price is decreased by 100%, it drops to zero, as the entire amount of the price is deducted from the original price.
9. **c.** 10% of $1000 is $100, so your monthly earnings after one year will be $1100. Each year thereafter, your earnings will increase by more than $100 per year (because 10% of $1100 is more than $100), and the end result will be more than $1500.
10. **b.** The only thing we can conclude with certainty is that she won between 20% and 30% of her races. To prove this rigorously, one could detour into an algebra calculation (let x = number of races entered in high school, let y = number of races entered in college, and show that $\dfrac{0.3x + 0.2y}{x + y}$ is between 20% and 30%). Try different values for x and y, and compute the win percentage of all the races Emily entered to see that answers **a** and **c** are not correct.

DOES IT MAKE SENSE?

7. Makes sense. If a country's population is declining, then the percent change will be negative (and several of Europe's countries have, indeed, experienced recent declines in population).
8. Makes sense. As a 100% increase corresponds with a doubling, a 200% increase corresponds with a tripling.
9. Makes sense. An older child could easily weigh 25% more than a younger child (think of 100-pound and 125-pound children).
10. Does not make sense. You cannot decrease your caloric intake by more than 100% (and you wouldn't want to do that for too long).
11. Does not make sense. Consider the case where I earn $100, and you earn $120. You earn $20 more than I do, which corresponds to 20% more than me (because 20% of $100 is $20). Even though I earn $20 less than you, I do not earn 20% less than you (because 20% of $120 is not $20). In fact, I earn 1/6 less than you do, which is about 16.7% less.
12. Does not make sense. Increasing a quantity by several successive percent changes is not equivalent to a one-time percent decrease that is the sum of the successive changes. This can be seen with a simple example: take $100 and increase it by 10% to $110, followed by another 10% increase to $121. Now take the same $100 and increase it by 20% to $120. Two successive 10% changes is not equivalent to a single 20% change, just like ten successive 10% changes is not equivalent to a 100% change.

13. Makes sense. This just means that the incidence of cancer for children living near toxic landfills was seven times larger than the incidence of cancer among other children.

14. Does not make sense. In a weighted average like this, the course average is computed by taking 75% of the pre-final work, and adding it to 25% of the final exam score. The student in this scenario would end up with a 65% course average, because $0.75 \times 60\% + 0.25 \times 80\% = 65\%$.

15. Makes sense. If the rate of return on the fund used to be 10%, then a 50% increase would result in a rate of return of 15%.

16. Makes sense. A 100% increase is the same as a doubling, and twice 2% is 4%.

BASIC SKILLS AND CONCEPTS

17. $2/5 = 0.4 = 40\%$.
18. $30\% = 0.3 = 3/10$.
19. $0.20 = 1/5 = 20\%$.
20. $0.85 = 85\% = 17/20$.
21. $150\% = 1.5 = 3/2$.
22. $2/3 = 0.666\ldots = 66.66\ldots\%$.
23. $4/9 = 0.444\ldots = 44.44\ldots\%$.
24. $1.25 = 125\% = 5/4$.
25. $5/8 = 0.625 = 62.5\%$.
26. $44\% = 0.44 = 11/25$.
27. $69\% = 0.69 = 69/100$.
28. $4.25 = 425\% = 17/4$.
29. $7/5 = 1.4 = 140\%$.
30. $121\% = 1.21 = 121/100$.
31. $4/3 = 1.333\ldots = 133.33\ldots\%$.
32. $0.666\ldots = 2/3 = 66.66\ldots\%$.
33. 8 to 4 = 2. 4 to 8 = 1/2. 8 is 200% of 4. Note that the ratio of B to A is just the reciprocal of the ratio of A to B, and that 200% is simply the ratio of A to B expressed as a percent.
34. 10 to 30 = 1/3. 30 to 10 = 3. 10 is 33.3% of 30. Note that the ratio of B to A is just the reciprocal of the ratio of A to B, and that 33.3% is simply the ratio of A to B expressed as a percent.
35. 150 to 400 = 3/8. 400 to 150 = 8/3. 150 is 37.5% of 400.
36. 450 to 400 = 9/8. 400 to 450 = 8/9. 450 is 112.5% of 400.
37. 52,252 to 16,268 = 3.21. 16,268 to 52,252 = 0.31. 52,252 is 321% of 16,268.
38. 40,229,000 to 88,458,000 = 0.455. 88,458,000 to 40,229,000 = 2.20. 40,229,000 is 45.5% of 88,458,000.
39. 3.9 million to 2.9 million = 1.34. 2.9 million to 3.9 million = 0.744. 3.9 million is 134% of 2.9 million.
40. 466 to 523 = 0.891. 523 to 466 = 1.12. 466 is 89.1% of 523.

41. 2,290,000 to 2,010,000 = 1.14. 2,010,000 to 2,290,000 = 0.877. 2,290,000 is 87.7% of 2,010,000.
42. $87,000 to $636,000 = 0.137. $636,000 to $87,000 = 7.31. $87,000 is 13.7% of $636,000.
43. 100 square meters to 25π square meters = $4/\pi$ = 1.27. 25π square meters to 100 square meters = $\pi/4$ = 0.785. 100 square meters is 127% of 25π square feet.
44. 87.8% to 55.8% = 1.57. 55.8% to 87.8% = 0.636. 87.8% is 157% of 55.8%.
45. 28 is 53.8% of 52 because 28/52 = 0.538.
46. 12 is 18.4% of 65.1 because 12/65.1 = 0.184.
47. 33,196 is 159% of 20,922 because 33,196/20,922 = 1.59.
48. 40.4 is 13.2% of 305 because 40.4/305 = 0.132.
49. 70.3 is 81.4% of 86.4 because 70.3/86.4 = 0.814.
50. 10,000 is 37.0% of 27,000 because 10,000/27,000 = 0.37.
51. Clint's absolute change in salary was $28,000 – $20,000 = $8000, and the relative change was $\frac{\$28,000-\$20,000}{\$20,000}=0.4=40\%$. Helen's absolute change was $35,000 – $25,000 = $10,000, and the relative change was $\frac{\$35,000-\$25,000}{\$25,000}=0.4=40\%$. Thus Helen's salary grew more in absolute terms, but the relative change was the same. This happened because we are comparing Helen's larger absolute change to her also larger initial salary.
52. The absolute change in Las Vegas' population was 565,000 people – 478,000 people = 87,00 people, and the relative change was $\frac{565,000-478,000}{478,000}=0.182=18.2\%$. The absolute change in Dallas' population was 1,245,000 people – 1,189,000 people = 56,000 people, and the relative change was $\frac{1,245,000-1,189,000}{1,189,000}=0.047=4.7\%$. Thus Las Vegas experienced a both larger absolute change, and a larger relative change.
53. The absolute change is 308 million – 249 million = 59 million people. The relative change is $\frac{308,000,000-249,000,000}{249,000,000}=0.237=23.7\%$.
54. The absolute change is 53 – 30 = 23. The relative change is $\frac{53-30}{30}=0.767=76.7\%$.

55. The absolute change is 1420 papers – 2226 papers = –806 papers. The relative change is $\frac{1420-2226}{2226} = -0.362 = -36.2\%$.

56. The absolute change is 511 million CDs – 942 million CDs = –431 million CDs. The relative change is $\frac{511,000,000-942,000,000}{942,000,000} =$ $-0.458 = -45.8\%$.

57. The relative difference is $\frac{266-220}{220} = 0.209 = 20.9\%$, which means the gestation period of humans (266 days) is 20.9 percent longer than the gestation period of grizzly bears (220 days).

58. The relative difference is $\frac{81.2-65.9}{65.9} = 0.232 = 23.2\%$, which means the 2009 life expectancy in Canada (81.2 years) is 23.3 percent greater than 2009 life expectancy in Russia (65.9).

59. The relative difference is $\frac{4200-2800}{4200} = 0.333 = 33.3\%$, which means the main span of the Tacoma Narrows bridge (2800 feet) is 33.3 percent shorter than the main span of the Golden Gate bridge (4200 feet).

60. The relative difference is $\frac{25.9-27.5}{27.5} = -0.0581 = -5.81\%$, which means the median age at first marriage of U.S. women (25.9 years) is 5.81 percent less than the median age at first marriage of U.S. men (27.5 years).

61. The relative difference is $\frac{25,500-21,400}{21,400} = 0.192 = 19.2\%$, which means the number of deaths due to poisoning in the United States in a year (25,500) is 19.2 percent greater than the number of deaths due to falls (21,400).

62. The relative difference is $\frac{190-127}{127} = 0.495 = 49.6\%$, which means the amount of rice produced by China in 2007 (190 million metric tons) as 49.6 percent greater than the amount of rice produced by India in 2007 (127 million metric tons).

63. Will's height is 122% of Wanda's height because 22% *more than* expresses a relative difference in heights, and this is equivalent to 100% + 22% *of* the reference height (i.e. Wanda's height).

64. Norway's area is 124% of Colorado's area because 24% *more than* expresses a relative difference in area, and this is equivalent to 100% + 24% *of* the reference area (i.e. Colorado's area).

65. Virginia's population is 82% of Georgia's population because 18% *less than* expresses a relative difference in population, and this is equivalent to 100% – 18% *of* the reference population (i.e. Georgia's population).

66. Zelda's net worth is 93.6% of Alicia's net worth because 6.4% *less than* expresses a relative difference in salary, and this is equivalent to 100% – 6.4% *of* the reference salary (i.e. Alicia's net worth).

67. Since the wholesale price is 40% *less than* the retail price, it is 60% *of* the retail price, which means it is 0.6 times the retail price.

68. The original price is 2 times as much of the sale price, because 100% (original price) is twice as large as 50% (sale price).

69. Since the retail cost is 30% *more than* the wholesale cost, it is 130% *of* the wholesale cost, which means it is 1.3 times the wholesale cost.

70. A 40% off sale means prices are discounted 40%. Since 40% of $80 is 0.4 × $80 = $32, the sale price is $80 – $32 = $48.

71. The absolute change is 2.8% – 2.3% = 0.5 percentage points. The relative change is $\frac{2.8-2.3}{2.3} = 0.217 = 21.7\%$.

72. The absolute change is 46.4% – 53.3% = –6.9 percentage points. The relative change is $\frac{46.4-53.3}{53.3} = -0.129 = -12.9\%$.

73. The absolute change is 78.5% – 66.9% = 11.6 percentage points. The relative change is $\frac{78.5-66.9}{66.9} = 0.173 = 17.3\%$.

74. The absolute change is 44% – 25% = 19 percentage points. The relative change is $\frac{44-25}{25} = 0.76 = 76\%$.

75. In the first case, 33% of city employees in Freetown ride the bus to work because 10% *more than* 30% is 33%. In the second case, 40% of the city employees in Freetown ride the bus, because 40% is 10 percentage points more than 30%.

76. The first statement implies that the precipitation is 180 inches, because 200% *of* 90 is two times as large as 90. The second statement means that the relative difference between the average and this year's precipitation is 200%, which is three times the average amount, or 270 inches.

77. The final cost is $760 + 0.076 × $760 = $817.76.

78. The pre-tax price is $107.69/1.062 = $101.40.

79. The total number of undergraduates is 2410/0.54 = 4463.

80. In 2007 there were 3.98/1.81 = 2.20 million foreclosures.

81. The cost for the dinner before the tip was $76.40/1.20 = $63.67.

82. If you leave $50 for a bill of $42.50, you left a $7.50 tip, which is 17.6% of $42.50 (because 7.50/42.50 = 0.176 = 17.6%).

83. Simon's gross pay is $2200/0.79 = $2785.

84. The balance in the account was $45/0.035 = $1286.

85. False. If the national economy began at E, and it shrinks at 4% annually, it would be at $E \times 0.96 \times 0.96 \times 0.96 = 0.885E$, which is 11.5% less than the original value.

86. False. Assign an arbitrary number to your salary, such as $100. A pay raise of 5% results in a new salary of $105. A 5% cut in the new salary yields $0.95 \times \$105 = \$99.75$. Thus your salary has changed (it's dropped 0.25% over the two changes in pay).

87. False. Assign an arbitrary number to your profits before the increases, such as $100. If your profits increase by 4% in the first year, they will be $104. If they decrease by 2% in the next year, they will be $0.98 \times \$104 = \$101.92$. This is an increase of 1.92%, not 2%.

88. False. Assign an arbitrary number to the original SAT scores, such as 1000. If the scores fell 20% one year, they would be at 800, and if they rose 30% the next year, they would be at $1.3 \times 800 = 1040$. This is an overall improvement of 4%, not 10%.

89. Not possible. A bill can decrease at most by 100%. Once you've deducted 100% from a bill, there's nothing more to pay.

90. Possible. Scott would be less than half again as tall as his son.

91. Possible. An increase of 100% means restaurant prices are twice what it used to be.

92. Not possible. Renee would have to run 10 kilometers instantaneously.

93. Possible. This means your computer is five times faster than my computer.

94. Not possible. At a maximum, your computer could be 100% slower than mine (in which case your computer doesn't work at all).

95. No, the mean score for both classes is not 85%. Assuming a 100-point exam, the first class scored a total of $25 \times 86 = 2150$ points, and the second class scored a total of $30 \times 84 = 2520$ points. Thus the combined number of points scored by 55 students is 2150 + 2520 = 4670, and the mean score for both classes is 4670/55 = 84.9%.

96. No, his new batting average is not .450. As in exercise 95, one can't average averages. In this exercise, we can't compute his new average as we don't know how many at-bats he's had in the previous games, but it can't be 4 at-bats (because there's no way he'd be batting .400 in that scenario), and this would be the only case where averaging averages would produce the correct result.

FURTHER APPLICATIONS

97. True. 10% of 60% is 1/10 of 60%, which is 6%.

98. False. 20% of 40% is $0.2 \times 40\% = 8\%$, not 80%.

99. False. Some of the hotels may have both a pool and a restaurant, and those would be counted twice if the percentages were just added together.

100. This is true as long as those who drive to school are not bus drivers who park the bus at school and attend classes there.

101. Speculative credit default swaps are worth $62 trillion $\times 0.80 = \$49.6$ trillion.

102. Since $37,729/$20,718 = 1.821, the annual income for adults with bachelor degrees is 182.1% *of* the income for those with a high school diploma, which means the bachelor degree income is 82.1% *more than* the high school income.

103. The relative change is $\dfrac{8.5 - 7.1}{7.1} = 0.197 = 19.7\%$.

104. The percentage change in the number of businesses is $\dfrac{1500 - 4700}{4700} = -0.681 = -68.1\%$. The percentage change in locations represented is $\dfrac{2500 - 5500}{5500} = -0.545 = -54.5\%$.

105. Before the losses the endowment was worth $222 million/0.43 = $516 million.

106. If the diagnoses began at D, and it drops at 4% a year, it would be at $D \times 0.982 \times 0.982 \times 0.982 \times 0.982 = 0.93E$, which is 7.0% less than the original value.

107. a. Before the loss, the Dow Jones Industrial average was at 10,365 + 778 = 11,143, so the percentage loss was $\dfrac{778}{11,143} = 0.07 = 7.0\%$.

b. Before the loss, the Dow Jones Industrial average was at 1739/0.774 = 2247, so the point loss as 2247 − 1739 = 508.

UNIT 3B

TIME OUT TO THINK

Pg. 149. 5% of $15 billion is $75 million — fifteen times the cost of the advertising campaign. The campaign is probably worth it, although it also depends on your profit margin for the ice cream. E.g., if you can expect a profit of $5 million or more from the additional $75 million in sales, then you'll make money by spending on the advertising. Of course, it's important to keep the uncertainty of the estimate in mind.

Pg. 150. This question should challenge the student to think about the enormous implications of being able to replace ALL current energy sources with (in an ideal sense) a single fusion reactor on a small creek. A good offshoot to this question is to ask how much taxpayer money it would be worth spending on the effort to achieve sustained nuclear fusion. FYI: nuclear fusion plants do not have nearly the same waste disposal problem as current fission plants. The product of fusion is helium, which is a harmless gas. The only nuclear waste from fusion plants would arise because neutrons from the fusion reactions would strike the reactor walls, gradually making the walls themselves radioactive. Not only does this mean far less nuclear waste than from fission plants, but most of the radioactive isotopes produced this way have far shorter half-lives than do uranium and plutonium, so the material does not require the same long-term disposal as fission waste.

Pg. 152. This question should give you a better idea of the vast size of the solar system and the relative size of objects in it.

Pg. 153. Detecting an Earth-like planet around a nearby star is like trying to see a pinhead orbiting a grapefruit — from a distance equivalent to that across the United States. The Kepler mission is attempting to find planets by looking for the change is a star's brightness caused by a planet passing between the star and the observer (called a transit).

Pg. 154. Not possible. To meet 700,000 people during a yearlong campaign, the Congressman would have to visit more than 1900 people each day. Going door-to-door, there's just not enough time.

QUICK QUIZ

1. **a.** The decimal point must move seven places to the left to transform 70,000,000 into scientific notation, and thus its value is 7×10^7.

2. **c.** 1277 is roughly 10^3, and 14,385 is of order 10^4, so their product is around 10^7.

3. **c.** 10^9 is larger than 10^5 by a factor of 10^4, which is ten thousand.

4. **c.** One person, who drives 15,000 miles in a year in a vehicle that gets 25 mpg, uses 600 gallons of gas per year. There are 300 million Americans,

and if each used this much gas, the total would be

$$3 \times 10^8 \text{ people} \times \frac{6 \times 10^2 \text{ gal}}{\text{person}} = 18 \times 10^{10} \text{ gal} =$$

1.8×10^{11} gallons of gasoline, which is 180 billion gallons. Of course, not everyone drives 15,000 miles every year (children, the elderly, and urban dwellers come to mind). On the other hand, this estimate doesn't even consider all the gas used by trucking, airlines, and other industries. Certainly the answer can't be **a** or **b**, as these estimates are much too small. 100 billion gallons is probably a conservative estimate.

5. **c.** A dollar bill is about 6 inches long, or about 15 cm long, and thus 8 million of them amounts to

$$8 \times 10^6 \text{ bills} \times \frac{1.5 \times 10^1 \text{ cm}}{\text{bill}} \times \frac{1 \text{ km}}{10^5 \text{ cm}} =$$

12×10^2 km, which is 1200 kilometers. This is enough to get into outer space, but not near enough to reach the moon.

6. **c.** If you know the song from the Broadway musical *Rent*, you may recall that there are 525,600 minutes in a year. 1.2×10^{-10} year is just over one ten-billionth of a year, which isn't even close to a minute (it's a small fraction of a second). Clearly the sun won't burn out in the next fraction of a second, nor in the next minute.

7. **b.** If 1 inch = 20 miles, then 6 inches is 6 × 20 = 120 miles.

8. **b.** $1 billion is $1000 million, so at $10 million per year, it will take 100 years to earn $1 billion.

9. **c.** Assuming you're willing to campaign for eight hours per day (which is roughly 500 minutes), and that you'll limit yourself to 10 minutes of talking at each house (including travel time between houses), you'll be able to visit 50 households per day, or 100 houses in two days. This translates into 500 houses in two weeks (campaigning five days per week), or 1000 households in a month, or 12,000 households in a year-long campaign, where you do nothing but campaigning. Clearly it would be impossible to carry out your plan before the election – pay for some TV advertisements instead.

10. **a.** The largest Division 1 college football stadiums hold about 100,000 fans. In a lottery with the stated odds, there's only one winning ticket for every 1,000,000 printed, which means there are 999,999 losing tickets. More likely than not, the fans in the stadium will be disappointed (and it's more likely still they will be disappointed in a smaller stadium).

DOES IT MAKE SENSE?

9. Makes sense. The page you are reading right now has two columns, each of which has about 50 lines, and there are roughly 10 words per line, for a total of 1000 words per page. A book with $10^5 = 100,000$ words would have 100 pages. A paperback with pages about half the size of this solutions manual would be two-hundred pages long.

10. Does not make sense. A very rough estimate for the number of minutes in a lifetime might use 100 years per life, 400 days per year, 20 hours per day, and 60 minutes per hour. This means somewhere between 10^7 and 10^8 minutes in a lifetime. Even if you could view several commercials each minute, you couldn't come anywhere close to 10^{50} commercials over a lifetime of continuous TV viewing.

11. Makes sense. At ten feet per floor, an apartment building with 20 floors would be 200 feet tall.

12. Does not make sense. With 300 million Americans, each would have to spend roughly $3 per year to reach $1 billon. Housing costs far exceed $3 per person per year.

13. Does not make sense. A typical NFL stadium holds 70,000 fans. At an unrealistic speed of 10 signatures per minute, it would take the football star 7000 minutes (roughly 100 hours) to provide signatures for all the fans (who would grow restless waiting in line for a signature after about 15 minutes).

14. Makes sense. This is a large company if it has more than 500 employees, and the salaries for the low-skilled jobs might be around $20,000 per year (about $10 per hour). $(5 \times 10^2) \times (2 \times 10^4) = 10^7$, so the sum of all these salaries is $10 million, which is on the order of what a CEO of a large company earns.

BASIC SKILLS AND CONCEPTS

15. a. $3 \times 10^3 = 3000 =$ three thousand .

b. $6 \times 10^6 = 6,000,000 =$ six million .

c. $3.4 \times 10^5 = 340,000 =$ three hundred forty thousand.

d. $2 \times 10^{-2} = 0.02 =$ two hundredths .

e. $2.1 \times 10^{-4} = 0.00021 =$ twenty-one hundred-thousandths.

f. $4 \times 10^{-5} = 0.00004 =$ four hundred - thousandths.

16. a. $8 \times 10^2 = 800 =$ eight hundred .

b. $5 \times 10^3 = 5000 =$ five thousand .

c. $9.6 \times 10^4 = 96,000 =$ ninety-six thousand .

d. $2 \times 10^{-3} = 0.002 =$ two thousandths .

e. $3.3 \times 10^{-5} = 0.000033 =$ thirty-three millionths.

f. $7.66 \times 10^{-2} = 0.0766 =$ seven hundred sixty - six ten-thousandths.

17. a. $233 = 2.33 \times 10^2$.

b. $126,547 = 1.26547 \times 10^5$.

c. $0.11 = 1.1 \times 10^{-1}$.

d. $9736.23 = 9.73623 \times 10^3$.

e. $124.58 = 1.2458 \times 10^2$.

f. $0.8642 = 8.642 \times 10^{-1}$.

18. a. $4327 = 4.327 \times 10^3$.

b. $984.35 = 9.8435 \times 10^2$.

c. $0.0045 = 4.5 \times 10^{-3}$.

d. $624.87 = 6.2487 \times 10^2$.

e. $0.1357 = 1.357 \times 10^{-1}$.

f. $98.180004 = 9.8180004 \times 10^1$.

19. a. $(3 \times 10^3) \times (2 \times 10^2) = 6 \times 10^5$.

b. $(4 \times 10^2) \times (3 \times 10^8) = 12 \times 10^{10} = 1.2 \times 10^{11}$.

c. $(3 \times 10^3) + (2 \times 10^2) = 3000 + 200 = 3200 = 3.2 \times 10^3$.

d. $(8 \times 10^{12}) \div (4 \times 10^4) = 2 \times 10^8$.

20. a. $(4 \times 10^7) \times (2 \times 10^8) = 8 \times 10^{15}$.

b. $(3.2 \times 10^5) \times (2 \times 10^4) = 6.4 \times 10^9$.

c. $(4 \times 10^3) + (5 \times 10^2) = 4000 + 500 = 4500 = 4.5 \times 10^3$.

d. $(9 \times 10^{13}) \div (3 \times 10^{10}) = 3 \times 10^3$.

21. a. 10^{35} is 10^9 (1 billion) times as large as 10^{26} .

b. 10^{27} is 10^{10} (10 billion) times as large as 10^{17} .

c. 1 billion is 10^3 (1000) times as large as 1 million.

d. 7 trillion is 10^9 (1 billion) times as large as 7 thousand.

e. 2×10^{-6} is 10^3 (1000) times as large as 2×10^{-9} .

f. 6.1×10^{29} is 10^2 (100) times as large as 6.1×10^{27} .

22. a. 5 billion (5×10^9) is 20 times as large as 250 million (2.5×10^8).

b. 9.3×10^2 is 3×10^4 (30,000) times as large as 3.1×10^{-2}.

c. 1×10^{-8} is 5×10^4 (50,000) times as large as 2×10^{-13}.

d. 3.5×10^{-2} is 5×10^5 (500,000) times as large as 7×10^{-8}.

e. 1 thousand (10^3) is 10^6 (1 million) times as large as 1 thousandth (10^{-3}).

f. 10^{12} is 10^{21} times as large as 10^{-9}.

23. My new music player has a capacity of 3.4×10^{11} bytes.

24. The estimated (world) nuclear energy production is $2.6.8 \times 10^{12}$ kilowatt-hours.

25. As of 2009, U.S. consumer credit (total amount borrowed) was $\$2.564 \times 10^{12}$.

26. The number of different eight-letter passwords that can be made with 26 letters and 10 numerals is approximately 2.8×10^{12}.

27. The diameter of a typical bacterium is about 1×10^{-6} meter.

28. A beam of light can travel the length of a football field in 3×10^{-8} seconds.

29. a. 300,000 is 3×10^5, and 100 is 1×10^2, so their product is 3×10^7, or 30,000,000. This is an exact answer as no estimation was necessary.

b. 5.1 million is about 5×10^6, and 1.9 thousand is about 2×10^3, so their product is about 1×10^{10}, which is 10 billion. The exact answer (computed with a calculator) is 9.69 billion.

c. Since 2.1×10^6 is about 2 million, $4 \times 10^9 \div 2.1 \times 10^6$ is about 2×10^3, or 2000. The exact answer is nearer to 1.9×10^3 (1904.76 is a rounded answer).

d. 33 multiplied by 3.1 is very close to 100, so $(33 \times 10^6) \times (3.1 \times 10^3)$ is about 100×10^9, which is 1×10^{11}. The exact answer is 1.023×10^{11}.

e. 4,288,364 is about 4×10^6, and 2132 is about 2×10^3, so their quotient is about 2×10^3, or 2000. The exact answer is 2011 (rounded).

f. $(6.129845 \times 10^6) \div (2.198 \times 10^4)$ is about $(6 \times 10^6) \div (2 \times 10^4) = 3 \times 10^2$, or 300. The exact answer is 279 (rounded).

30. a. $(5.6 \times 10^9) \div (2 \times 10^2) = 2.8 \times 10^7$. This is an exact answer as no estimation is necessary (provided you can divide 5.6 by 2 in your head – estimate 5.6 billion as 6 billion if not, to arrive at an approximate answer of 3×10^7).

b. Since 4 divided by 2.6 is about 2, 4 trillion ÷ 260 million = $(4 \times 10^{12}) \div (2.6 \times 10^8)$ is about 2×10^4 = 20,000. The exact answer is 15385 (rounded).

c. $9000 \times 54,986$ is close to $(1 \times 10^4) \times (5 \times 10^4)$, which is 5×10^8. The exact answer is 4.95×10^8 (rounded).

d. 3 billion ÷ 25,000 is close to $(3 \times 10^9) \div (3 \times 10^4)$, which is 10^5. The exact answer is 1.2×10^5.

e. 5987×341 is about $(6 \times 10^3) \times (3 \times 10^2)$, which is 1.8×10^6. Because we rounded 341 all the way down to 300, a better approximation is 2×10^6. The exact answer is 2,041,567, or 2.04×10^6 (rounded).

f. $43 \div 765$ is about $(4 \times 10^1) \div (8 \times 10^2)$, which is 5×10^{-2}, or 0.05. The exact answer is 0.056 (rounded).

31. Answers will vary regarding the estimates made, but most people spend more money on gas each month than on coffee. If you buy one coffee per day (but perhaps not every day), spending $1–2 per coffee, that's around $30–40 per month,. On the other hand, if you fill up your gas tank twice per month, spending around $35 to fill a tank, that's around $70–80 per month.

32. Answers will vary regarding the estimates made, but it's certainly possible to walk across the United States in a year. If you walked at a modest rate of 2 miles per hour, for 8 hours each day, you would walk 16 miles per day. Over the course of one year (365 days), you'd end up walking 5840 miles, which is almost enough to go there and back again (it's about 3000 miles from New York to California). Thus even with rest days scheduled, you'd have no trouble walking the distance in a year.

33. Assuming you sleep 7 hours per day, and that you study less than 7 hours per day, you'll sleep more than you study. In particular, if you sleep 7 hours

each night, you'll sleep 2555 hours over the course of a year. If you study 6 hours per day over the course of a school year (30 weeks, or two semesters), you'll study 1260 hours per year.

34. Answer will vary, but the average percent of income spent on food is around 14% while the percent spent on transportation is around 18%.

35. Assuming 1 beat per second, one can estimate the number of heart beats in a day with a unit conversion:

$1 \text{ d} \times \dfrac{24 \text{ hr}}{\text{d}} \times \dfrac{60 \text{ min}}{\text{hr}} \times \dfrac{60 \text{ sec}}{\text{min}} \times \dfrac{1 \text{ beat}}{\text{sec}}$, which is about 86,400 beats per day (answers will vary).

36. Assuming the average person walks 2 miles per day and there are 2000 steps per mile, one can estimate the number of steps taken in a day with

$1 \text{ d} \times \dfrac{2 \text{ mi}}{\text{d}} \times \dfrac{2000 \text{ steps}}{\text{mi}} = 4000$ steps per day.

(answers will vary).

37. Answers will vary, but assuming a daily water intake of 2 pints, one can estimate the annual water consumption with a unit conversion:

$1 \text{ yr} \times \dfrac{365 \text{ d}}{\text{yr}} \times \dfrac{2 \text{ pt}}{\text{d}} \times \dfrac{1 \text{ qt}}{2 \text{ pt}} \times \dfrac{1 \text{ gal}}{4 \text{ qt}}$, which is about 90 gallons per year.

38. Answers will vary. Page 158 of the text has two columns, each with about 40 lines, and each line has about 10 words. Thus there are approximately 800 words on that page. If we treat that page as representative of the entire book, which has about 800 pages, there are about 640,000 words in the book.

39. Assuming you drive (or ride) about 10 miles per day and drive 350 days each year, the total would be 3500 miles.

40. If you listen to music 1–3 hours per day, you would spend 30–90 hours per month listening to music.

41. Table 3.1 states that 4 million joules are required for one hour of running, and that an average candy bar supplies 1 million joules of energy. Thus four candy bars would be needed for each hour of running, which means you'd need to eat 24 candy bars to supply the energy for six hours of running.

42. The average home uses 50 million joules per day, which amounts to 1.5 billion joules per month (assuming a 30-day month). Divide 1.5 billion joules per month by 12 million joules per liter of oil to arrive at 125 liters per month.

43. One kilogram of uranium-235 releases 5.6×10^{13} joules, which is 35,000 times as much as the energy released by one kilogram of coal (1.6×10^9 joules): $\dfrac{5.6 \times 10^{13}}{1.6 \times 10^9} = 35,000$.

44. One liter of water supplies enough hydrogen to produce 7×10^{13} joules of energy through fusion, and this is almost 6 million times as much energy released by burning a liter of oil (1.2×10^7 joules):

$\dfrac{7 \times 10^{13}}{1.2 \times 10^7} = 5,833,333$.

45. $\dfrac{5 \times 10^7 \text{ joules}}{\text{home}} \times \dfrac{1 \text{ liter H}_2\text{O}}{7 \times 10^{13} \text{ joules}} = 7 \times 10^{-7} \dfrac{\text{liters}}{\text{home}}$.

This is just a little less than one millionth of a liter.

46. $\dfrac{5 \times 10^{20} \text{ joules}}{\text{world}} \times \dfrac{1 \text{ liter H}_2\text{O}}{7 \times 10^{13} \text{ joules}} =$

$7.14 \times 10^6 \dfrac{\text{liters}}{\text{world}}$. This is about 7 million liters.

47. $\dfrac{1 \times 10^{20} \text{ joules}}{\text{yr}} \times \dfrac{1 \text{ kg uranium}}{5.6 \times 10^{13} \text{ joules}} = 1.8 \times 10^6 \dfrac{\text{kg}}{\text{yr}}$.

Thus 1.8 million kg of uranium would be needed to supply the annual energy needs of the United States.

48. The sun generates 1×10^{34} joules each year. A simple unit conversion tells us how much energy is generated by the sun in a second:

$\dfrac{1 \times 10^{34} \text{ j}}{\text{yr}} \times \dfrac{1 \text{ yr}}{365 \text{ d}} \times \dfrac{1 \text{ d}}{24 \text{ hr}} \times \dfrac{1 \text{ hr}}{60 \text{ min}} \times \dfrac{1 \text{ min}}{60 \text{ sec}} =$

$\dfrac{3.2 \times 10^{26} \text{ j}}{\text{sec}}$.

This is more than enough to supply U.S. energy needs for a year (about 3 million times as much as is needed, in fact).

49. Since 2 cm represents 100 km, 1 cm represents 50 km. Since there are 5,000,000 cm in 50 km, the scale is 500,000 to 1.

50. There are 633,600 inches in 10 miles, as shown here: $10 \text{ mi} \times \dfrac{5280 \text{ ft}}{1 \text{ mi}} \times \dfrac{12 \text{ in.}}{1 \text{ ft}} = 633,600$ inches, and thus the scale is 633,600 to 1.

51. 1 cm represents 500 km. Since there are 50,000,000 cm in 500 km, the scale is 50,000,000 to 1.

52. Since 0.5 in. represents 1 km, 1 in. represents 2 km. Since there are

$2 \text{ km} \times \dfrac{100,000 \text{ cm}}{1 \text{ km}} \times \dfrac{1 \text{ in.}}{2.54 \text{ cm}} = 78,740.16$ in. in 2 km, the scale is 78,740.16 to 1.

53. In order to scale down each of the actual diameters and distances listed in the table, begin by dividing by 10,000,000,000 (10 billion). Since this produces tiny answers when units of kilometers are used, it is best to convert to a more convenient unit. The table below shows diameters listed in millimeters (rounded to the nearest tenth of a millimeter), and distances listed in meters (rounded to the nearest meter).

Planet	Model Diameter	Model distance from Sun
Mercury	0.5 mm	6 m
Venus	1.2 mm	11 m
Earth	1.3 mm	15 m
Mars	0.7 mm	23 m
Jupiter	14.3 mm	78 m
Saturn	12.0 mm	143 m
Uranus	5.2 mm	287 m
Neptune	4.8 mm	450 m

54. As noted in Example 8, *Alpha Centauri* is about 4.1×10^{13} km from Earth. The amount of time needed to reach *Alpha Centauri* traveling at 50,000 km/hr can be found by dividing the distance by the rate of speed:

$$\text{time} = \frac{4.1 \times 10^{13} \text{ km}}{50,000 \text{ km/hr}} = 8.2 \times 10^{8} \text{ hr},$$

which is 820 million hours. A quick conversion shows that this is nearly 100,000 years. Thus interstellar travel is beyond our means until we design a ship that will last 100,000 years, and that will support many generations of the crew, or until we build a ship that travels much faster than 50,000 km/hr.

55. a. The scale on this timeline would be 4.5 billion years to 100 yards, and thus 1 billion years is equivalent to 1/4.5 of 100 meters, which amounts to 22.2 yards.
b. Since 10,000 years is 1/100,000 of one billion years, we only need to divide 22.2 yards by 100,000 to find the distance that goes with 10,000 years. This gives 0.000222 yards, or

$$0.000222 \text{ yd} \times \frac{36 \text{ in.}}{1 \text{ yd}} = 0.008 \text{ inches.}$$

56. a. The scale on this timeline would be 4.5 billion years to 12 hours, and thus 1 billion years is equivalent to 1/4.5 of 12 hours, which amounts to 2.67 hours.
b. Since 10,000 years is 1/100,000 of one billion years, we only need to divide 2.67 hours by 100,000 to find the distance that goes with 10,000

years. This gives 0.0000267 hours or

$$0.0000267 \text{ hr} \times \frac{3600 \text{ sec}}{1 \text{ hr}} = 0.096 \text{ seconds.}$$

FURTHER APPLICATIONS

57. $\dfrac{2.4 \times 10^{6} \text{ births}}{\text{yr}} \times \dfrac{1 \text{ yr}}{365 \text{ d}} \times \dfrac{1 \text{ d}}{24 \text{ hr}} \times \dfrac{1 \text{ hr}}{60 \text{ min}} =$

$4.6 \dfrac{\text{births}}{\text{min}}$.

58. $\dfrac{2.2 \times 10^{6} \text{ marriages}}{\text{yr}} \times \dfrac{1 \text{ yr}}{365 \text{ d}} \times \dfrac{1 \text{ d}}{24 \text{ hr}} =$

$251 \dfrac{\text{marriages}}{\text{hr}}$.

59. $\dfrac{40,000 \text{ deaths}}{\text{yr}} \times \dfrac{1 \text{ yr}}{365 \text{ d}} = 110 \dfrac{\text{deaths}}{\text{day}}$.

60. $\dfrac{\$1.27 \times 10^{10}}{\text{yr}} \times \dfrac{1 \text{ yr}}{365 \text{ d}} \times \dfrac{1 \text{ d}}{24 \text{ hr}} \times \dfrac{1 \text{ hr}}{60 \text{ min}} =$

$\$24,000/\text{min}$.

61. a. $\dfrac{3.05 \times 10^{8} \text{ crimes}}{\text{yr}} \times \dfrac{1 \text{ yr}}{365 \text{ d}} \times \dfrac{1 \text{ d}}{24 \text{ hr}} \times \dfrac{1 \text{ hr}}{60 \text{ min}} \times$

$\dfrac{1 \text{ min}}{60 \text{ sec}} = 9.7 \dfrac{\text{crimes}}{\text{min}}$.

b. $\dfrac{3.05 \times 10^{8} \text{ crimes}}{3.05 \times 10^{8} \text{ Americans}} = 1 \dfrac{\text{crime}}{\text{American}}$

62. $1.6 \times 10^{6} \text{ prisoners} \times \dfrac{1 \text{ arena}}{50,000 \text{ prisoners}} = 32$ arenas.

63. There are 305 million Americans, so the amount consumed per person is $\dfrac{7.6 \times 10^{9} \text{ lb}}{3.05 \times 10^{8} \text{ people}} = 25$ pounds per person. This is 25 lb/12 months = 2.1 pounds per person per month.

64. The thickness of a stack of ten $1 bills is about one millimeter, and this can be used to convert $5.2 billion into a height.

$$\$5.2 \times 10^{9} \times \frac{1 \text{ mm}}{\$10} \times \frac{1 \text{ km}}{10^{6} \text{ mm}} = 520 \text{ km}.$$

65. a. $1 \text{ cm}^{3} \times \left(\dfrac{10^{4} \ \mu\text{m}}{1 \text{ cm}}\right)^{3} \times \dfrac{1 \text{ cell}}{100 \ \mu\text{m}^{3}} = 1 \times 10^{10} \text{ cells}$, or 10 billion cells.
b. One liter is 1000 milliliters, or 1000 cubic centimeters, so there are 1000 times as many cells in a liter as there are in a cubic centimeter, which comes to 1×10^{13} cells (see part a).
c. If one liter of water weighs 1 kilogram, then a person who weighs 70 kg has a volume of 70 liters. From part b, we know each liter contains

1×10^{13} cells, and thus we need only multiply that result by 70 to find the number of cells in a human body. This results in 7×10^{14} cells.

66. Answers will vary, but if you assume there are 200 million drivers in the U.S. (2/3 of the population), and each uses 1000 gallons of gas per year, then roughly 2 trillion kg of carbon dioxide was added to the atmosphere over the past year:

$$2 \times 10^8 \text{ drivers} \times \frac{1000 \text{ gal}}{\text{driver}} \times \frac{10 \text{ kg}}{\text{gal}} = 2 \times 10^{12} \text{ kg}.$$

67. If we assume an average of three people per household, there are 100 million households in the U.S. (because there are 300 million people). If 4.5 trillion gallons is enough to supply all households for five months, then $\dfrac{4.5 \times 10^{12}}{5} = 9 \times 10^{11}$ gallons is sufficient for one month. Thus each household uses $\dfrac{9 \times 10^{11} \text{ gal}}{1 \times 10^8 \text{ households}} = 9{,}000$ gallons per month. Answers will vary regarding whether this is reasonable, but considering water used for bathing, washing, drinking, cooking, cleaning, and upkeep of the lawn/garden, this is within the ballpark.

68. a. Energy = power × time, so we need to multiply the solar power by one second, and then take 0.06% of the result, followed by 1% of that result to account for the fact that not all solar power is converted into plant matter.

$$180{,}000 \times 10^{12} \text{ W} = 1.8 \times 10^{17} \frac{\text{j}}{\text{s}} \times 1 \text{ s} =$$

1.8×10^{17} j. This is the amount of energy that reaches the earth each second. Multiply by 0.0006, and then by 0.01 (the decimal equivalent of 0.06% and 1%) to find the amount of energy stored in plant matter each second – this results in 1.08×10^{12} joules.

b. If 1.08×10^{12} joules of energy are used every second, that's the same as 1.08×10^{12} watts, or about 1 terawatt. This is only 10% of the world's electricity demand, so it would not be enough.

c. To avoid depleting plant life, it's necessary to use fossil fuels, which provide the energy stored by plants over thousands of years.

69. a. The volume of a sphere is $V = \frac{4}{3}\pi r^3$, and thus the volume of the white dwarf will be $\frac{4}{3}\pi(6400 \text{ km})^3$. Density is mass per unit volume, so the density of the white dwarf will be

$$\frac{2 \times 10^{30} \text{ kg}}{\frac{4}{3}\pi(6400 \text{ km})^3} \times \left(\frac{1 \text{ km}}{10^5 \text{ cm}}\right)^3 = 1821 \frac{\text{kg}}{\text{cm}^3}.$$

b. Since a teaspoon is about 4 cubic centimeters, and each cubic centimeter has mass of 1821 kg (part a), a teaspoon will have a mass of 7300 kg, which is about the mass of a tank.

c. Following the calculations in part a, the density is $\dfrac{2.8 \times 10^{30} \text{ kg}}{\frac{4}{3}\pi(10 \text{ km})^3} \times \left(\dfrac{1 \text{ km}}{10^5 \text{ cm}}\right)^3 = 7 \times 10^{11} \dfrac{\text{kg}}{\text{cm}^3}$, which means one cubic centimeter of this material is more than ten times the mass of Mount Everest.

70. Answers will vary, but if a ream of paper (500 sheets) weighs 8 pounds, then each sheet will weigh 1/500 of 8 pounds, which is 0.016 lb.

71. Careful measurements show that a penny is about 1.5 mm thick, a nickel 1.8 mm, a dime 1.3 mm, and a quarter 1.7 mm thick. The easiest way to make these measurements is to measure a stack of ten coins, and divide the answer by ten. Although a quarter is almost the thickest coin (among these), its value is 2.5 times as much as the thinnest coin, the dime, and yet it's thickness is not anywhere near 2.5 times as thick as a dime (it's about 1.3 times as thick). So while you'll get more dimes in a stack that is as tall as you are, the value of that stack won't be as much as the value of the stack of quarters – take the quarters.

72. Answers will vary considerably, depending upon the sand that is used to make the estimate.

73. Answers will vary considerably, depending on the amount of light pollution in the area where one might make an estimate.

UNIT 3C

TIME OUT TO THINK

Pg. 163. Random errors might occur by setting the time incorrectly or if your clock fluctuates in a random way. Systematic errors might occur if you deliberately set your clock a few minutes ahead or behind, or if your clock consistently runs slightly fast or slow.

Pg. 164. With regard to the constitutional issue, there is no correct answer and courts have been divided on the issue when it has come before them. With regard to the political issue, people who are missed in the census tend to be poorer people who reside in regions typically represented by Democratic Congress members. Thus, statistical sampling is likely to increase the number of Democrats in Congress at the expense of the Republicans. This would be a good topic for a discussion either during or outside of class.

Pg. 167(1st). To know your true weight, we would have to have measured it on a very carefully calibrated scale. Even in that case, it would be difficult to be sure that it is your true weight, since there are always random errors that can occur in measurement.

Pg. 167(2nd). Answers will vary. This would be a good topic for a discussion either during or outside of class.

QUICK QUIZ

1. **b**. The best economists can do when making projections into the future is to base their estimates on current trends, but when these trends change, it often proves the predictions wrong.

2. **a**. There are two significant digits in 5.0×10^{-1}, while the other answers have only one.

3. **b**. 1.020 has four significant digits, 1.02 has three, and 0.000020 has only two.

4. **a**. Random errors can either be too high or too low, and averaging three readings is likely to reduce random errors because the high readings typically cancel the low readings.

5. **b**. If you place the thermometers in sunlight, this is a problem with your system of measurement, and the readings will all be too high, which is a systematic error.

6. **c**. Since all the scores are affected the same way (50 points too low), this is an example of a systematic error.

7. **b**. The absolute error in all cases was –50 points, but unless all students had the same score (very unlikely), the relative errors will be different.

8. **a**. Because the scale is able to report your weight to the nearest 1/10 of a pound, it is fairly precise (in comparison to standard bathroom scales), but its accuracy is lacking as it is off by more than 30 pounds (in 146 pounds).

9. **a**. Reporting the debt to the nearest penny is very precise, though the debt is so large that we really don't know it to that level of precision, and thus it is not likely to be very accurate.

10. **a**. Multiplying the gas mileage by the tank capacity will produce the number of miles the car can go on a full tank (290 miles), so the question boils down to this: "How many significant digits should be used when reporting the answer?" Since there are two significant digits in 29 mpg, and three in 10.0 gallons, we should use two significant digits in the answer (use the rounding rule for multiplication), and thus the answer is 290 miles.

DOES IT MAKE SENSE?

7. Does not make sense. Predicting the federal deficit for the next year to the nearest million dollars is nearly impossible.

8. Makes sense. It is difficult to estimate the population (in both developing and developed countries), and it is reasonable to claim the error in these estimates may be 10% or more.

9. Does not make sense. Unless you have access to an exceptionally precise scale, you could never measure your weight to that level of precision (and even with an excellent scale, your weight changes at the level reported when you sweat, breath, lose a few hairs, etc.).

10. Does not make sense. It is very unlikely that anyone could count the number of people attending a rally to the nearest thousand people when the number of attendees is near two million..

11. Does not make sense. A typical yard stick may be precise to the nearest 1/16 of an inch, but certainly not to the nearest micrometer.

12. Makes sense. Suppose you measure your weight with a scale that is precise to the nearest 1/10 of a pound, but you fail to take your shoes and clothes off before stepping on the scale. The reading will not be very accurate (off by a pound or more), and increasing the level of precision to, say, 1/100 of a pound won't help matters.

13. Makes sense. Provided the company's revenue is $1 billion, $1 million would be only 0.1% of revenue, and it wouldn't be considered a large error.

14. Does not make sense. Random errors can also affect accuracy (and in just about every measurement made, the measuring device has a finite level of precision that prevents perfect accuracy).

BASIC SKILLS & CONCEPTS

15. a. 3.   b. 88.   c. 0.
    d. 185.   e. 1945.   f. 3.
    g. 6.   h. 1500.   i. –14.

16. a. 567.5; 570.   b. 23.5; 20.
    c. 34.5; 30.   d. 123.5; 120.
    e. –34.8; –30.   f. 45.5; 50.
    g. –76.3; –80.   h. 32.5; 30.
    i. 0.0; 0.

17. There are four significant digits, and it is precise to the nearest dollar.

18. There are five significant digits, and it is precise to the nearest 0.001 mph.

19. There is one significant digit, and it is precise to the nearest 10 mph.

20. There is one significant digit, and it is precise to the nearest 0.01 centimeter.

21. There are six significant digits, and it is precise to the nearest 0.00001 mile.

22. There are two significant digits, and it is precise to the nearest 10,000 years.

23. There are two significant digits, and it is precise to the nearest 1000 seconds.

24. There are 3 significant digits, and it is precise to the nearest 0.000001 meter.

25. There are seven significant digits, and it is precise to the nearest 0.0001 pound.

26. There is one significant digit, and it is precise to the nearest 0.00001 liter.

27. There are four significant digits, and it is precise to the nearest 0.1 km/s.

28. There are four significant digits, and it is precise to the nearest one billion kg.

29. $45 \times 32.1 = 1430.$

30. $45 \times 32.1 = 1444.5.$

31. $231.89 \div 0.034 = 6800.$

32. $231.89 \div 0.034 = 6820$ (the ones place is significant).

33. $(2.3 \times 10^5) \times (7.963 \times 10^3) = 1.83149 \times 10^3.$

34. $(6.667 \times 10^3) \times (8.9421 \times 10^{-2}) = 5.962 \times 10^2.$

35. Random errors may occur when birds are miscounted, and systematic errors may happen the same bird is are counted more than once (if it leaves and then returns to the region) or a bird that enters the region is not seen.

36. Random errors may occur when people are miscounted, and systematic errors may happen when homeless people are not counted, or when college students are counted twice.

37. Random errors could occur if the average is calculated incorrectly. Systematic errors might occur if people repeatedly understate their weight.

38. Random errors could occur using different timing devices, and a systematic error could occur if the timing devices are not calibrated.

39. Random errors may be introduced if the scale weighing the cans is read incorrectly, and systematic errors could occur if the scale is not properly zeroed out (set to read zero before the can is placed on it).

40. Random errors may occur due to miscounting of the M&Ms®.

41. Random errors could occur if the thermometer used to measure the temperatures is read incorrectly, while systematic errors may occur if the thermometer is not calibrated correctly or is in a location that affects its reading, such as direct sunlight.

42. Random errors could occur if the ballots are miscounted, either by hand or machine, while systematic errors may occur if ballots are not counted or counted twice.

43. Problem (1) is a random error because the mistakes may be too high or two low. Problem (2) is a systematic error, because the tax payer likely underreported his income.

44. Problem (1) is a random error because the number of people with AIDS is either too high or too low, depending on the incorrect diagnosis. Problem (2) is a systematic error as those who never seek help result in an undercounting of the number of people with AIDS.

45. This is a systematic error that results in all altitude readings being 2780 lower than they should be.

46. Random errors are involved here, most likely due to hurried measurements or cutting, which leads to lengths that are sometimes too long, and sometimes too short.

47. The absolute error is measured value – true value, or 67.5. in. – 68.0 in. = –0.5 in.. The relative error is $\dfrac{\text{measured value} - \text{true value}}{\text{true value}} = \dfrac{67.5 \text{ in} - 68.0 \text{ in}}{68.0 \text{ in}} = 0.007 = 0.7\%.$

48. The absolute error is measured value – true value, or 30 lb – 29 lb = 1 lb. The relative error is $\dfrac{\text{measured value} - \text{true value}}{\text{true value}} = \dfrac{30 \text{ lb} - 29 \text{ lb}}{29 \text{ lb}} = 3.4\%.$

49. The absolute error is 60 mi/hr – 58 mi/hr = 2 mi/hr. The relative error is (60 mi/hr – 58 mi/hr) / 58 mi/hr = 0.034 = 3.4%.

50. The absolute error is $9.95 – $8.95 = $1.00. The relative error is ($9.95 – $8.95) / $8.95 = 0.112 = 11.2%.

51. The absolute error is 4.75 oz – 5 oz = –0.25 cup. The relative error is (4.75 oz – 5 oz)/5 oz = –0.05 = –5.0%.

52. The absolute error is 13 mi – 13.34 mi = –0.34 mi. The relative error is –0.34 mi/13.34 mi = –0.025 = –2.5%.

53. The absolute error is 24.65 cm – 24.5 cm = 0.15 cm. The relative error is (24.65 cm – 24.5 cm) / 24.5 cm = 0.006 = 0.6%.

54. The absolute error is 2 votes. The relative error is 2 votes/2563 votes = 0.0008 = 0.08%.

55. The measurement obtained by the tape measure is more accurate because the value is closer to your true height than the value obtained at the doctor's office (1/8 inch versus 0.4 inch). However, the laser at the doctor's office is more precise as it measures to the nearest 0.05 (or 1/20) inch, while the tape measure measures to the nearest 1/8 inch.

56. The laser at the doctor's office is both more precise and more accurate, as it measures your height exactly (while the tape measure is off by

1/8 inch), and it measures to the nearest 0.05 (or 1/20) inch compared to the nearest 1/8 inch.

57. The digital scale at the gym is both more precise and more accurate. It is more precise because it measures to the nearest 0.01 kg, while the health clinic's scale measures to the nearest 0.5 kg, and it is more accurate because its reported weight is nearer to your true weight than the scale at the health clinic.

58. The scale at the health clinic is more accurate because the error in measuring your true weight is only 0.05 kg, while the error of the digital scale is 0.07 kg. The digital scale is more accurate, because it gives readings to the nearest 0.01 kg compared to the clinic's scale, which gives readings to the nearest 0.5 kg.

59. A calculator gives 12 lb – 0.1 lb = 11.9 lb. This should be rounded to the nearest 1 lb because that's the level of precision of 12 lb. The final answer is 12 lb.

60. A calculator gives 43 mi/hr × 0.25 hr = 10.75 mi. However, as both numbers have only two significant digits, we must use only two in the final answer: 11 mi

61. A calculator gives 102 km/065 hr = 156.923 km/hr. However, as both numbers have only two significant digits, we must use only two in the final answer: 150 km/hr.

62. A calculator gives 60,000 households × $445.79/household = $26,747,400. However, as the first number has only one significant digit, we must use only one in the final answer: $30 million.

63. The least precise measurement is 36 miles, which is precise to the nearest mile, so the answer should be rounded to the nearest mile. 36 mi + 2.2 mi = 38.2 mi, which is 38 mi when rounded to the correct level of precision.

64. 50 kg + 1.25 kg = 51.25 kg, but the answer must be reported to the nearest 10 kg, as that's the level of precision of the first weight. Thus the final answer is 50 kg.

65. The cost is $2.1 million/120,345 people = $17.45 per person. However, as the first measurement has only two significant digits, so must the answer, so we round to $17 per person.

66. A calculator gives $21.43 ÷ 450 lb = $0.0476222... However, as the first number has only two significant digits, we must use only two in the final answer: $0.048/lb.

FURTHER APPLICATIONS

67. Random or systematic errors could be present, (for example, a car could be counted twice or not counted). The measurement is not believable with the given precision.

68. Random or systematic errors could be present (for example, if vote were not counted or voting machines did not operate properly). The measurement is not believable with the given precision. Recounts of votes are usually taken if the totals for candidates only differ by a small number of voters, especially in large elections.

69. Systematic errors could be present if the equipment (such as a transit) used to measure the height is faulty, and random errors could occur in several ways (e.g. if a transit is used, and it wasn't aimed precisely at the top of the building). But even considering these factors, the figure is believable with the given precision.

70. Random or systematic errors could be present, (for example, a person could be counted twice or not counted) but the precision implies that the number of *Smith*s is known with an error of $305,000,000 \times 0.00001 = \pm3,000$, which is believable.

71. Systematic errors could arise depending on how the area of a lake is defined and how it is measured (should we measure at the current water level, or at the highest recorded water level?), and random errors could easily arise due to changes in the shape of the lake over time, or errors in recording the data. The fact is not believable because (as explained above), it is rather difficult to define how the area of a lake should be measured, let alone measure such a large lake to the nearest square mile.

72. This measurement could have many sources of errors, both random and systematic (for example, transient people might get counted twice). The measurement is not believable as the level of precision (to the nearest person) is unattainable. In the time it would take to conduct the survey, many people would have been born and died, and people immigrating to the country change its population on a daily basis.

73. This measurement could have many sources of errors, both random and systematic (for example, people that were killed may not be reported missing and some people that were killed may never be found). The measurement is not believable as the level of precision (to the nearest person) is unattainable, especially in the chaos following a major natural disaster.

74. With good accounting, the circulation of the magazine could be known to the nearest subscriber at a given instant of time; it is believable.

75. a. Since each cut can be off by 0.25 inches, the maximum error in either direction will be 20 × 0.25 in. = 5 in. The lengths of the boards can be between 48 in. – 5 in. = 43 in. and 48 in. + 5 in. = 53 in.

b. Since each cut can be off by 0.005%, the lengths of the boards can be between $48 \times (0.995)^{20} = 17.20$ in. and $48 \times (1.005)^{20} = 53.03$ in.

UNIT 3D

TIME OUT TO THINK

Pg. 173. Answers will vary. Assuming today's price is \$3.00, the index would be $\frac{\$3.00}{\$0.567} \times 100 = 529.1$.

Pg. 174. For 1965 $\frac{31.2¢}{119.6¢} \times 100 = 26.1$., Similar calculations will verify the values in the last column of Table 3.3.

Pg. 177. The two curves would cross in 1982, but the general trends would look the same.

QUICK QUIZ

1. **b.** The 1985 index of 210.9 is a little more than twice as large as the 1975 index of 100, so the price of gas in 1985 is roughly twice as much as the price in 1975.
2. **c.** If you know the price of gas in 1970, you can divide today's price by the 1970 price to get the index number for the current year.
3. **b.** Like most indexes, the CPI is designed to allow one to compare prices from one year to another.
4. **c.** To compare prices in one year to prices in another, one can just divide the CPI from one year by the other – this tells you the factor by which prices in one year differ from prices in another.
5. **c.** The CPI in 2008 was 215.3, and it was 152.4 in 1995. Thus prices in 2008 are 41% more than prices in 1995 (because 215.3/152.4 = 1.41). If the CPI were recalibrated so that 1995 = 100, the new CPI in 2005 would be 141, which is lower than 215.3.
6. **b.** As long as the computers being compared are of comparable power, since the prices have declined, the index would decrease.
7. **a.** If the cost of college has increased faster than the CPI, but one's salary has only kept pace with the CPI, then the cost of college as a percentage of salary has increased, making it more difficult to afford.
8. **a.** If your salary increases faster than the CPI, then it has more purchasing power than in previous years.
9. **c.** Measured in 2006 dollars, gas was less than \$1.50 per gallon in 1998–1999, and this is lower than any other time shown on the chart.
10. **c.** In order to reflect the fact that housing prices have tripled from 1985 to 2005, the index would also triple, from 100 to 300.

DOES IT MAKE SENSE?

5. Does not make sense. One must consider the affect of inflation on the price of gas, and compare the prices in, say, 2006 dollars in order to make a valid comparison.
6. Makes sense. As long as the speaker of the statement lives in a country where the CPI has increased over the past seven years (i.e. where there has been inflation), a stable salary would lose purchasing power over time.
7. Makes sense. A penny in Franklin's day would be worth something on the order of a dollar today.
8. Makes sense. As long as the price of a car has increased at a rate lower than the CPI over the last couple decades, a car would be cheaper when compared to prices (in today's dollars) of twenty years ago.
9. Does not make sense. The reference year that is chosen for an index number does not affect the trends of inflation, so if milk is more expensive in 1995 dollars, it should also be more expensive in 1975 dollars.
10. Does not make sense. Students on financial aid rely on government programs for funding, and the money spent on these programs is directly tied to the CPI.

BASIC SKILLS & CONCEPTS

11. To find the index number, take the current price and divide it by the 1975 price: \$2.50/\$0.567 = 4.409 = 440.9%. The price index number is 440.9 (the percentage sign is dropped).
12. To find the index number, take the current price and divide it by the 1975 price: \$2.80/\$0.567 = 4.938 = 493.8%. The price index number is 493.8 (the percentage sign is dropped).
13. The price index number in 2005 is 407.4, which means prices in 2005 were 407.4% of the prices in 1975. Thus \$10 spent on gas in 1975 is equivalent to \$10 × 407.4% = \$8 × 4.074 = \$32.59.
14. To find the factor by which 2005 prices were greater than 1995 prices, divide their index numbers: 407.4/212.5 = 1.9171. This means prices in 2005 were 191.71% of prices in 1995, and thus \$12 spent in 1995 is equivalent to \$12 × 1.9171 = \$23.01 in 2005 dollars.
15. To find the fraction of a tank you could purchase, divide the 1985 price by the 2005 price: $\frac{119.6¢}{231.0¢} = 0.52 = 52\%$, so you could buy 0.52 of a tank with \$10 in 2005.

16. With 1995 as the reference value, the price index number for that year is 100. To find the index for 1955, divide the 1955 price by the 1995 price, convert to a percent, and drop the percent sign:

$$\frac{29.1¢}{120.5¢} = 0.241 = 24.1\%$$, so the index is 24.1.

Follow the same procedure to find the index for 1965: $\frac{31.2¢}{120.5¢} = 0.259 = 25.9\%$, so the index is 25.9. Do the same thing for the remaining years to arrive at the following index numbers. 1975 = 47.1. 1985 = 99.3. 1995 = 100.0. 2005 = 191.7.

17. Divide the 2008 CPI by the 1976 CPI to find the factor by which prices in 2008 were larger than prices in 1977: $\frac{CPI_{2008}}{CPI_{1976}} = \frac{215.3}{56.9} = 3.784$. This means prices in 2008 were about 3.784 times larger than prices in 1976, so $20,000 in 1976 is equivalent to $20,000 \times \frac{215.3}{56.9} = \$75,677$ in 2008.

18. Divide the 2006 CPI by the 1985 CPI to find the factor by which prices in 2005 were larger than prices in 1981: $\frac{CPI_{2005}}{CPI_{1985}} = \frac{201.6}{107.6} = 1.874$. This means prices in 2006 were about 1.874 times larger than prices in 1985, so $40,000 in 1981 is equivalent to $40,000 \times \frac{201.6}{107.6} = \$74,944$ in 2006.

19. Inflation is the relative change in the CPI, which is $\frac{CPI_{1985} - CPI_{1980}}{CPI_{1980}} = \frac{107.6 - 82.4}{82.4} = 0.306 = $ 30.6%. Note that this is inflation over the span of five years (that is, it is not an annual rate of inflation).

20. Inflation is the relative change in the CPI, which is $\frac{CPI_{2008} - CPI_{2000}}{CPI_{2000}} = \frac{215.3 - 172.2}{172.2} = 0.250 = $ 25.0%. Note that this is inflation over the span of eight years (that is, it is not an annual rate of inflation).

21. The price in 2005 dollars is $$\$0.25 \times \frac{CPI_{2005}}{CPI_{1976}} = \$0.25 \times \frac{195.3}{56.9} = \$0.86$$

22. The price in 2006 dollars is $$\$1500 \times \frac{CPI_{2006}}{CPI_{1980}} = \$1500 \times \frac{201.6}{82.4} = \$3670$$

23. The price in 1980 dollars is $$\$9.00 \times \frac{CPI_{1980}}{CPI_{2008}} = \$9.00 \times \frac{82.4}{215.3} = \$3.44$$

24. The price in 1980 dollars is

$$\$85 \times \frac{CPI_{1985}}{CPI_{2008}} = \$85 \times \frac{107.6}{215.3} = \$42.48.$$

25. The purchasing power of a 1976 dollar in terms of 2006 dollars is $$\$1 \times \frac{CPI_{2006}}{CPI_{1976}} = \$1 \times \frac{201.6}{56.9} = \$3.54.$$

26. The purchasing power of a 1979 dollar in terms of 2008 dollars is $$\$1 \times \frac{CPI_{2008}}{CPI_{1979}} = \$1 \times \frac{215.3}{72.6} = \$2.97.$$

27. In Palo Alto, the price would be $300,000 \times \frac{365}{87}$, which is $1.26 million. In Sioux City, the price would be $300,000 \times \frac{47}{87} = \$162,000$. In Boston, the price would be $300,000 \times \frac{182}{87} = \$627,600$.

28. In Juneau, the price would be $570,000 \times \frac{100}{182}$, which is $313,000. In Manhattan, the price would be $570,000 \times \frac{495}{182} = \$1.55$ million. In Tulsa, the price would be $570,000 \times \frac{52}{182} = \$163,000$.

29. In Spokane, the price would be $250,000 \times \frac{78}{75}$, which is $260,000. In Denver, the price would be $250,000 \times \frac{87}{75} = \$290,000$. In Juneau, the price would be $250,000 \times \frac{100}{75} = \$333,000$.

30. In Providence, the price would be $1 \text{ million} \times \frac{91}{495} = \$184,000$. In Spokane, the price would be $1 \text{ million} \times \frac{78}{495} = \$158,000$. In Tulsa, it would be $1 \text{ million} \times \frac{52}{495} = \$105,000$.

31. Health care spending increased by a percent of $\frac{\$2.4 \times 10^{12} - \$85 \times 10^9}{\$85 \times 10^9} = 27 = 2700\%$, whereas the overall rate of inflation was $\frac{CPI_{2007} - CPI_{1976}}{CPI_{1976}} = \frac{207.3 - 56.9}{56.9} = 2.64 = 264\%$.

32. The relative change in cost for an airline ticket was $\frac{\$420 - \$230}{\$230} = 0.83 = 83\%$. The overall rate

of inflation was $\dfrac{\text{CPI}_{2008} - \text{CPI}_{1980}}{\text{CPI}_{1980}}$

$= \dfrac{215.3 - 82.4}{82.4} = 1.61 = 161\%$.

33. The relative change in the cost of college was $\dfrac{\$25,143 - \$14,857}{\$14,857} = 0.69 = 69\%$. The rate of

inflation was $\dfrac{\text{CPI}_{2008} - \text{CPI}_{1989}}{\text{CPI}_{1989}} = \dfrac{215.3 - 124.0}{124.0}$

$= 0.74 = 74\%$.

34. The relative change in the cost of college was $\dfrac{\$6585 - \$2929}{\$2929} = 1.25 = 125\%$. The rate of

inflation was $\dfrac{\text{CPI}_{2008} - \text{CPI}_{1989}}{\text{CPI}_{1989}} = \dfrac{215.3 - 124.0}{124.0}$

$= 0.74 = 74\%$.

35. The relative change in the price of a home was $\dfrac{\$170,000 - \$75,300}{\$75,300} = 1.26 = 126\%$. The rate of

inflation was $\dfrac{\text{CPI}_{2008} - \text{CPI}_{1990}}{\text{CPI}_{1990}} = \dfrac{215.3 - 130.7}{130.7}$

$= 0.65 = 65\%$.

36. The relative change in the price of a home was $\dfrac{\$275,000 - \$129,600}{\$129,600} = 1.12 = 112\%$. The rate of

inflation was $\dfrac{\text{CPI}_{2008} - \text{CPI}_{1990}}{\text{CPI}_{1990}} = \dfrac{215.3 - 130.7}{130.7}$

$= 0.65 = 65\%$

37. As shown in the first line of the table, $0.25 in 1938 dollars is worth $2.78 in 1996 dollars.

38. As shown in the table, $1.00 in 1956 dollars is worth $5.77 in 1996 dollars.

39. In 1996, actual dollars are 1996 dollars.

40. 2005 dollars are worth less than 1996 dollars due to inflation.

41. The 1979 minimum wage, measured in 1979 dollars, was $2.90. To convert this to 1996 dollars, use the CPI from 1996 and 1979.

$$\$2.90 \times \frac{\text{CPI}_{1996}}{\text{CPI}_{1979}} = \$2.90 \times \frac{156.9}{72.6} = \$6.27 .$$

This agrees with the entry in the table.

42. The 1968 minimum wage was $7.21, measured in 1996 dollars. The 2008 minimum wage was $5.12, measured in 1996 dollars. The 1968 minimum wage has more purchasing power.

43. The purchasing power of the minimum wage was highest in 1968, when its value in 1996 dollars was highest ($7.21). Since all entries in the last column are listed in 1996 dollars, we can make valid comparisons between values in the column.

44. Answers will vary.

TECHNOLOGY EXERCISES

53. $100 in 1980 has the same buying power as $261.93 in 2009.

54. $10 in 2009 has the same buying power as $0.94 in 1920.

55. $25 in 1930 has the same buying power as $323.10 in 2009.

56. $1000 in 2008 has the same buying power as $46.91 in 1915.

57. *A* will be greater than *B*.

58. *C* will be less than *D*.

UNIT 3E

TIME OUT TO THINK

Pg. 185. Although women were admitted at a significantly higher rate than men in Department A, the total number of men admitted is more than five times the total number of women admitted in the department. Thus it would be difficult to say that the department favors women overall. However, it is conceivable that women gained some preference in admissions, perhaps in an effort to increase the low female enrollment. Alternatively, it may simply be that because the department is more popular among men, the relatively few female applicants tended to be more qualified (i.e., women applied only if they were very confident of their abilities). Without investigating the applicant pools in more depth, we cannot draw any conclusion about discrimination.

Pg. 187(1st). Answers will vary. One point to consider is if a woman has previously had breast cancer, a biopsy might seem like a particularly good idea. Similarly, if there is a strong family history of breast cancer, the biopsy might also be recommended. Also, how much of a factor cost should play in the decision. This would be a good topic for a discussion either during or outside of class.

Pg. 187(2nd). There is a 90% chance that you'll pass the test, in which case the police would presumably begin to believe in your innocence. However, there is a 10% chance that you'll fail. If the police are aware that most people who fail are still actually innocent, then this might not hurt you. However, most people assume the tests are very reliable, and the police are therefore likely to be even more adamant about your guilt if you fail the test. This would be a good topic for a discussion either during or outside of class.

QUICK QUIZ

1. **a**. As stated in the text surrounding the table, the old treatment had a better overall treatment rate, even though the new treatment performed better in each category.

2. **a**. 63% refers to the percent of men admitted to Department B.

3. **b**. Even though Derek had a higher GPA in each of the two years, we can't be sure his overall GPA was higher than Terry's – Simpson's paradox may be at play.

4. **a**. A *false negative* means the test detected no cancer (that's the *negative* part) even though the person has it (the *false* part).

5. **c**. A *false positive* means the test detected steroids (that's the *positive* part), but the person never used steroids (that's the *false* part).

6. **c**. The last row in the column labeled *Tumor is benign* shows the total of those who did not have malignant tumors.

7. **b**. Those who had false negatives (15) and false positives (1485) make up the group who had incorrect test results.

8. **c**. Imagine a test group of 1000 women, where 900 are actually pregnant, and 100 are not. Of those who are pregnant, 1% (that is, 9 women) will test negative. Of those who aren't pregnant, 99% (that is, 99 women) will test negative. Thus 108 women test negative, and 99 of them actually aren't pregnant. Since 99/108 is not 99% (it's closer to 92%), statement **c** is not true (it may be true in other scenarios, but in general, it is not).

9. **b**. A person earning $200,000 will save 2.9% of his income, which is $5800. A person earning $50,000 will save 4.4% of his income, which is $2200. Thus the person earning $200,000 or more will save more total tax dollars than someone earning between $40,000 and $50,000.

10. **c**. A person earning more than $200,000 will see his tax bill fall by 2.9% (see Republican table).

DOES IT MAKE SENSE?

5. Makes sense. If Simpson's paradox is at work, both categories could show an improvement with the new drug even though overall, the old drug may have done a better job.

6. Does not make sense. It is not clear who played the better game – one would have to look at the actual baskets made to determine who scored more points.

7. Does not make sense. There are scenarios (see discussion in text concerning mammograms and drug tests, for example) where a positive test may not correlate well with the probability that a bag contains banned materials, even though the test is 98% accurate.

8. Does not make sense. See discussion in text concerning polygraph tests.

9. Does not make sense. Both sides can make a valid argument for their position (see discussion in text about tax cuts).

10. Makes sense. If the percent increase in the annual budget was less than the CPI, the purchasing power of dollars received is lower this year than last, which amounts to a cut in the budget.

BASIC SKILLS & CONCEPTS

11. a. As shown in the tables, Josh had a higher batting average in the first half of the season.
    b. As shown in the tables, Josh had a higher batting average in the second half of the season.
    c. Jude had the higher overall batting average (80/200 = .400 versus 85/220 = .386).
    d. This illustrates Simpson's paradox because it's a case where one person (Josh) performed better in two of two categories (the first and second halves of the season), and yet Jude outperformed Josh over the course of the entire season.

12. a. As shown in the tables, Justice had a higher batting average in both 1995 and 1996.
    b. Justice's combined batting average was (104 + 45)/(411 + 140) = 0.270 and Jeter's combined batting average was (12 + 183)/(48 + 582) = 0.310.
    c. From (b), Jeter had the highest combined batting average.
    d. This illustrates Simpson's paradox because it's a case where one person (Justice) performed better in two out of two categories (1995 and 1996), and yet Jeter outperformed Justice over the course of two seasons.

13. a. New Jersey had higher scores in both categories (283 versus 281, and 252 versus 250), but Nebraska had the higher overall average (277 versus 272).
    b. The explanation lies in Simpson's paradox: it's possible for one state (Nebraska) to score lower in both categories, and yet have a higher overall percentage. This is due to the different racial makeup of the two state's populations. The white students are scoring better than the nonwhite students in both states, and Nebraska has a larger percentage of white students than New Jersey, so they influence the overall scores more heavily than the white students in New Jersey.
    c. The verification is an exercise in a weighted average. 87% of the population had an average of 281, and 13% of the population had an average of 250, so the overall average is 0.87(281) + 0.13(250) = 277.

d. As in part **c**, we only have to compute a weighted average: $0.66(283) + 0.34(252) = 272$.

e. See part **b**.

14. a. The SAT scores all decreased by about 3 points in each of the grade categories.

    b. The overall SAT scores increased by 10 points between 1988 and 1998.

    c. This is an illustration of Simpson's paradox because SAT scores went down in each of the five grade categories, and yet in the overall picture, they increased.

15. a. The death rate for whites was $8400/4,675,000 = 0.0018 = 0.18\%$. For nonwhites, it was $500/92,000 = 0.0054 = 0.54\%$. Overall, the death rate was $8900/4,767,000 = 0.0019 = 0.19\%$.

    b. The death rate for whites was $130/81,000 = 0.0016 = 0.16\%$. For nonwhites, it was $160/47,000 = 0.0034 = 0.34\%$. Overall, the death rate was $290/128,000 = 0.0023 = 0.23\%$.

    c. Simpson's paradox is at work here because the death rates for TB in each category (white and nonwhite) were higher in New York City than in Richmond, and yet the overall death rate due to TB was higher in Richmond. The paradox arises because Richmond had a different racial makeup than New York City: it had a much higher percentage of nonwhite residents than New York, and as the death rate for TB was much higher among nonwhites than whites in both cities, the higher percentage of nonwhites in Richmond has a more pronounced influence on the death rate.

16. Simpson's paradox is at work here because the Gazelles saw a larger time improvement than the Cheetahs in each category (10s versus 9s among those who weight trained, and 2s versus 1s among those who did not), and yet the Cheetahs realized a larger time improvement across the entire team. To determine the percentage of each team that used weight training, we need to use the idea of a weighted average. Suppose the ratio of Gazelles who used weight training is represented by x. Then the ratio of those who did not use weight training is $1 - x$. The weighted average across the entire team is 6.0 s, so we must solve $10x + 2(1 - x) = 6$ for x. This results in $x = 0.5$, so 50% of the Gazelles used weight training. In a similar fashion, the percent of Cheetahs who used weight training can be determined: $9x + 1(1 - x) = 6.2$, which results in a solution of $x = 0.65$. Thus 65% of the Cheetahs used weight training. As the table shows, weight training improves race times on both teams much more dramatically than using no weight training, and since the Cheetahs had a higher percentage of runners who used weight training, it makes sense they had a better overall improvement in times.

17. a. There are 10,000 total participants with tumors in the study (lower right hand entry), and 1% of them (100) have malignant tumors. Since the test is 90% accurate, 90 of those with malignant tumors will be true positives, while the other 10 will be false negatives. 99% of the women (9900) will have benign tumors. 90% of these (8910) will be true negatives, while 10% of these (990) will be false positives. The only numbers in the table not yet verified are the first two entries in the Total column; these are simply the sum of the rows in which they lie.

    b. Of the 1080 who have positive mammograms, only 90 are true positives, so only $90/1080 = 8.3\%$ of them actually have cancer.

    c. 100 of the women have cancer (malignant tumors), and 90 of those will have a true positive test result, which is 90%. Thus if you really have cancer, the test will detect it 90% of the time.

    d. Of the 8920 who have a negative mammogram, only 10 of them are false negatives, which translates to a probability of $10/8920 = 0.11\%$.

18. a. Beginning with the last row, there are 2000 employees, and 1% of them (20) use drugs, while the other 99% (1980) do not. The first column shows the 20 drug users, and 85% of them (17) will be detected when they lie about their drug use, while 3 of them will avoid detection. The second column shows the 1980 non-users, and 85% of them (1683) will pass the polygraph when they tell the truth that they don't use drugs. The other 297 of them will be falsely accused of using drugs, because they will fail the test. The entries in last column are simply the sum of the rows in which they lie.

    b. 314 are accused of lying, but only 17 of them are actually lying; the remaining 297 (the falsely accused) are telling the truth. $297/314 = 94.6\%$ are falsely accused.

    c. 1686 are found to be truthful, and 1683 of them actually are telling the truth, and thus $1683/1686 = 99.8\%$ of those found truthful really were telling the truth.

19. a. Beginning with the last row, the sample size is 4000, and 1.5% of them (60) have the disease, while the remaining 3940 do not. The first column shows the 60 with the disease, and the test detects 90% of them (54), but misses 6 of them. The second column shows the 3940 who do not have the disease, and the test says 90% of them (3546) do not have the disease (a negative test), but it says 10% of them (394) do have the disease. The entries in the last column are simply the sum of the rows in which they lie.

    b. 54 of the 60 (90%) who have the disease test positive.

c. 54 of the 448 (12%) who test positive actually have the disease. In part **b**, the answer of 90% is the ratio of those who test positive out of those who have the disease, while the answer of 12% here is the ratio of those who have the disease among those that test positive.

d. As shown in part **c**, if you test positive, you have a 12% chance of actually having the disease. This is 8 times the overall incidence rate (1.5%), which means there is reason for concern, and yet it's still a fairly low chance that you actually have the disease.

20. One can argue that funding for the program is being cut because there was a 1% rise in the budget, and yet the CPI is 3%, which means the purchasing power of the new budget has decreased. On the other hand, the funding has certainly increased from $1 billion to $1.01 billion.

FURTHER APPLICATIONS

21. a. Spelman won 10/29 = 34% of its home games and 12/16 = 75% of its away games, while Morehouse won 9/28 = 32% of its home games and 56/76 = 74% of its away games. Since Spelman is better than Morehouse in each category, it's the better team.

b. Morehouse won 65/104 = 62.5% of all the games they played, while Spelman won 22/45 = 49% of all the games they played. Based on these figures, Morehouse is the better team.

c. Disregarding the strength of the opponents each college played, it's universally accepted that the team with a higher percentage of wins is the better team, and thus the claim in part **b** makes more sense. Additionally, it's more difficult to win away games than home games, and while both teams have an impressive away-game win percentage, Morehouse complied its overall record of 62.5% with many more away games.

22. a. Drug B cured 101/900 = 11.2% of female patients and 196/200 = 98% of male patients, while Drug A cured 5/100 = 5% of female patients and 400/800 = 50% of male patients. Since Drug B outperformed drug A in both categories, it's the more effective drug.

b. Drug A cured 405/900 = 45% of all patients, while Drug B cured 297/1100 = 27% of all patients, so Drug A is more effective than Drug B.

c. Because the drugs had such different effects on men and women, the individual cure rates should be cited and used for evaluating the drugs (that is, the claim in part **a** makes more sense).

23. a. Note that 10% of the 5000 at risk people is 500, and this is the sum of the first row in the first table. For the 20,000 people in the general population, note that 0.3% of 20,000 is 60, and this is the sum of the first row in the second table. 95% of the 500 infected people in the at risk group should test positive, and 5% should test negative – take 95% and 5% of 500 to verify the first row entries in the first table. 95% of the 4500 at risk people who aren't infected should test negative, while 5% should test positive – take 95% and 5% of 4500 to verify the second row in the first table. A similar process will show that the numbers in the second table are also correct.

b. 475/500 = 95% of those with HIV test positive. 475/700 = 67.9% of those who test positive have HIV. The percentages are different because the number of people in each group (those who have HIV and those who test positive) is different.

c. As shown in part **b**, if you test positive, and you are in the at risk group, you have a 67.9% chance of carrying the disease. This is much greater than the overall percentage of those who have the disease (10%), which means if you test positive, you should be concerned.

d. 57/60 = 95% of those with HIV test positive. 57/1054 = 5.4% of those who test positive have HIV. The two percentages are different because the number of people in each group (those who have HIV and those who test positive) is different.

e. As shown in part **d**, if you test positive, and you are in the general population, you have a 5.4% chance of carrying the disease. This is larger than the overall percentage of those who have the disease (0.3%), but it's still small enough that it's best to wait for more tests before becoming alarmed.

24. a. Excelsior Airlines has a higher percentage of on-time flights in each of the five cities shown in the table.

b. First, compute the number of overall on-time arrivals for Excelsior by multiplying the percents in each row by the number of arrivals for each city, and adding these together:
0.889(559) + 0.948(233) + 0.914(232) + 0.831(605) + 0.858(2146) = 3274 on-time flights. Divide this by the total number of flights (3775) to find the overall on-time percentage: 3274/3775 = 86.7%.

Next, do the same thing for Paradise:
0.856(811) + 0.921(5255) + 0.855(448) + 0.713(449) + 0.767(262) = 6438 on-time flights, which means an overall on-time percentage of 6438/7225 = 89.1%.

c. Simpson's paradox is evident here because Excelsior had a higher percentage of on-time flights in each of the five cities, yet Paradise had the higher overall percentage of on-time flights.

25. The data suggest a hiring preference for women because a higher percentage of women were hired in each of the two categories (white-collar and blue-collar jobs). On the other hand, if one looks at the overall picture, it turns out a higher percentage of male applicants was hired. (There were 20% of 200 applicants = 40 female workers hired for white-collar jobs, and 85% of 100 applicants = 85 female workers hired for blue-collar jobs. Thus there were 125 workers hired from a pool of 300 applicants, which is 125/300 = 41.7%. There were 15% of 200 applicants = 30 male workers hired for white-collar jobs, and 75% of 400 applicants = 300 male workers hired for blue-collar jobs. Thus there were 330 workers hired from a pool of 600 applicants, which is 330/600 = 55%.) This is an example of Simpson's paradox because females were hired at a greater rate in both categories of workers, and yet males were hired at a greater rate overall. The paradox can be resolved by realizing that there were many more males hired for the blue-collar jobs, which are more abundant than the white-collar jobs, and thus the male-dominated blue-collar jobs have a greater influence on the overall hiring rate.

26. Treatment A had a better cure rate in each of the two trials (20% versus 15% in the first trial, and 85% versus 75% in the second trial). The overall cure rate for Treatment A was 125/300 = 41.7%, while the overall cure rate for Treatment B was 330/600 = 55%, and thus Treatment B had the better overall cure rate. This is an example of Simpson's paradox because Treatment A performed better in each of the trials, and yet Treatment B performed better overall. The paradox can be resolved by realizing that there were more people in the second trial who received Treatment B.

27. – 30. Answers will vary.

31. a. The absolute difference in savings is $12,838 – $211 = $12,627. A single person earning $41,000 will save $211/$41,000 = 0.5% of income. A single person earning $530,000 will save $12,838/$530,000 = 2.4% of income.

    b. The absolute difference in savings is $13,442 – $1208 = $12,234. A married couple earning $41,000 will save $1208/$41,000 = 2.9% of income. A married couple earning $530,000 will save $13,442/$530,000 = 2.5% of income.

UNIT 4A

TIME OUT TO THINK

Pg. 201. Answers will vary. This would be a good topic for a discussion either during or outside of class.

Pg. 203. Answers will vary, but considerations could include ways to free up time to study other than cutting back on work hours, the need to take out student loans, and future estimates of earnings based on completing a college degree. This would be a good topic for a discussion either during or outside of class.

QUICK QUIZ

1. **a**. Evaluating your budget allows you to look critically at your cash flow, which affects personal spending.
2. **a**. Your cash flow is determined by the amount of money you earn (income), and the amount you spend.
3. **b**. If your cash flow is negative, you are spending more than you take in.
4. **c**. You should prorate all once-per-year expenses and include them in your monthly budget.
5. **b**. Housing typically costs about one-third of your income.
6. **c**. As a percentage of income, health care expenses are not too alarming, though they grow rapidly as one ages.
7. **a**. You can't save without money left over at the end of the month, which corresponds to a positive cash flow.
8. **c**. Trey spends about $5 per day on cigarettes, which comes to $150 per month.
9. **c**. Kira spends $7.50 per day on soda, so over the course of a year, she spends nearly $3000.
10. **b**. Each week, you use about 22 gallons of gas, because (400 mi)/(18 mi/gal) = 22.2 gal. With gas at $3/gal, this comes to $66/week, or $3432/year. A car that gets 50 mi/gal will use about one-third of the gas used by your old car (because 50 is almost three times as large as 18), which means it will cost about $1100/year for gas. The difference between these two values is the amount you save, around $2200.

DOES IT MAKE SENSE?

7. Does not make sense. All the smaller expenses do add up, and they have a significant influence on your budget.
8. Makes sense. If you have a negative monthly cash flow, your debt will rise.
9. Makes sense. When prorated as a per-month expense, an $1800 vacation costs $150 per month.
10. Makes sense. Cash flow is determined by income and spending, and one way to turn a negative cash flow into a positive cash flow (other factors being equal) is to earn more money.
11. Does not make sense. Divide $15,000 by 365 (days per year) to find that an annual expense of $15,000 comes to $41 per day. Pizza and a soda do not cost that much.
12. Does not make sense. You generally get what you pay for, and cheap insurance usually goes hand-in-hand with minimal benefits and hidden costs.

BASIC SKILLS & CONCEPTS

13. Maria spends $20 each week on coffee, and using 52 weeks per year, this comes to $1040 per year. She spends $130 each month on food, which is $1560 per year. The amount she spends on coffee is $1040/$1560 = 67% of the amount she spends on food.
14. Jeremy spends $6 each week on the newspaper, which comes to $312 per year. He spends $20 per week, or $1040 per year on gas. The amount he spends on the *New York Times* is $312/$1040 = 30% of the amount he spends on gas.
15. Suzanne spends $85 per month for her cell phone usage, which is $1020 per year. This is $1020/$200 = 510% of the amount she spends on health insurance.
16. Homer spends $10 per week on lottery tickets, which comes to $520 per year. He spends $400 each month on rent, or $4800 per year. The amount he spends on lottery tickets is $520/$4800 = 11% of the amount he spends on rent.
17. Sheryl spends $9 each week on cigarettes, which comes to $468 per year. She spends $30 each month on dry cleaning, or $360 per year. The amount she spends on cigarettes is $468/$360 = 130% of the amount she spends on dry cleaning.
18. Ted spends $60 every two weeks on concert tickets, which is $30 per week. Using 52 weeks per year, he spends $1560 per year on tickets, which is $1560/$500 = 312% of the amount he spends on car insurance.
19. Vern spends $21 per week on beer, which amounts to $1092 per year. This is $1092/$700 = 156% of the amount he spends on textbooks.
20. Sandy spends $35 every two weeks, which is $17.50 every week on gas. This comes to $910 per year. She spends $60 per month, or $720 per year for her TV/Internet services. The amount she spends on gas is $910/$720 = 126% of the amount she spends on TV/Internet services.
21. Since 18%/12 = 1.5%, you spend 1.5% of $650 on interest each month, which is $0.015 × $650 =

$9.75. Over the span of a year, you'll spend $117 on interest.

22. Since 21%/12 = 1.75%, Brooke spends 1.75% of $900, or $0.0175 \times \$900 = \$15.75$ on interest each month. Over the course of a year, she'll spend $189 on interest.

23. Vic's balance is $2200 – $300 = $1900. He spends 3% of $1900, or $0.03 \times \$1900 = \$57$ each month on interest. This comes to $684 per year.

24. Deanna pays 9% of $700, or $0.09 \times \$700 = \$63.00$ on interest each month. Over the course of a year, she'll spend $756 on interest.

25. Sara spends $6000 per semester, or $12,000 per year, which is $12,000/12 = $1000 per month.

26. Jake spends $600 \times 15 = \$9000$ for 15 credit-hours each quarter, and $350 for books, which comes to $9350 each quarter, or $28,050 per year. Thus his monthly cost is $28,050 /12 = $2337.50 per month.

27. Lan spends $650 \times 2 = \$1300$ per year on automobile insurance, $125 \times 12 = \$1500$ per year for health insurance, and $400 per year on life insurance. The total cost is $3200, which means he spends $3200/12 = $266.67 per month.

28. Each year, Juan spends $500 \times 12 = \$6000$ on rent, $800 \times 2 = \$1600$ on insurance, and $900 at the health club, for a total of $8500 per year. His monthly cost is $8500/12 = $708.

29. Raul spends $200 + $245 + $100 + $300 = $845 each year on these contributions, or $845/12 = $70.42 per month.

30. Using 52 weeks per year, Randy spends $25 \times 52 + \$45 \times 4 = \$1480$ on these expenses each year. That's $1480/12 = $123 per month.

31. Income = $600 \times 12 + \$400 \times 12 + \$5000 = \$17,000$ per year. Expenses = $450 \times 12 + \$50 \times 48 + \$3000 \times 2 + \$100 \times 48 = \$18,600$ per year. Thus annual cash flow is $17,000 – $18,600 = –$1600, and monthly cash flow is –$1600/12 = –$133.

32. Income = $1200 \times 12 + \$7000 + \$8000 = \$29,400$ per year. Expenses = $600 \times 12 + \$70 \times 48 + \$7500 + \$40 \times 12 + \$200 \times 12 + \$65 \times 12 = \$21,720$ per year. Thus annual cash flow is $29,400 – $21,720 = $7680, and monthly cash flow is $7680/12 = $640.

33. Income = $2300 \times 12 = \$27,600$. Expenses = $800 \times 12 + \$90 \times 48 + \$125 \times 12 + \$360 \times 2 + \$400 \times 2 + \$25 \times 48 + \$400 \times 12 + \$85 \times 12 = \$23,960$. Thus annual cash flow is $27,600 – $23,960 = $3640, and monthly cash flow is $3640/12 = $303.

34. Income = $32,000 + \$200 \times 12 = \$34,400$ per year. Expenses = $700 \times 12 + \$150 \times 48 + \$450 \times 12 + \$150 \times 12 + \$500 \times 2 + \$200 \times 12 + \$600 + \$800 \times 12 = \$36,400$. Thus annual cash

flow is $34,400 – $36,400 = –$2000, and monthly cash flow is –$2000/12 = –$167.

35. The woman spends $900/$3200 = 28% of her income on rent (i.e. housing), which is below average.

36. The couple spends $400/$3500 = 11% on entertainment, which is above average.

37. The man spends $200/$3600 = 5.6% on health care, which is about average.

38. The couple earns $45,500/12 = $3792 per month, and spends $700/$3792 = 18% on transportation, which is slightly below average.

39. The couple spends $600/$4200 = 14% on health care, which is above average.

40. The family earns $48,000/12 = $4000 per month, and spends $1500/$4000 = 37.5% on housing, which is above average.

41. The cost of using the old car is computed below.
Gas:
$$\frac{250 \text{ mi}}{\text{wk}} \times \frac{1 \text{ gal}}{21 \text{ mi}} \times \frac{\$3.50}{1 \text{ gal}} \times \frac{52 \text{ wk}}{\text{yr}} \times 5 \text{ yr} = \$10,833 .$$

Insurance: $\dfrac{\$400}{\text{yr}} \times 5 \text{ yr} = \$2000$.

Repairs: $\$75,000 = Pe^{0.045 \times 35}$.
Total: $10,833 + $2000 + $7500 = $20,333.
The cost for using the new car is computed below.
Gas:
$$\frac{250 \text{ mi}}{\text{wk}} \times \frac{1 \text{ gal}}{45 \text{ mi}} \times \frac{\$3.50}{1 \text{ gal}} \times \frac{52 \text{ wk}}{\text{yr}} \times 5 \text{ yr} = \$5056 .$$

Insurance: $\dfrac{\$800}{\text{yr}} \times 5 \text{ yr} = \$4000$.

Purchase Price: $16,000.
Total: $5056 + $4000 + $16,000 = $25, 056.
Using the old car is less expensive, but not by a large factor. After five years, if you use the old car, you'll have a junky car, whereas if you bought the new car, you'd have a nice car after five years.

42. Over five years, the old car would cost $18,200 for gas, $3000 for insurance, and $6000 for repairs, for a total of $27,200. The new car would cost $5460 for gas, $4000 for insurance, and $12,000 to buy it, for a total of $21,460. (See details in exercise 41, which is identical except for the numbers used). Using the new car is less expensive over five years.

43. If you buy the car for $22,000, and sell it three years later for $10,000, you will have spent $12,000. If you lease the car for three years (36 months) you will spend $1000 + $250 \times 36 = \$10,000$. It is cheaper to lease in this case.

44. If you buy the car for $22,000, and sell it four years later for $8000, you will have spent $14,000. If you lease the car for four years ($48 months),

you will spend $1000 + $300 × 48 = $15,400. It is cheaper to buy the car in this case.

45. At the in-state college, you will spend $4000 + $700 × 12 = $12,400 each year. At the out-of-state college, you will spend $6500 + $450 × 12 = $11,900. It will cost less out-of-state.

46. If you go to Concord, you will spend $3000 + $800 × 12 = $12,600. If you go to Versalia, you will spend $16,000 − $10,000 + $350 × 12 + $2000 = $12,200. It is cheaper to attend Versalia.

47. If you take the course, you will spend $1500, and use 150 hours of time that could be used to earn money in a job. If you work those 150 hours, you will earn $1500.

48. If you take the part-time job, you will earn $15 × 20 = $300 per week, though you will spend $150 on entertainment, which comes to a net earnings of $150 per week. If you take the full-time job, you will earn $12 × 40 = $480 per week. If finances are the only consideration, the full-time job is the better choice.

FURTHER APPLICATIONS

49. Note that it costs $10 less per month to operate the new dryer, and thus in 62 months, you would have saved $620, which is long enough to pay for the new dryer.

50. The cost for installing the solar system is $18,400 × (100% − 40%) = $11,040. It would take

approximately $\dfrac{\$11,040}{\$85/\text{month}} = 130$ months or

$130 \text{ months} \times \dfrac{1 \text{ yr}}{12 \text{ months}} = 10.8 \text{ years}$.

51. a. If you didn't have the policy, you'd pay all of the costs of the claims, which is $450 + $925 = $1375. If you did have the policy, you'd pay two years of premiums (2 × $550 = $1100), all of the $450 claim, and $500 of the $925 claim, for a grand total of $2050.
b. Without the insurance policy, your cost would be $450 + $1200 = $1650. With the policy, you'd pay premiums for two years, and $200 on each claim for a total of 2 × $650 + 2 × $200 = $1700.
c. Without the policy, your cost would be $200 + $1500 = $1700. With the policy, you'd pay premiums for two years, $200 for the first claim, and $1000 for the second claim, for a total of 2 × $300 + $200 + $1000 = $1800.

52. Under Plan A, you'll pay $1000 for the down payment, $400 for each of 24 months (two years), and $10,000 for the residual, which totals to $1000 + $400 × 24 + $10,000 = $20,600. Under Plan B, the cost will be $500 + $250 × 36 + $9500 = $19,000. Under Plan C, the cost will be $175 × 48

+ $8000 = $16,400, and this is the least expensive plan.

53. a. You'll pay $25 for each of the office visits, $200 for each trip to the emergency room, and $1000 for the surgery, plus one year of premiums, for a grand total of $25 × 3 + $200 × 2 + $1000 + $350 × 12 = $5675.
b. If you did not have the insurance policy, your cost is the total of the numbers in the second column, which is $8220.

54. a. You'll pay $25 for each office visit, $400 for the January 23rd trip to the emergency room, $500 for the September 23rd trip to the emergency room, $1400 for the April 13th surgery, $5000 for the June 14th surgery, and one year of premiums, for a grand total of $25 × 2 + $400 + $500 + $1400 + $5000 + $300 × 12 = $10,950.
b. You'll pay $25 for each office visit, $200 for each trip to the emergency room, $1400 for the April 13th surgery, $1500 for the June 14th surgery, and one year of premiums, for a grand total of $25 × 2 + $200 × 2 + $1400 + $1500 + $700 × 12 = $11,750.
c. With no insurance, you would pay all of the costs listed in the table out-of-pocket, for a total of $10,700. This is cheaper than both Plan A and Plan B, though going without health insurance is very risky: if you have a huge expense (such as extensive care while recovering from a car wreck), you have to pay all of it.

UNIT 4B

TIME OUT TO THINK

Pg. 215. Looking at figure 4.3, students could guess that the value at 3% would be closer to the value at 2% since the graph at 4% rises more quickly. At 3%, the value would be $\$224 \times (1.03)^{535} \approx 1.65 \times 10^9$. At 6%, the value would be $\$224 \times (1.06)^{535} \approx 7.74 \times 10^{15}$. Small increases in the interest rate will cause large changes in the accumulated value since, over 535 years, the value at the end of each year will be larger.

Pg. 217. With n = 1, we get back the formula for compounding once a year. This should be the case because annual compounding means n = 1.

Pg. 220. It is important that students can locate the e^x key on their calculator and become acquainted with the value of e.. For some calculators e^x is the inverse of the LN (natural log) key.

Pg. 223. Even though the annual interest rates may not be constant, they will usually be close to the average annual interest rate, which can be used to make financial decision. You may have a choice of investments with different expected average returns (and different levels of risk). The comparison may therefore still help you decide which type of investment is best for you, given the amount you have to deposit. For example, suppose in Example 9 you have a choice between a high risk mutual fund that historically averages 10% return and a low risk CD that offers 7% return. If you have $40,000 to deposit in the college fund now, the low-risk investment may be the best bet because you'll be assured of reaching your $100,000 goal. But if you have only $16,000 available now, you might choose the higher risk in hopes that the higher return will get you to your goal. FYI: the specific calculations are still valid if the APY at the assumed interest rate turns out to be the average annual interest rate; we cover this in more detail in Unit 4B.

QUICK QUIZ

1. **b**. Compound interest always yields a greater balance than simple interest when the APR is the same.

2. **a**. If you begin with a principle P, and add 5% to its value after one year, the result is $P + 0.05P = 1.05P$, which means the principle increases by a factor of 1.05 each year.

3. **c**. The compound interest formula states $A = P \times (1 + \text{APR})^Y$. With an APR of 6.6%, the balance after five years would be $A = P \times (1 + 0.066)^5$, which means the account increases in value by a factor of 1.066^5.

4. **a**. The APR of 4% is divided evenly into four parts so that each quarter (three months), the account increases in value by 4%/4 = 1%.

5. **c**. Compounding interest more often always results in a greater annual percentage yield.

6. **b**. The APY is the same as the APR with annual compounding, but it's larger in all other cases.

7. **a**. After 20 years, the account earning 4% APR will have grown by a factor of $1.04^{20} = 2.19$, whereas the account earning 2% APR will have grown by a factor of $1.02^{20} = 1.49$. Thus the 4% APR account will have earned about one and a half times as much interest.

8. **a**. The continuously compounded interest formula reads $A = P \times e^{(\text{APR} \times Y)}$, and thus after two years, the balance is $A = \$500 \times e^{(0.06 \times 2)} = \$500 \times e^{0.12}$.

9. **a**. The compound interest formula assumes a constant APR for as many years as you have your money invested in an account.

10. **c**. Bank accounts that earn compound interest grow by larger amounts as time goes by, and this is a hallmark of exponential growth.

DOES IT MAKE SENSE?

9. Does not make sense. You earn more interest under compound interest when the APR is the same.

10. Makes sense. The APY is a function of both the APR and the number of compounding periods. If one bank had more compounding periods than the other, its APY would be greater.

11. Does not make sense. A bank with an APR of 5.9% compounded daily is a better deal than a bank with 6% APR compounded annually (all other things being equal) because the APY in the first case is greater.

12. Does not make sense. There is a diminishing return when banks offer to compound interest more often, and even under the situation where a bank compounds interest continuously (i.e. more often than every trillionth of a second), the APY has a finite limit.

13. Makes sense. One's bank account grows based on the APY, and an APR of 5% could certainly result in an APY of 5.1% if the number of compounding periods per year was just right.

14. Makes sense. At 4% APR (compounded annually), and over the span of twenty years, the value of an account will grow by a factor of $1.04^{20} = 2.19$, which is more than double the original amount.

BASIC SKILLS & CONCEPTS

15. $2^3 = 2 \times 2 \times 2 = 8$.

16. $3^4 = 3 \times 3 \times 3 \times 3 = 81$.

17. $4^3 = 64$.

18. $3^{-2} = \dfrac{1}{3^2} = \dfrac{1}{9}$.

19. $16^{1/2} = \sqrt{16} = 4$.

20. $81^{1/2} = \sqrt{81} = 9$.

21. $64^{-1/3} = \dfrac{1}{64^{1/3}} = \dfrac{1}{\sqrt[3]{64}} = \dfrac{1}{4}$.

22. $2^3 \times 2^5 = 2^{3+5} = 2^8 = 256$.

23. $3^4 \div 3^2 = 3^{4-2} = 3^2 = 9$.

24. $6^2 \times 6^{-2} = 6^{2+(-2)} = 6^0 = 1$.

25. $25^{1/2} \div 25^{-1/2} = 25^{1/2-(-1/2)} = 25^1 = 25$.

26. $3^3 + 2^3 = 27 + 8 = 35$.

27. $x = 12$ (add 3 to both sides).

28. $y = 3$ (subtract 4 from both sides).

29. $z = 16$ (add 10 to both sides).

30. $x = 4$ (divide both sides by 2).
31. $p = 4$ (divide both sides by 3).
32. $y = 4$ (subtract 2, and divide both sides by 4).
33. $z = 4$ (add 1, and divide both sides by 5).
34. $y = -2$ (subtract 1, and divide both sides by -6).
35. $3x - 4 = 2x + 6 \Rightarrow 3x = 2x + 10 \Rightarrow x = 10$.
36. $5 - 4s = 6s - 5 \Rightarrow 10 - 4s = 6s \Rightarrow 10 = 10s \Rightarrow s = 1$.
37. $3a + 4 = 6 + 4a \Rightarrow 3a - 2 = 4a \Rightarrow a = -2$.
38. $3n - 16 = 53 \Rightarrow 3n = 69 \Rightarrow n = 23$.
39. $6q - 20 = 60 + 4q \Rightarrow 6q = 80 + 4q \Rightarrow 2q = 80 \Rightarrow q = 40$.
40. $5w - 5 = 3w - 25 \Rightarrow 5w = 3w - 20 \Rightarrow 2w = -20 \Rightarrow w = -10$.
41. $t/4 + 5 = 25 \Rightarrow t/4 = 20 \Rightarrow t = 80$.
42. $2x/3 + 4 = 2x \Rightarrow 4 = 4x/3 \Rightarrow 4x = 12 \Rightarrow x = 3$.
43. You'll earn 4% of $700, or $0.04 \times \$700 = \$28$, each year. After five years, you will have earned $5 \times \$28 = \$140$ in interest, so that your balance will be $840.
44. Each year, you'll earn 2% of $1200 = $0.02 \times \$1200 = \$24$. After five years, you will have earned $5 \times \$24 = \$120$ in interest, and your balance will be $1320.
45. Each year, you'll earn 2.5% of $3200 = $0.025 \times \$3200 = \$80$. After five years, you will have earned $5 \times \$80 = \$400$ in interest, and your balance will be $3600.
46. Each year, you'll earn 3.2% of $1800 = $0.032 \times \$1800 = \$57.60$. After five years, you will have earned $5 \times \$57.60 = \$288$ in interest, and your balance will be $2088.
47.

	Suzanne		Derek	
Year	Interest	Balance	Interest	Balance
0	-----	$3000	-----	$3000
1	$75	$3075	$75	$3075
2	$75	$3150	$77	$3152
3	$75	$3225	$79	$3231
4	$75	$3300	$81	$3311
5	$75	$3375	$83	$3394

Suzanne's balance increases by $375, or 12.5% of its original value. Derek's increases by $394, or 13.1% of its original value. (Note on values shown in the table: the balance in one year added to next year's interest does not necessarily produce next year's balance due to rounding errors. Each value shown is rounded correctly to the nearest cent).

48.

	Ariel		Travis	
Year	Interest	Balance	Interest	Balance
0	-----	$5000	-----	$5000
1	$150	$5150	$150	$5150
2	$150	$5300	$155	$5305
3	$150	$5450	$159	$5464
4	$150	$5600	$164	$5628
5	$150	$5750	$169	$5797

Ariel's balance increases by $750, or 15% of its original value. Travis' increases by $797, or 15.9% of its original value.

49. $A = \$10,000(1 + 0.04)^{10} = \$14,802.44$.
50. $A = \$10,000(1 + 0.05)^{20} = \$26,532.98$.
51. $A = \$15,000(1 + 0.032)^{25} = \$32,967.32$.
52. $A = \$3000(1 + 0.04)^{12} = \$4803.10$.
53. $A = \$5000(1 + 0.031)^{12} = \$7212.30$.
54. $A = \$40,000(1 + 0.085)^{30} = \$462,330.07$.
55. $A = \$10,000\left(1 + \dfrac{0.02}{4}\right)^{4 \cdot 10} = \$12,207.94$.
56. $A = \$2000\left(1 + \dfrac{0.03}{365}\right)^{365 \cdot 5} = \$2323.65$.
57. $A = \$25,000\left(1 + \dfrac{0.03}{365}\right)^{365 \cdot 5} = \$29,045.68$.
58. $A = \$10,000\left(1 + \dfrac{0.0275}{12}\right)^{12 \cdot 5} = \$11,472.21$.
59. $A = \$2000\left(1 + \dfrac{0.05}{12}\right)^{12 \cdot 15} = \$4227.41$.
60. $A = \$30,000\left(1 + \dfrac{0.045}{365}\right)^{365 \cdot 15} = \$58,918.54$.
61. $A = \$25,000\left(1 + \dfrac{0.037}{4}\right)^{4 \cdot 30} = \$75,472.89$.
62. $A = \$15,000\left(1 + \dfrac{0.042}{12}\right)^{12 \cdot 15} = \$28,133.20$.
63. The APY is the relative increase in the balance of a bank account over the span of one year. The easiest way to compute it when the APR is known is to find the one-year balance, compute the relative increase, and express the answer as a percent. When the principal is not given, any amount can be used – here, we will use $100.

1-year balance: $A = \$100\left(1+\dfrac{0.055}{365}\right)^{365\cdot1} =$ 105.65. The relative increase is $\$5.65/\$100 = 5.65\%$, so the APY is 5.65%.

64. See exercise 63 for details. The one-year balance is $A = \$100\left(1+\dfrac{0.042}{12}\right)^{12\cdot1} = \$104.28$. The relative increase is $\$4.28/\$100 = 4.28\%$, so the APY is 4.28%.

65. See exercise 63 for details. The one-year balance is $A = \$100\left(1+\dfrac{0.042}{12}\right)^{12\cdot1} = \$104.28$. The relative increase (APY) is $\$4.28/\$100 = 4.28\%$.

66. See exercise 63 for details. The one-year balance is $A = \$100\left(1+\dfrac{0.0225}{4}\right)^{4\cdot1} = \$102.27$. The relative increase (APY) is $\$2.27/\$100 = 2.27\%$.

67. The one, five, and twenty-year balances are:

One year: $A = \$10,000e^{0.035\times1} = \$10356.20$.

Five years: $A = \$10,000e^{0.035\times5} = \$11,912.46$.

Twenty years: $A = \$10,000e^{0.035\times20} = \$20,137.53$.

To compute the APY, find the relative increase in the balance of the account after one year.
APY = $\$356.20/\$10,000 = 3.56\%$.

68. The one, five, and twenty-year balances are:

One year: $A = \$2000e^{0.031\times1} = \$2062.97$.

Five years: $A = \$2000e^{0.031\times5} = \$2335.32$.

Twenty years: $A = \$2000e^{0.031\times10} = \$3717.86$.
To compute the APY, find the relative increase in the balance of the account after one year.
APY = $\$62.97/\$2000 = 3.14\%$.

69. The one, five, and twenty-year balances are:

One year: $A = \$7000e^{0.045\times1} = \$7322.20$.

Five years: $A = \$7000e^{0.045\times5} = \$8766.26$.

Twenty years: $A = \$7000e^{0.045\times20} = \$17,217.22$.
To compute the APY, find the relative increase in the balance of the account after one year.
APY = $\$322.20/\$7000 = 4.60\%$.

70. The one, five, and twenty-year balances are:

One year: $A = \$3000e^{0.075\times1} = \$3233.65$.

Five years: $A = \$3000e^{0.075\times5} = \$4364.97$.

Twenty years: $A = \$3000e^{0.075\times20} = \$13,445.07$.
To compute the APY, find the relative increase in the balance of the account after one year.
APY = $\$233.65/\$3000 = 7.79\%$.

71. The one, five, and twenty-year balances are:

One year: $A = \$3000e^{0.06\times1} = \$3185.51$.

Five years: $A = \$3000e^{0.06\times5} = \$4049.58$.

Twenty years: $A = \$3000e^{0.06\times20} = \$9960.35$.
To compute the APY, find the relative increase in the balance of the account after one year.
APY = $\$185.51/\$3000 = 6.18\%$.

72. The one, five, and twenty-year balances are:

One year: $A = \$500e^{0.027\times1} = \$513.68$.

Five years: $A = \$500e^{0.027\times5} = \$572.27$.

Twenty years: $A = \$500e^{0.027\times20} = \$858.00$.
To compute the APY, find the relative increase in the balance of the account after one year.
APY = $\$13.68/\$500 = 2.74\%$.

73. Solve $\$25,000 = P(1+0.05)^8$ for P to find
$P = \dfrac{\$25,000}{(1+0.05)^8} = \$16,920.98$.

74. Solve $\$25,000 = P\left(1+\dfrac{0.045}{4}\right)^{4\cdot8}$ for P to find
$P = \dfrac{\$25,000}{\left(1+\dfrac{0.045}{4}\right)^{4\cdot8}} = \$17,477.00$.

75. Solve $\$25,000 = P\left(1+\dfrac{0.06}{12}\right)^{12\cdot8}$ for P to find
$P = \dfrac{\$25,000}{\left(1+\dfrac{0.06}{12}\right)^{12\cdot8}} = \$15,488.10$.

76. Solve $\$25,000 = P\left(1+\dfrac{0.04}{365}\right)^{365\cdot8}$ for P to find
$P = \dfrac{\$25,000}{\left(1+\dfrac{0.04}{365}\right)^{365\cdot8}} = \$18,154.04$.

77. Solve $\$120,000 = P\left(1+\dfrac{0.04}{365}\right)^{365\cdot15}$ for P to find
$P = \dfrac{\$120,000}{\left(1+\dfrac{0.04}{365}\right)^{365\cdot15}} = \$65,859.56$.

78. Solve $\$120,000 = P\left(1+\dfrac{0.055}{365}\right)^{365\cdot15}$ for P to find
$P = \dfrac{\$120,000}{\left(1+\dfrac{0.055}{365}\right)^{365\cdot15}} = \$52,591.47$.

79. Solve $\$120,000 = P\left(1+\dfrac{0.028}{4}\right)^{4 \cdot 15}$ for P to find

$$P = \dfrac{\$120,000}{\left(1+\dfrac{0.028}{4}\right)^{4 \cdot 15}} = \$78,961.07 \,.$$

80. Solve $\$120,000 = P\left(1+\dfrac{0.035}{12}\right)^{12 \cdot 15}$ for P to find

$$P = \dfrac{\$120,000}{\left(1+\dfrac{0.035}{12}\right)^{12 \cdot 15}} = \$71,040.91 \,.$$

FURTHER APPLICATIONS

81. After 10 years, Chang has $705.30; after 30 years, he has $1403.40. After 10 years, Kio has $722.52; after 30 years, she has $1508.74. Kio has $17.22, or 2.4% more than Chang after 10 years. She has $105.34, or 7.5% more than Chang after 30 years.

82. After 10 years, José has $2586.61; after 30 years, he has $7691.46. After 10 years, Marta has $2611.21; after 30 years, she has $7912.99. Marta has $24.60, or 0.95% more than José after 10 years. She has $221.53, or 2.9% more than José after 30 years.

83. To compute the APY, find the one-year balance in the account, using any principal desired ($100 is used here), and then compute the relative increase in the value of the account over one year.
One-year balance, compounded quarterly:

$$A = \$100\left(1+\dfrac{0.066}{4}\right)^{4 \cdot 1} = \$106.77 \,.$$

APY = $6.77/$100 = 6.77%.
One-year balance, compounded monthly:

$$A = \$100\left(1+\dfrac{0.066}{12}\right)^{12 \cdot 1} = \$106.80 \,.$$

APY = $6.80/$100 = 6.80%.
One-year balance, compounded daily:

$$A = \$100\left(1+\dfrac{0.066}{365}\right)^{365 \cdot 1} = \$106.82 \,.$$

APY = $6.82/$100 = 6.82%.
As the number of compounding periods per year increases, so does the APY, though the rate at which it increases slows down.

84. To compute the APY, find the one-year balance in the account, using any principal desired ($100 is used here), and then compute the relative increase in the value of the account over one year.
One-year balance, compounded quarterly:

$$A = \$100\left(1+\dfrac{0.05}{4}\right)^{4 \cdot 1} = \$105.09 \,.$$

APY = $5.09/$100 = 5.09%.
One-year balance, compounded monthly:

$$A = \$100\left(1+\dfrac{0.05}{12}\right)^{12 \cdot 1} = \$105.12 \,.$$

APY = $5.12/$100 = 5.12%.
One-year balance, compounded daily:

$$A = \$100\left(1+\dfrac{0.05}{365}\right)^{365 \cdot 1} = \$105.13 \,.$$

APY = $5.13/$100 = 5.13%.
As the number of compounding periods per year increases, so does the APY, though the rate at which it increases slows down.

85.

	Account 1		Account 2	
Year	Interest	Balance	Interest	Balance
0	-----	$1000	-----	$1000
1	$55	$1055	$57	$1057
2	$58	$1113	$60	$1116
3	$61	$1174	$63	$1179
4	$65	$1239	$67	$1246
5	$68	$1307	$70	$1317
6	$72	$1379	$74	$1391
7	$76	$1455	$79	$1470
8	$80	$1535	$83	$1553
9	$84	$1619	$88	$1640
10	$89	$1708	$93	$1733

Account 1 has increased in value by $708, or 70.8%. Account 2 has increased by $733, or 73.3%. (Note on values shown in the table: the balance in one year added to next year's interest does not necessarily produce next year's balance due to rounding errors. Each value shown is rounded correctly to the nearest dollar).

86. a. If there is only one compounding period during the year, the balance will increase by the APR in one year. Thus, the APY is the APR.
b. With more than one compounding per year, the APY is always greater than the APR. The APY reflects the cumulative effects of several compounding periods during the year. At the end of the year, the balance will be greater than if there had been only one compounding period.
c. APY does *not* depend on the starting principal. It gives the relative increase (as a percent) in the balance.
d. The more compounding periods per year, the greater the APY.

87. a. After 5 years, Rosa has $3000(1.04)^5 =$ $3649.96; after 20 years, she has $3000(1.04)^{20} =$ $6573.37. Julian has $2500(1.05)^5 = \$3190.70$ after 5 years, and he has $2500(1.05)^{20} =$ $6633.24 after 20 years.

b. For Rosa, ($3649.96 – $3000.00)/$3649.96 = 18% of the balance after 5 years is interest and ($6573.37 – $3000.00)/$6573.37 = 54% of the balance after 20 years is interest. For Julian, ($3190.70 – $2500.00)/$3190.70 = 22% of the balance after 5 years is interest and ($6633.24 – $2500.00)/$6633.24 = 62% of the balance after 20 years is interest.

c. The longer the investment time, the higher the overall returns.

88. a. After 5 years, Paula has $4000e^{0.048 \times 5}$ = $5085.00; after 20 years, she has $4000e^{0.048 \times 20}$ = $10,446.79. Petra has $3600e^{0.056 \times 5}$ = $4763.27 after 5 years, and she has $3600e^{0.056 \times 20}$ = $11.033.48 after 20 years.

b. For Paula, ($5085.00 – $4000.00)/$5085.00 = 21% of the balance after 5 years is interest and ($10,446.79 – $4000.00)/$10,446.79 = 62% of the balance after 20 years is interest. For Petra, ($4763.27 – $3600.00)/$4763.27 = 24% of the balance after 5 years is interest and ($11,033.48 – $3600.00)/$11,033.48 = 67% of the balance after 20 years is interest.

c. The longer the investment time, the higher the overall returns.

89. For Plan A, solve $120,000 = P(1.05)^{30}$ for P to find $P = \dfrac{\$120,000}{(1.05)^{30}} = \$27,765.29$. For Plan B, solve $120,000 = Pe^{0.048 \times 30}$ for P to find $P = \dfrac{\$120,000}{e^{0.048 \times 30}} = \$28,431.33$.

90. Answers will vary.

91. To obtain an exact solution for this problem, one must use logarithms (studied in a later chapter). If your initial investment P is to triple, we must solve $3P = P(1.08)^t$ for t in order to find out how long it takes. Begin by dividing both sides by P (it will cancel from both sides), and then take the logarithm of both sides: $\log 3 = \log(1.08)^t$. A property of logarithms says the exponent t can be moved in front of the logarithm, as such: log 3 = t log(1.08). Now divide both sides by log 1.08 to arrive at the answer: $t = (\log 3)/(\log 1.08) = 14.3$ years. Thus it will take about 14.3 years for your investment to triple in value. Another way to come to the solution is to try various values of t in $(1.08)^t$ – you will have found a solution when $(1.08)^t$ is about 3.

92. See exercise 91. Solve $1.5P = P(1.07)^t$ for t to arrive at $t = (\log 1.5)/(\log 1.07) = 6$ years.

93. See exercise 91. Solve $100,000 = \$1000(1.07)^t$ for t. Begin by dividing both sides by $1000; this yields $100 = (1.07)^t$. Now take the logarithm of both sides, and apply a property of logarithms to get log 100 = t log 1.07. Divide both sides by log 1.07 to find $t = (\log 100)/(\log 1.07) = 68.1$ years. Trial and error may also produce the same result if you are patient.

94. a.

n	1	4	12	365	500	1000
APY	12.00	12.55	12.68	12.75	12.75	12.75

b. The one-year balance (using P = $100) is $A = \$100e^{0.12 \times 1} = \$112.75$, and thus the APY is $12.75/$100 = 12.75%.

c.

Annual Percentage Yield (APY) with APR = 12%

d. The APY is higher with continuous compounding than with any other periodic compounding.

e. At the end of one year, you will have $A = \$500e^{0.12 \times 1} = \$563.75$. After five years, you will have $A = \$500e^{0.12 \times 5} = \$911.06$.

TECHNOLOGY EXERCISES

98. a. $6^{12} = 2,176,782,336$

b. $1.01^{40} = 1.488864$

c. $20 \times 1.05^{16} = 43.657492$.

d. $4^{-5} = 0.00097656$

e. $1.08^{-20} = 0.214548$

99. a. FV(0.10,5,0,100)=$161.05.
b. FV(0.02,535,0,224) = $8,940,049.24.

100. a. FV(0.03,20,0,500) = $903.06.
b. FV(0.06,20,0,500) = $1,603.57. The amount is less than double.
c. FV(0.03,49,0,500) = $1,631.02. The amount is less than double.

d. FV(0.03,20,0,1000) = $1,806.11. The amount is less than double.

101. a. FV(0.03/12,60,0,5000) = $5,808.08.

b. FV(0.045/12,30*12,0,800) = $3,078.16.

c. FV(0.0375/365,365*50,0,1000) = $6,520.19.

102. a. EFFECT(0.04,4) = 0.04060401 = 4.0604%.

b. EFFECT(0.04,12) = 0.040741543 = 4.0742%.

c. EFFECT(0.04,365) = 0.040808493 = 4.0808%.

d. EFFECT(0.04,100000) = 0.0408106 = 4.0811%. Using a very large value for the number of compoundings is one way to estimate the continuous compounding rate.

103. a. $e^{3.2} = 24.5325$

b. $e^{0.065} = 1.0672$

c. $100 \times e^{0.04} = 104.0811$. So the APY is $4.081/$100 = 4.0811%.

UNIT 4C

TIME OUT TO THINK

Pg. 232. Your best choice in any particular situation will depend on your financial circumstances. Most people don't have nearly $40,000 to put into a savings account, and therefore would opt for the regular payments of a savings plan. However, if you are lucky enough to get a sudden windfall of at least $40,000, such as an inheritance, you might decide to use it as a lump sum for the college fund.

Pg. 237. Answers will vary, but the DJIA will most likely be below the all-time high of 14,164. Whether money invested in 2000 or 2005 would be worth more or less depends on the current value of the DJIA, but for money invested in 1995, the mutual fund is likely worth more today.

Pg. 238. Younger people have more time to recover if investments fall due to volatile investments, such as stocks and are likely less dependent on their savings since they are still working while people who are retired or nearing retirement would have less time to recover their investments and are more likely to be using their investments as a source of income. Opinions will vary on the veracity of the advice.

Pg. 243. The fund performed better in 2004 and 2005 since more value was lost in the 2006 investment.

QUICK QUIZ

1. **a**. As the number of compounding periods n increases, so does the APY, and a higher APY means a higher accumulated balance.

2. **c**. As long as the savings plan in which you are investing money has a positive rate of return, the balance will increase as time increases.

3. **c**. The total return on a five-year investment is simply the percent change of the balance over five years.

4. **b**. The annual return is the APY that gives the same overall growth in five years as the total return.

5. **a**. If you deposit $100 per month for ten years (120 months), you have deposited a total of $12,000 into the savings plan. Since the balance was $22,200, you earned $22,200 − $12,000 = $10,200 in interest.

6. **a**. If you can find a low risk, high return investment, that's the best of both worlds, and adding high liquidity (where it's easy to access your money) is like icing on the cake. Good luck.

7. **b**. Market capitalization is the share price of a company times the number of outstanding shares. Company B has the greatest market capitalization of $9 per share × 10,000,000 shares = $90,000,000, which is greater than the market capitalization of $10,000,000 for companies A and C.

8. **a**. The P/E ratio is the share price divided by earnings per share over the past year.

9. **b**. If the bond is selling at 103 points, it is selling at 103% of its face value, which is 1.03 × $5000 = $5150.

10. **c**. The one-year return is simply a measure of how well the mutual fund has done over the last year, and it could be higher or lower than the three-year return (which measures how well the fund has done over the last three years).

DOES IT MAKE SENSE?

9. Does not make sense. With an APR of 4%, the savings plan formula gives a balance of

$$A = \frac{\$25\left[\left(1+\dfrac{0.04}{12}\right)^{12\cdot30} - 1\right]}{\left(\dfrac{0.04}{12}\right)} = \$17,351 \text{ after } 30$$

years, which probably wouldn't cover expenses for even one year of retirement (and certainly interest earned on that balance would not be enough for retirement). You should plan to save considerably more than $25 per month for a retirement plan.

10. Does not make sense. When you find an investment that guarantees an APR of 15% for the next 30 years, please tell me about it.

11. Does not make sense. Stocks can be a risky investment (you might lose all of your money), and most financial advisors will tell you to diversify your investments.

12. Makes sense. A liquid investment is one where it is easy to access your money.

13. Does not make sense. Stocks are considered a risky investment (especially in the short term). In general, an investment with a greater return is even more risky, and thus the claim that there is no risk at all is dubious, at best.

14. Makes sense. Financial advisors generally tell retired people (who depend on their life savings for income) to invest in low-risk funds, lest they lose a big portion of their nest egg. U.S. Treasury bills, notes and bonds are considered low-risk investments.

BASIC SKILLS & CONCEPTS

15. $x^2 = 25 \Rightarrow (x^2)^{1/2} = 25^{1/2} \Rightarrow x = \sqrt{25} = 5$. Another solution is $x = -5$.

16. $y^3 = 27 \Rightarrow (y^3)^{1/3} = 27^{1/3} \Rightarrow y = \sqrt[3]{27} = 3$.

17. $(x-4)^2 = 36 \Rightarrow ((x-4)^2)^{1/2} = 36^{1/2} \Rightarrow$
    $x - 4 = \sqrt{36} \Rightarrow x = 4 + 6 = 10$. Another solution is $x = -2$.

18. $p^{1/3} = 3 \Rightarrow (p^{1/3})^3 = 3^3 \Rightarrow p = 27$.

19. $(t/3)^2 = 16 \Rightarrow ((t/3)^2)^{1/2} = 16^{1/2} \Rightarrow$
    $t/3 = \sqrt{16} \Rightarrow t = 3 \times 4 = 12$. Another solution is $x = -12$.

20. $w^2 + 2 = 27 \Rightarrow w^2 = 25 \Rightarrow w = \sqrt{25} = 5$. Another solution is $x = -5$.

21. $u^9 = 512 \Rightarrow (u^9)^{1/9} = 512^{1/9} \Rightarrow u = \sqrt[9]{512} = 2$.

22. $v^3 + 4 = 68 \Rightarrow v^3 = 64 \Rightarrow v = \sqrt[3]{64} = 4$.

23. $A = \dfrac{\$150\left[\left(1+\dfrac{0.03}{12}\right)^{12} - 1\right]}{\left(\dfrac{0.03}{12}\right)} = \$1824.96$.

24. $A = \dfrac{\$100\left[\left(1+\dfrac{0.025}{12}\right)^{12\times5} - 1\right]}{\left(\dfrac{0.025}{12}\right)} = \$6384.05$.

25. $A = \dfrac{\$400\left[\left(1+\dfrac{0.04}{12}\right)^{12\times3} - 1\right]}{\left(\dfrac{0.04}{12}\right)} = \$15,272.63$.

26. $A = \dfrac{\$250\left[\left(1+\dfrac{0.05}{12}\right)^{12\times2} - 1\right]}{\left(\dfrac{0.05}{12}\right)} = \$6296.48$.

Note that 24 months is 2 years.

27. You save for 40 years, so the value of the IRA is
    $$A = \dfrac{\$75\left[\left(1+\dfrac{0.05}{12}\right)^{12\times40} - 1\right]}{\left(\dfrac{0.05}{12}\right)} = \$114,451.51.$$
    Since you deposit $75 each month for 40 years, your total deposits are $\dfrac{\$75}{\text{mo}} \times \dfrac{12 \text{ mo}}{\text{yr}} \times 40 \text{ yr} = \$36,000$. The value of the account is just over three times the amount you deposited.

28. She saves for 40 years, so the value of the IRA is
    $$A = \dfrac{\$50\left[\left(1+\dfrac{0.0625}{12}\right)^{12\times40} - 1\right]}{\left(\dfrac{0.0625}{12}\right)} = \$106,595.63.$$
    Since she deposits $50 each month for 40 years, her total deposits are $\dfrac{\$50}{\text{mo}} \times \dfrac{12 \text{ mo}}{\text{yr}} \times 40 \text{ yr} = \$24,000$. The value of her account is more than four times the value of the amount invested.

29. $A = \dfrac{\$300\left[\left(1+\dfrac{0.035}{12}\right)^{12\times18} - 1\right]}{\left(\dfrac{0.035}{12}\right)} = \$90,091.51$.

    You have deposited $\dfrac{\$300}{\text{mo}} \times \dfrac{12 \text{ mo}}{\text{yr}} \times 18 \text{ yr} = \$64,800$, which is a little less than three-fourths of the value of the account.

30. $A = \dfrac{\$200\left[\left(1+\dfrac{0.045}{12}\right)^{12\times18} - 1\right]}{\left(\dfrac{0.045}{12}\right)} = \$66,373.60$.

    You have deposited $\dfrac{\$200}{\text{mo}} \times \dfrac{12 \text{ mo}}{\text{yr}} \times 18 \text{ yr} = \$43,200$, which is about two-thirds of the value of the account.

31. Solve $\$85,000 = \dfrac{PMT\left[\left(1+\dfrac{0.05}{12}\right)^{12\times15}-1\right]}{\left(\dfrac{0.05}{12}\right)}$ for

 PMT. $PMT = \dfrac{\$85,000\left(\dfrac{0.05}{12}\right)}{\left[\left(1+\dfrac{0.05}{12}\right)^{12\times15}-1\right]} = \$318.01$.

 You should deposit $318.01 each month.

32. Solve $\$2,000,000 = \dfrac{PMT\left[\left(1+\dfrac{0.06}{12}\right)^{12\times30}-1\right]}{\left(\dfrac{0.06}{12}\right)}$

 for   *PMT.*

 $PMT = \dfrac{\$2,000,000\left(\dfrac{0.06}{12}\right)}{\left[\left(1+\dfrac{0.06}{12}\right)^{12\times30}-1\right]} = \$1991.01$.   You

 should deposit $1991.01 each month.

33. Solve $\$15,000 = \dfrac{PMT\left[\left(1+\dfrac{0.055}{12}\right)^{12\times3}-1\right]}{\left(\dfrac{0.055}{12}\right)}$ for

 PMT. $PMT = \dfrac{\$15,000\left(\dfrac{0.055}{12}\right)}{\left[\left(1+\dfrac{0.055}{12}\right)^{12\times3}-1\right]} = \$384.19$.

 You should deposit $384.19 each month.

34. Solve $\$5,000,000 = \dfrac{PMT\left[\left(1+\dfrac{0.045}{12}\right)^{12\times45}-1\right]}{\left(\dfrac{0.045}{12}\right)}$

 for   *PMT.*

 $PMT = \dfrac{\$5,000,000\left(\dfrac{0.045}{12}\right)}{\left[\left(1+\dfrac{0.045}{12}\right)^{12\times45}-1\right]} = \$2863.70$.   You

 should deposit $2863.70 each month.

35. First, find out how large your retirement account needs to be in order to produce $100,000 in interest (at 6% APR) each year. You want 6% of the total balance to be $100,000, which means the

total balance should be $100,000/0.06 = $1,666,667. Now solve

 $\$1,666,667 = \dfrac{PMT\left[\left(1+\dfrac{0.06}{12}\right)^{12\times30}-1\right]}{\left(\dfrac{0.06}{12}\right)}$ for

 PMT.

 $PMT = \dfrac{\$1,666,667\left(\dfrac{0.06}{12}\right)}{\left[\left(1+\dfrac{0.06}{12}\right)^{12\times30}-1\right]} = \$1659.18$.   You

 should deposit $1659.18 each month.

36. First, find out how large your retirement account needs to be in order to produce $200,000 in interest (at 6% APR) each year. You want 6% of the total balance to be $200,000, which means the total balance should be $200,000/0.06 = $3,333,333. Now solve

 $\$3,333,333 = \dfrac{PMT\left[\left(1+\dfrac{0.06}{12}\right)^{12\times40}-1\right]}{\left(\dfrac{0.06}{12}\right)}$

 for *PMT.*

 $PMT = \dfrac{\$3,333,333\left(\dfrac{0.06}{12}\right)}{\left[\left(1+\dfrac{0.06}{12}\right)^{12\times40}-1\right]} = \$1673.79$.

 You should deposit $1673.79 each month.

37. The total return is the relative change in the investment, and since you invested $6000 (100 shares at $60 per share), the total return is $\dfrac{\$9400-\$6000}{\$6000} = 0.567 = 56.7\%$.   The   annual return is the APY that would give the same overall growth in five years, and the formula for computing it is $\left(\dfrac{A}{P}\right)^{(1/Y)}-1$. Thus the annual return is $\left(\dfrac{\$9400}{\$6000}\right)^{(1/5)}-1 = 0.094 = 9.4\%$.

38. The total return is the relative change in the investment, or $\dfrac{\$12,500-\$8000}{\$8000} = 0.563 = 56.3\%$.

 The annual return is the APY that would give the same overall growth in 20 years, and the formula for computing it is $\left(\dfrac{A}{P}\right)^{(1/Y)}-1$. Thus the annual

return is $\left(\dfrac{\$12,500}{\$8000}\right)^{(1/20)}-1=0.023=2.3\%$.

39. The total return is $\dfrac{\$11,300-\$6500}{\$6500}=73.8\%$. The

annual return is $\left(\dfrac{\$11,300}{\$6500}\right)^{(1/20)}-1=2.8\%$.

40. You invested $5000 (200 shares at $25 per share),

so the total return is $\dfrac{\$8500-\$5000}{\$5000}=70.0\%$. The

annual return is $\left(\dfrac{\$8500}{\$5000}\right)^{(1/3)}-1=19.3\%$.

41. The total return is $\dfrac{\$2000-\$3500}{\$3500}=-42.9\%$. The

annual return is $\left(\dfrac{\$2000}{\$3500}\right)^{(1/3)}-1=-17.0\%$.

42. The total return is $\dfrac{\$3000-\$5000}{\$5000}=-40.0\%$. The

annual return is $\left(\dfrac{\$3000}{\$5000}\right)^{(1/5)}-1=-9.7\%$.

43. The total return is $\dfrac{\$12,600-\$7500}{\$7500}=68.0\%$. The

annual return is $\left(\dfrac{\$12,600}{\$7500}\right)^{(1/10)}-1=5.3\%$.

44. The total return is $\dfrac{\$2200-\$10,000}{\$10,000}=-78.0\%$.

The annual return is

$\left(\dfrac{\$2200}{\$10,000}\right)^{(1/10)}-1=-14.1\%$.

45. $250 invested in stocks would be worth $250(1+0.06)^{108}=\$135,199$. For bonds and cash, the investments would be worth $250(1+0.021)^{108}=\$2,359$, and $250(1+0.01)^{108}=\$732$, respectively.

46. The $10 investment in stocks would be worth $10(1+0.06)^{108}=\$5,408$, which is more than the investments in bonds and cash, which would be worth $75(1+0.021)^{108}=\$708$, and $500(1+0.01)^{108}=\$1,464$, respectively.

47. a. The symbol for Intel stock is INTC.
b. Intel stock closed at $15.48 per share yesterday.

c. The total value of shares traded today is $15.48/share × 64 million shares = $990 million.
d. 64 million/5580 million = 1.1% of all Intel shares have been traded so far today.
e. You should expect a dividend of 100 × $15.48 × 0.0362 = $56.04.
f. The earnings per share is $15.48/19.77 = $0.783 = $0.78/share.
g. Intel earned a total profit of $0.783/share × 5580 million shares = $4369 million, so Intel earned a total profit of about $4.37 billion.

48. a. The symbol for Wal-Mart stock is WMT.
b. Wal-Mart stock closed at $50.00 per share yesterday.
c. The total value of shares traded today is $50.00/share × 17.28 million shares = $864 million.
d. 17.28 million/3910 million = 0.44% of all Wal-Mart shares have been traded so far today.
e. You should expect a dividend of 100 × $50.00 × 0.0218 = $109.00.
f. The earnings per share is $50.00/14.88 = $3.36 = $3.36/share.
g. Wal-Mart earned a total profit of $3.36/share × 3910 million shares = $13,137 million, so Wal-Mart earned a total profit of about $13.1 billion.

49. a. The earnings per share for COSTCO is $48.30/17.25 = $3.80/share.
b. The stock is slightly overpriced.

50. a. The earnings per share for General Mills is $52.65/16.14 = $3.26/share.
b. The stock is slightly overpriced.

51. a. The earnings per share for IBM is $101.89/11.30 = $9.02/share.
b. The stock is priced just about right.

52. a. The earnings per share for Google is $393.50/28.78 = $13.67/share.
b. The stock overpriced.

53. – 54. Answers will vary.

55. The current yield on a bond is its annual interest payment divided by its current price. A $1000 bond with a coupon rate of 2% pays $1000 × 0.02 = $20 per year in interest, so this bond has a current yield of $20/$950 = 2.11%.

56. The current yield on a bond is its annual interest payment divided by its current price. A $1000 bond with a coupon rate of 2.5% pays $1000 × 0.025 = $25 per year in interest, so this bond has a current yield of $25/$1050 = 2.38%.

57. The annual interest payment on this bond is $1000 × 0.055 = $55, so its current yield is $55/$1100 = 5%.

58. The annual interest payment on this bond is $10,000 × 0.03 = $300, so its current yield is $300/$9500 = 3.16%.

59. The price of this bond is 105% × $1000 = $1050, and it has a current yield of 3.9%, so the annual interest earned is $1050 × 0.039 = $40.95.

60. The price of this bond is 98% × $1000 = $980, and its current yield is 1.5%, which means the annual interest will be $980 × 0.015 = $14.70.

61. The price of this bond is 114.3% × $1000 = $1143, and its current yield is 6.2%, which means the annual interest will be $1143 × 0.062 = $70.87.

62. The price of this bond is 102.5% × $10,000 = $10,250, and it has a current yield of 3.6%, so the annual interest earned is $10,250 × 0.036 = $369.

63. a. You would buy $5000/$10.93 = 457.46 shares.
   b. Your investment would be worth
   $$\$5000 \times (1 + 0.0320)^5 = \$5852.86.$$
   c. Your investment would be worth
   $$\$5000 \times (1 + 0.0369)^{10} = \$7183.54.$$

64. a. You would buy $2500/$10.82 = 231.05 shares.
   b. Your investment would be worth
   $$\$2500 \times (1 + 0.0482)^5 = \$3163.45.$$
   c. Your investment would be worth
   $$\$2500 \times (1 + 0.0619)^{10} = \$4558.02.$$

FURTHER APPLICATIONS

65. After 10 years, the balance in Yolanda's account is
$$A = \frac{\$200 \left[\left(1 + \frac{0.05}{12}\right)^{12 \times 10} - 1 \right]}{\left(\frac{0.05}{12}\right)} = \$31,056.46. \quad \text{She}$$
deposits $200 per month, so her total deposits are $\frac{\$200}{\text{mo}} \times \frac{12 \text{ mo}}{\text{yr}} \times 10 \text{ yr} = \$24,000$. Zach's account is worth
$$A = \frac{\$2400 \left[\left(1 + \frac{0.05}{1}\right)^{1 \times 10} - 1 \right]}{\left(\frac{0.05}{1}\right)} = \$30,186.94. \quad \text{He}$$
deposits $2400 per year, so his total deposits are $\frac{\$2400}{\text{yr}} \times 10 \text{ yr} = \$24,000$. Yolanda comes out ahead even though both deposited the same amount of money because the interest in her account is compounded monthly, while Zach's is compounded yearly, which means Yolanda enjoys a higher APY.

66. After 10 years, the balance in Polly's account is
$$A = \frac{\$50 \left[\left(1 + \frac{0.06}{12}\right)^{12 \times 10} - 1 \right]}{\left(\frac{0.06}{12}\right)} = \$8193.97. \quad \text{She}$$
deposits $50 per month, so her total deposits are $\frac{\$50}{\text{mo}} \times \frac{12 \text{ mo}}{\text{yr}} \times 10 \text{ yr} = \$6000$. Quint's account is worth
$$A = \frac{\$40 \left[\left(1 + \frac{0.065}{12}\right)^{12 \times 10} - 1 \right]}{\left(\frac{0.065}{12}\right)} = \$6736.13.$$
He deposits $40 per month, so his total deposits are $\frac{\$40}{\text{mo}} \times \frac{12 \text{ mo}}{\text{yr}} \times 10 \text{ yr} = \$4800$. Polly comes out ahead despite the fact that she has the lower APR, because she deposited more each month.

67. After 10 years, the balance in Juan's account is
$$A = \frac{\$400 \left[\left(1 + \frac{0.06}{12}\right)^{12 \times 10} - 1 \right]}{\left(\frac{0.06}{12}\right)} = \$65,551.74. \quad \text{His}$$
total deposits are $\frac{\$400}{\text{mo}} \times \frac{12 \text{ mo}}{\text{yr}} \times 10 \text{ yr} = \$48,000$. The balance in Maria's account is
$$A = \frac{\$5000 \left[(1 + 0.065)^{10} - 1 \right]}{(0.065)} = \$67,472.11. \quad \text{Her}$$
total deposits are $\frac{\$5000}{\text{yr}} \times 10 \text{ yr} = \$50,000$. Maria comes out ahead because she has a higher APR (and APY, it turns out), and she deposits more money over the course of the 10 years.

68. After 10 years, the balance in George's account is
$$A = \frac{\$40 \left[\left(1 + \frac{0.07}{12}\right)^{12 \times 10} - 1 \right]}{\left(\frac{0.07}{12}\right)} = \$6923.39. \quad \text{His}$$
total deposits are $\frac{\$40}{\text{mo}} \times \frac{12 \text{ mo}}{\text{yr}} \times 10 \text{ yr} = \$4800$. Harvey's balance is

$$A = \frac{\$150\left[\left(1+\dfrac{0.075}{4}\right)^{4\times10}-1\right]}{\left(\dfrac{0.075}{4}\right)} = \$8818.79. \quad \text{His}$$

total deposits are $\dfrac{\$150}{\text{qtr}} \times \dfrac{4\ \text{qtr}}{\text{yr}} \times 10\ \text{yr} = \$6000$.

Harvey comes out ahead because he deposited more money, and had a higher APR (and APY).

69. Your balance will be $A = \dfrac{\$50\left[\left(1+\dfrac{0.07}{12}\right)^{12\cdot15}-1\right]}{\left(\dfrac{0.07}{12}\right)}$

= $15,848.11, so you won't reach your goal.

70. Your balance will be $A = \dfrac{\$75\left[\left(1+\dfrac{0.07}{12}\right)^{12\cdot15}-1\right]}{\left(\dfrac{0.07}{12}\right)}$

= $23,772.17, so you won't reach your goal.

71. Your balance will be $A = \dfrac{\$100\left[\left(1+\dfrac{0.06}{12}\right)^{12\cdot15}-1\right]}{\left(\dfrac{0.06}{12}\right)}$ = $29,081.87, so

you won't reach your goal.

72. Your balance will be $A = \dfrac{\$200\left[\left(1+\dfrac{0.05}{12}\right)^{12\cdot15}-1\right]}{\left(\dfrac{0.05}{12}\right)}$ = $53,457.79 so

you will reach your goal.

73. The total return is $\dfrac{\$8.25-\$6.05}{\$6.05} = 36.4\%$.

Incidentally, this is also the annual return (because you bought the stock a year ago), and it doesn't matter how many shares you bought.

74. The total return is $\dfrac{\$8.25-\$46.25}{\$46.25} = -82.2\%$.

75. The total return was $\dfrac{\$22,000,000-\$5000}{\$5000} =$ 439,900%. The annual return was $\left(\dfrac{\$22,000,000}{\$5000}\right)^{(1/50)} -1 = 18.3\%$, which is much higher than the average annual return for large-company stocks.

76. The monthly deposit would be $4.50 × 30 = $135. The final value of the savings plan for the ex-smoker will be $A = \dfrac{\$135\left[\left(1+\dfrac{0.09}{12}\right)^{12\cdot30}-1\right]}{\left(\dfrac{0.09}{12}\right)}$

= $247,150, so the article was correct.

77. a. At age 35, the balance in Mitch's account is $A = \dfrac{\$1000\left[(1+0.07)^{10}-1\right]}{(0.07)} = \$13,816.45$. At this

point, it is no longer appropriate to use the savings plan formula as Mitch is not making further deposits into the account. Instead, use this balance as the principal in the compound interest formula, and compute the balance 40 years later. $A = \$13,816.45(1+0.07)^{40} = \$206,893.82$. (Note that the rounded balance of $13,816.45 was not used in this computation, but rather the more exact answer stored in a calculator – this is the way it would happen in a banking institution).

b. At age 75, the balance in Bill's account is $A = \dfrac{\$1000\left[(1+0.07)^{40}-1\right]}{(0.07)} = \$199,635.11$.

c. Mitch deposited $1000 per year for ten years, which is $10,000. Bill deposited $1000 per year for 40 years, which is $40,000, or four times as large as Mitch's total deposits.

TECHNOLOGY EXERCISES

87. a. FV(0.04/12,12*25,100,0) = $51,412.95
   b. FV(0.08/12,12*25,100,0) = $95,102.64.
      The amount is less than double
   c. FV(0.04/12,12*50,100,0) = $190,935.64.
      The amount is more than double.

88. a. Abe deposits $50 \times 12 \times 40 = \$24,000$ and Beatrice deposits $100 \times 12 \times 20 = \$24,000$.

   b. Abe will have a total of FV(0.055/12,12*40,50,0)=$87,051.98 while Beatrice will have a total of FV(0.055/12,12*20,100,0)=$43,562.74. Abe has more money since he started investing earlier, which took more advantage of compound interest.

89. a. $2.8^{1/4} = 1.293569$
   b. $120^{1/3} = 4.932424$
   c. We need to solve the equation $1850 = 250 \times (1+r)^{15}$. Using algebra, rewrite the equation as $\dfrac{1850}{250} = (1+r)^{15}$.

Now raise both sides to the reciprocal power of 15, i.e. to the 1/15 power, and then subtract 1 to

find $r = \left(\dfrac{1850}{250}\right)^{1/15} - 1 = 0.1427 = 14.27\%$.

UNIT 4D

TIME OUT TO THINK

Pg. 252. This question should help students realize how installment loans work. More than half the payment goes to interest because it is early in the loan term when the balance is high, and the 9% interest rate is calculated on this entire balance. Late in the term, when the balance is low, interest will make only a small portion of the payments. For example, when the balance is down to $500, the monthly interest is only $0.0075 \times \$500 = \$3.75$, so almost all of the $95.01 monthly payment will be going to principal at that point.

Pg. 235. Answers will vary, but in general: the shorter term loan is better if you can afford the higher monthly payments; the longer term loan is better if you need to minimize your monthly payments.

Pg. 255. As long as there are no hidden fees, yes! The lower interest rate will save in total interest during the year. And the bank will require monthly payments, which should help enforce your discipline in paying off the loan. (Since the credit card requires only relatively small minimum payments, you must be self-disciplined to pay it off in a year.) Of course, all this assumes that you don't simply go deeper into debt as a result of having lower payments.

Pg. 258. Interest rates will vary, but the payments will be higher with higher interest rates and lower with lower interest rates.

Pg. 260. The 15-year loan is better if you are sure you can afford the higher monthly payments; for example, if you have a stable, long-term job and plenty of savings just in case you are laid off or quit. Otherwise, the 30-year loan may be safer. For example, if you have a new job and little savings, you may not want the added risk that comes with required high monthly payments. Also, the 30-year mortgage could be paid off early by making extra payments towards the principle. Make sure there is no prepayment penalty (fees that are assessed if you pay off a mortgage early).

Pg. 261. Answers will vary, but one circumstance might be someone who only plans to live in a house for a short time and expects the value of the house to increase. (Given the recent housing crisis, this may no longer be a good idea.)

QUICK QUIZ

1. **a**. Monthly payments go up when the loan principal is larger because you are borrowing more money.
2. **a**. The payment will be higher for a 15-year loan because there is less time to pay off the principal.
3. **b**. A higher APR means more money goes to paying off interest, and this corresponds with a higher payment.
4. **b**. Most of an early payment goes to interest, because the principal is large at the beginning stages of a loan, and thus the interest is also large.
5. **c**. Every year you'll pay $12,000, and thus after ten years, you'll pay $120,000.
6. **c**. Most credit card loans only require that you make a minimum payment each month; there is no specified time in which you must pay off a loan.
7. **c**. A two-point origination fee just means that you must pay 2% of the loan principal in advance, and 2% of $200,000 is $4000.
8. **b**. Add $500 to 1% (one point) of the loan principle of $120,000 to find the advanced payment required.
9. **c**. Refinancing a loan is not a good idea if you've nearly paid the loan off.
10. **a**. A shorter loan always has higher monthly payments (all other things being equal) because there is less time to pay off the principal, and you'll spend less on interest because the principal decreases more quickly.

DOES IT MAKE SENSE?

7. Makes sense. For a typical long-term loan, most of the payments go toward interest for much of the loan term. See Figure 4.8 in the text.
8. Makes sense. This plan is the essence of refinancing a loan.
9. Does not make sense. Making only the minimum required payment on a credit card is asking for financial trouble as the interest rates on credit cards are typically exorbitant. You'll end up spending a lot of your money on interest.
10. Does not make sense. Credit card companies often offer teaser rates to get new customers – after three months, the interest rate will balloon to who knows what level, and that's what matters in the long run.
11. Makes sense. In the worst-case scenario, the ARM loan will be at 6% in the last year you expect to live in the home, so it's certain you'll save money on the first two years, and you may even save during the last year.
12. Does not make sense. While it's true that you'll save money on interest if you take a 15-year loan, there are many scenarios where it's better to take a

30-year loan (for example: you may not be able to afford the higher payments that go with a 15-year loan; if interest rates are low, there are tax benefits and investment strategies that make a 30-year loan a wiser choice).

BASIC SKILLS & CONCEPTS

13. a. The starting principal is $80,000 with an annual interest rate of 7%. You'll make 12 payments each year (one per month) for 20 years, and each payment will be $620.
b. Since you make 12 payments per year for 20 years, you'll make $12 \times 20 = 240$ payments in total, which amounts to $240 \times \$620 = \$148,800$ over the term of the loan.
c. Since the loan principal is $80,000, you'll pay $148,800 – $80,000 = $68,800 in interest, and of course $80,000 of your payments will go toward the principal.

14. a. The starting principal is $15,000 with an annual interest rate of 9%. You'll make 12 payments each year (one per month) for 10 years, and each payment will be $190.
b. Because you make 12 payments per year for 10 years, you'll make $12 \times 10 = 120$ payments in total, which amounts to $120 \times \$190 = \$22,800$ over the term of the loan.
c. Because the loan principal is $15,000, you'll pay $22,800 – $15,000 = $7,800 in interest, and of course $15,000 of your payments will go toward the principal.

15. a. The monthly payment is
$$PMT = \frac{\$50,000\left(\frac{0.10}{12}\right)}{1-\left(1+\frac{0.10}{12}\right)^{-12\times20}} = \$482.51.$$
b. The total payment is $482.51 \times 12 \times 20 = $115,802.40.
c. The money spent on interest is $115,802.40 – $50,000 = $65,802.40, while $50,000 goes toward the principal.

16. a. The monthly payment is
$$PMT = \frac{\$12,000\left(\frac{0.08}{12}\right)}{1-\left(1+\frac{0.08}{12}\right)^{-12\times10}} = \$145.59.$$
b. The total payment is $145.59 \times 12 \times 10 = $17,470.80.
c. The money spent on interest is $17,470.80 – $12,000 = $5470.80, while $12,000 goes toward the principal.

17. a. The monthly payment is
$$PMT = \frac{\$200,000\left(\frac{0.075}{12}\right)}{1-\left(1+\frac{0.075}{12}\right)^{-12\times30}} = \$1398.43.$$
b. The total payment is $1398.43 \times 12 \times 30 = $503,434.80.
c. The money spent on interest is $503,434.80 – $200,000 = $303,434.80, while $200,000 goes toward the principal.

18. a. The monthly payment is
$$PMT = \frac{\$150,000\left(\frac{0.075}{12}\right)}{1-\left(1+\frac{0.075}{12}\right)^{-12\times15}} = \$1390.52.$$
b. The total payment is $1390.52 \times 12 \times 15 = $250,293.60.
c. The money spent on interest is $250,293.60 – $150,000 = $100,293.60, while $150,000 goes toward the principal.

19. a. The monthly payment is
$$PMT = \frac{\$200,000\left(\frac{0.09}{12}\right)}{1-\left(1+\frac{0.09}{12}\right)^{-12\times15}} = \$2028.53.$$
b. The total payment is $2028.53 \times 12 \times 15 = $365,135.40.
c. The money spent on interest is $365,135.40 – $200,000 = $165,135.40, while $200,000 goes toward the principal.

20. a. The monthly payment is
$$PMT = \frac{\$100,000\left(\frac{0.085}{12}\right)}{1-\left(1+\frac{0.085}{12}\right)^{-12\times15}} = \$984.74.$$
b. The total payment is $984.74 \times 12 \times 15 = $177,253.20.
c. The money spent on interest is $177,253.20 – $100,000 = $77,253.20, while $100,000 goes toward the principal.

21. a. The monthly payment is
$$PMT = \frac{\$10,000\left(\frac{0.12}{12}\right)}{1-\left(1+\frac{0.12}{12}\right)^{-12\times3}} = \$332.14.$$
b. The total payment is $322.14 \times 12 \times 3 = $11,957.04.
c. The money spent on interest is $11,957.04 – $10,000 = $1957.04, while $10,000 goes toward the principal.

22. a. The monthly payment is

$$PMT = \frac{\$10,000\left(\frac{0.10}{12}\right)}{1-\left(1+\frac{0.10}{12}\right)^{-12\times5}} = \$212.47 \,.$$

b. The total payment is $\$212.47 \times 12 \times 5 = \$12,748.20$.

c. The money spent on interest is $\$12,748.20 - \$10,000 = \$2748.20$, while $\$10,000$ goes toward the principal.

23. a. The monthly payment is

$$PMT = \frac{\$150,000\left(\frac{0.08}{12}\right)}{1-\left(1+\frac{0.08}{12}\right)^{-12\times15}} = \$1433.48 \,.$$

b. The total payment is $\$1433.48 \times 12 \times 15 = \$258,026.40$.

c. The money spent on interest is $\$258,026.40 - \$150,000 = \$108,026.40$, while $\$150,000$ goes toward the principal.

24. a. The monthly payment is

$$PMT = \frac{\$100,000\left(\frac{0.07}{12}\right)}{1-\left(1+\frac{0.07}{12}\right)^{-12\times30}} = \$665.30 \,.$$

b. The total payment is $\$665.30 \times 12 \times 30 = \$239,508.00$.

c. The money spent on interest is $\$239,508.00 - \$100,000 = \$139,508.00$, while $\$100,000$ goes toward the principal.

25. The monthly payment is

$$PMT = \frac{\$150,000\left(\frac{0.085}{12}\right)}{1-\left(1+\frac{0.085}{12}\right)^{-12\times30}} = \$1153.37 \,.$$

To compute the interest owed at the end of one month, multiply the beginning principal of $\$150,000$ by the monthly interest rate of 8.5%/12. This gives $\$150,000(0.085/12) = \$1062.50$. Because the monthly payment is $\$1153.37$, the amount that goes toward principal is $\$1153.37 - \$1062.50 = \$90.87$. Subtract this from $\$150,000$ to get a new principal of $\$150,000 - \$90.87 = \$149,909.13$.

For the second month, repeat this process, but begin with a principal of $\$149,909.13$. The results are shown in the following table through the third month – note that rounding errors at each step propagate through the table, which means that our answers may differ slightly from those that a bank would compute.

End of month	Interest	Payment toward principal	New Principal
1	$1062.50	$90.87	$149,909.13
2	$1061.86	$91.51	$149,817.62
3	$1061.21	$92.16	$149,725.46

26. The monthly payment is

$$PMT = \frac{\$24,000\left(\frac{0.08}{12}\right)}{1-\left(1+\frac{0.08}{12}\right)^{-12\times15}} = \$229.36 \,.$$

To compute the interest owed at the end of one month, multiply the beginning principal of $\$24,000$ by the monthly interest rate of 8%/12. This gives $\$24,000(0.08/12) = \$160$. Because the monthly payment is $\$229.36$, the amount that goes toward principal is $\$229.36 - \$160 = \$69.36$. Subtract this from $\$24,000$ to get a new principal of $\$24,000 - \$69.36 = \$23,930.64$.

For the second month, repeat this process, but begin with a principal of $\$23,930.64$. The results are shown in the following table through the third month – note that rounding errors at each step propagate through the table, which means that our answers may differ slightly from those that a bank would compute.

End of month	Interest	Payment toward principal	New Principal
1	$160.00	$69.36	$23,930.64
2	$159.54	$69.82	$23,860.82
3	$159.07	$70.29	$23,790.53

27. For the 3-year loan at 7% APR, the monthly payment is $PMT = \dfrac{\$12,000\left(\frac{0.07}{12}\right)}{1-\left(1+\frac{0.07}{12}\right)^{-12\times3}} = \$370.53$.

The monthly payment for the 4-year loan is $\$290.15$, and for the 5-year loan, it is $\$243.32$ (the computations being similar to those used for the 3-year loan). Since you can afford only the payments on the 5-year loan, that loan best meets your needs.

28. For the 2-year loan at 8% APR, the monthly payment is $PMT = \dfrac{\$4000\left(\frac{0.08}{12}\right)}{1-\left(1+\frac{0.08}{12}\right)^{-12\times2}} = \$180.91$.

The monthly payment for the 3-year loan is

$127.20, and for the 4-year loan, it is $101.45 (the computations being similar to those used for the 3-year loan). Since you can afford payments on the 3-year and 4-year loans, either would work for your budget.

29. a. The monthly payment is

$$PMT = \frac{\$5000\left(\dfrac{0.18}{12}\right)}{1-\left(1+\dfrac{0.18}{12}\right)^{-12\times1}} = \$458.40.$$

b. Your total payments are $458.40 × 12 = $5500.80.

c. The interest is $500.80/$5500.80 = 9.1% of the total payments.

30. The monthly payment is

$$PMT = \frac{\$5000\left(\dfrac{0.20}{12}\right)}{1-\left(1+\dfrac{0.20}{12}\right)^{-12\times2}} = \$254.48.$$

Your total payments are $254.48 × 24 = $6107.52.

c. The interest is $1107.52/$6107.52 = 18.1% of the total payments.

31. The monthly payment is

$$PMT = \frac{\$5000\left(\dfrac{0.21}{12}\right)}{1-\left(1+\dfrac{0.21}{12}\right)^{-12\times3}} = \$188.38.$$

Your total payments are $188.38 × 36 = $6781.68.

c. The interest is $1781.68/$6781.68 = 26.3% of the total payments.

32. The monthly payment is

$$PMT = \frac{\$5000\left(\dfrac{0.22}{12}\right)}{1-\left(1+\dfrac{0.22}{12}\right)^{-12\times1}} = \$467.97.$$

Your total payments are $467.97 × 12 = $5615.64.

c. The interest is $615.64/$5615.64= 11.0% of the total payments.

33. Complete the table as shown in the first month. To find the interest for the second month, compute $1093.00 × 0.015 = $16.40. To find the new balance, compute $1093.00 + $75 + $16.40 – $200 = $984.40. Continue in this fashion to fill out the rest of the table. Note that rounding errors at each step will propagate through the table: a credit card company computing these balances might show slightly different values.

Month	Pmt	Expenses	Interest	New balance
0				$1200.00
1	$200	$75	$18.00	$1093.00
2	$200	$75	$16.40	$984.40
3	$200	$75	$14.77	$874.17
4	$200	$75	$13.11	$762.28
5	$200	$75	$11.43	$648.71
6	$200	$75	$9.73	$533.44
7	$200	$75	$8.00	$416.44
8	$200	$75	$6.25	$297.69
9	$200	$75	$4.47	$177.16
10	$200	$75	$2.66	$54.82

In the 11th month, a partial payment of $54.82 + $54.82 × 0.015 + $75 = $130.64 will pay off the loan.

34. To find the interest for the first month, compute $1200 × 0.015 = $18. To find the new balance, compute $1200 + $75 + $18 – $300 = $993. Continue in this fashion to fill out the rest of the table. Note that rounding errors at each step will propagate through the table.

Month	Pmt	Expenses	Interest	New balance
0				$1200.00
1	$300	$75	$18.00	$993.00
2	$300	$75	$14.90	$782.90
3	$300	$75	$11.74	$569.64
4	$300	$75	$8.54	$353.18
5	$300	$75	$5.30	$133.48

In the 6th month, a partial payment of $133.48 + $133.48 × 0.015 + $75 = $210.48 will pay off the loan.

35. Complete the table as shown in the first month. To find the interest for the second month, compute $179.50 × 0.015 = $2.69. To find next month's balance, compute $179.50 + $150 + $2.69 – $150 = $182.19. Continue in this fashion to fill out the rest of the table. Note that rounding errors at each step will propagate through the table: a credit card company computing these balances might slow slightly different values.

Month	Pmt	Expenses	Interest	Balance
0				$300.00
1	$300	$175	$4.50	$179.50
2	$150	$150	$2.69	$182.19
3	$400	$350	$2.73	$134.92
4	$500	$450	$2.02	$86.94

5	$0	$100	$1.30	$188.24
6	$100	$100	$2.82	$191.06
7	$200	$150	$2.87	$143.93
8	$100	$80	$2.16	$126.09

36. a. The monthly interest payment is $4000(0.06/12) = $20.

b. The monthly interest payment is $4000(0.24/12) = $80, or four times as much as the teaser rate.

37. Under Option 1, the monthly payment is

$$PMT = \frac{\$200,000\left(\frac{0.08}{12}\right)}{1-\left(1+\frac{0.08}{12}\right)^{-12\times30}} = \$1467.53, \text{ and the}$$

total cost of the loan is $1467.53 × 12 × 30 = $528,310.80. Under Option 2, the monthly payment is

$$PMT = \frac{\$200,000\left(\frac{0.075}{12}\right)}{1-\left(1+\frac{0.075}{12}\right)^{-12\times15}} = \$1854.02, \text{ and the}$$

total cost of the loan is $1854.02 × 12 × 15 = $333,723.60. You'll pay considerably more interest over the term of the loan in Option 1, but you may be able to afford the payments under that option more easily.

38. Under Option 1, the monthly payment is

$$PMT = \frac{\$75,000\left(\frac{0.08}{12}\right)}{1-\left(1+\frac{0.08}{12}\right)^{-12\times30}} = \$550.32, \text{ and the}$$

total cost of the loan is $550.32 × 12 × 30 = $198,115.20. Under Option 2, the monthly payment is

$$PMT = \frac{\$75,000\left(\frac{0.07}{12}\right)}{1-\left(1+\frac{0.07}{12}\right)^{-12\times15}} = \$674.12, \text{ and the}$$

total cost of the loan is $674.12 × 12 × 15 = $121,341.60. You'll pay considerably more interest over the term of the loan in Option 1, but you may be able to afford the payments under that option more easily.

39. Under Option 1, the monthly payment is

$$PMT = \frac{\$60,000\left(\frac{0.0715}{12}\right)}{1-\left(1+\frac{0.0715}{12}\right)^{-12\times30}} = \$405.24, \text{ and the}$$

total cost of the loan is $405.24 × 12 × 30 =

$145,886.40. Under Option 2, the monthly payment is

$$PMT = \frac{\$60,000\left(\frac{0.0675}{12}\right)}{1-\left(1+\frac{0.0675}{12}\right)^{-12\times15}} = \$530.95, \text{ and the}$$

total cost of the loan is $530.95 × 12 × 15 = $95,571.00. See Exercise 37 for pros and cons.

40. Under Option 1, the monthly payment is

$$PMT = \frac{\$180,000\left(\frac{0.0725}{12}\right)}{1-\left(1+\frac{0.0725}{12}\right)^{-12\times30}} = \$1227.92, \text{ and}$$

the total cost of the loan is $1227.92 × 12 × 30 = $442,041.20. Under Option 2, the monthly payment is

$$PMT = \frac{\$180,000\left(\frac{0.068}{12}\right)}{1-\left(1+\frac{0.068}{12}\right)^{-12\times15}} = \$1597.83, \text{ and the}$$

total cost of the loan is $1597.83 × 12 × 15 = $287,609.40. See Exercise 38 for pros and cons.

41. Under Choice 1, your monthly payment is

$$PMT = \frac{\$120,000\left(\frac{0.08}{12}\right)}{1-\left(1+\frac{0.08}{12}\right)^{-12\times30}} = \$880.52, \text{ and the}$$

closing costs are $1200. For Choice 2, the payment is

$$PMT = \frac{\$120,000\left(\frac{0.075}{12}\right)}{1-\left(1+\frac{0.075}{12}\right)^{-12\times30}} = \$839.06, \text{ and the}$$

closing costs are $1200 + $120,000(0.02) = $3600. You'll save $880.52 − $839.06 = $41.46 each month with Choice 2, though it will take $3600/($41.46 per month) = 87 months (about 7 years) to recoup the higher closing costs, and thus Choice 2 is the better option only if you intend to keep the house for at least 7 years.

42. Under Choice 1, your monthly payment is

$$PMT = \frac{\$120,000\left(\frac{0.085}{12}\right)}{1-\left(1+\frac{0.085}{12}\right)^{-12\times30}} = \$922.70, \text{ with no}$$

closing costs. For Choice 2, the payment is

$$PMT = \frac{\$120,000\left(\dfrac{0.075}{12}\right)}{1-\left(1+\dfrac{0.075}{12}\right)^{-12\times30}} = \$839.06 \text{, and the}$$

closing costs are $1200 + $120,000(0.04) = $6000. You'll save $922.70 – $839.06 = $83.64 each month with Choice 2, though it will take $6000/($83.64 per month) = 72 months (6 years) to recoup the higher closing costs, and thus Choice 2 is the better option only if you intend to keep the house for at least 6 years.

43. Under Choice 1, your monthly payment is

$$PMT = \frac{\$120,000\left(\dfrac{0.0725}{12}\right)}{1-\left(1+\dfrac{0.0725}{12}\right)^{-12\times30}} = \$818.61 \text{, and the}$$

closing costs are $1200 + $120,000(0.01) = $2400. For Choice 2, the payment is

$$PMT = \frac{\$120,000\left(\dfrac{0.0675}{12}\right)}{1-\left(1+\dfrac{0.0675}{12}\right)^{-12\times30}} = \$778.32 \text{, and the}$$

closing costs are $1200 + $120,000(0.03) = $4800. You'll save $818.61 – $778.32 = $40.29 each month with Choice 2, though it will take $2400/($40.29 per month) = 60 months (5 years) to recoup the higher closing costs, and thus Choice 2 is the better option only if you intend to keep the house for at least 5 years.

44. Under Choice 1, your monthly payment is

$$PMT = \frac{\$120,000\left(\dfrac{0.075}{12}\right)}{1-\left(1+\dfrac{0.075}{12}\right)^{-12\times30}} = \$839.06 \text{, and the}$$

closing costs are $1000. For Choice 2, the payment is

$$PMT = \frac{\$120,000\left(\dfrac{0.065}{12}\right)}{1-\left(1+\dfrac{0.065}{12}\right)^{-12\times30}} = \$758.48 \text{, and the}$$

closing costs are $1500 + $120,000(0.04) = $6300. You'll save $839.06 – $758.48 = $80.58 each month with Choice 2, though it will take $5300/($80.58 per month) = 66 months (5.5 years) to recoup the higher closing costs, and thus Choice 2 is the better option only if you intend to keep the house for at least 5.5 years.

45. a. The monthly payment is

$$PMT = \frac{\$30,000\left(\dfrac{0.09}{12}\right)}{1-\left(1+\dfrac{0.09}{12}\right)^{-12\times20}} = \$269.92 \,.$$

b. The monthly payment is

$$PMT = \frac{\$30,000\left(\dfrac{0.09}{12}\right)}{1-\left(1+\dfrac{0.09}{12}\right)^{-12\times10}} = \$380.03 \,.$$

c. If you pay the loan off in 20 years, the total payments will be $269.92 × 12 × 20 = $64,780.80. If you pay it off in 10 years, the total payments will be $380.03 × 12 × 10 = $45,603.60.

46. a. The monthly payment is

$$PMT = \frac{\$60,000\left(\dfrac{0.08}{12}\right)}{1-\left(1+\dfrac{0.08}{12}\right)^{-12\times25}} = \$463.09 \,.$$

b. The monthly payment is

$$PMT = \frac{\$60,000\dfrac{\left(\dfrac{0.08}{12}\right)}{12}}{1-\left(1+\dfrac{0.08}{12}\right)^{-12\times15}} = \$573.39 \,.$$

c. If you pay the loan off in 25 years, the total payments will be $463.09 × 12 × 25 = $138,927. If you pay it off in 15 years, the total payments will be $573.39 × 12 × 15 = $103,210.20.

47. Following example 10 in the text, the interest on the $150,000 loan in the first year will be approximately 7% × $150,000 = $10,500, which means the monthly payment will be about $10,500/12 = $875. With the 5% ARM, the interest will be approximately 5% × $150,000 = $7500, and thus the monthly payment will be about $7500/12 = $625. You'll save $875 – $625 = $250 each month with the ARM. In the third year, the rate on the ARM will be 1.5% higher than the fixed rate loan, and thus the yearly interest payments will differ by $150,000 × 0.015 = $2250, which amounts to $187.50 per month.

48. Following example 10 in the text, the interest on the $125,000 loan in the first year will be approximately 8.5% × $125,000 = $10,625, which means the monthly payment will be about $10,625/12 = $885.42. With the 5.5% ARM, the interest will be approximately 5.5% × $125,000 = $6875, and thus the monthly payment will be about $6875/12 = $572.92. You'll save about $313 each month with the ARM. In the second year, the

rate on the ARM will be 1.5% higher than the fixed rate loan, and thus the yearly interest payments will differ by $125,000 × 0.015 = $1875, which is about $156 per month.

FURTHER APPLICATIONS

49. Solve

$$\$500 = \frac{P\left(\dfrac{0.09}{12}\right)}{1-\left(1+\dfrac{0.09}{12}\right)^{-12\times30}} = P\frac{\left(\dfrac{0.09}{12}\right)}{1-\left(1+\dfrac{0.09}{12}\right)^{-12\times30}}$$

for P by computing the fraction on the right, and dividing it into $500. This results in P = $62,141 (rounded to the nearest dollar), and it represents the largest loan you can afford with monthly payments of $500. The loan will pay for 80% of the house you wish to buy (you must come up with a 20% down payment). Thus 80% × (*house price*) = $62,141, which means *house price* = $62,141/0.80 = $77,676. You can afford a house that will cost about $78,000.

50. a. $PMT = \dfrac{\$200,000\left(\dfrac{0.06}{12}\right)}{1-\left(1+\dfrac{0.06}{12}\right)^{-12\times30}} = \$1199.10.$

b. $PMT = \dfrac{\$186,046\left(\dfrac{0.055}{12}\right)}{1-\left(1+\dfrac{0.055}{12}\right)^{-12\times20}} = \$1279.79.$

c. The total payout on the original loan would be $1199.10 × 360 = $431,676.

d. The total payout with the refinancing plan would be the total of the 60 payments at the original amount, the 240 payments at the new amount, and the administrative costs. This would be 60 × $1199.10 + 240 × $1279.79 + $2000 = $381,095.60.

e. The refinancing option leads to a lower total payout, but also to higher monthly payments. If the higher payments would not be a financial hardship, the refinancing option would be the better option. The homeowner might also want to factor in the tax benefits of interest payments.

51. a. The monthly payment for the first loan is

$$PMT = \frac{\$10,000\left(\dfrac{0.08}{12}\right)}{1-\left(1+\dfrac{0.08}{12}\right)^{-12\times15}} = \$95.57.\quad \text{The}$$

$171,823.60 (*n* = 26); and $171,776.80. The total payout when *n* = 52 is shown below; the others are done in a similar fashion.

payments for the other two loans are calculated similarly; you should get $130.17 and $158.34, respectively.

b. For the first loan, you'll pay $95.57 × 12 × 15 = $17,202.60 over its term. The total payments for the other loans are computed in a similar fashion – you should get $31,240.80 and $19,000.80, respectively. Add them together to get $67,444.20.

c. The monthly payment for the consolidated loan

will be $PMT = \dfrac{\$37,500\left(\dfrac{0.085}{12}\right)}{1-\left(1+\dfrac{0.085}{12}\right)^{-12\times20}} = \$325.43,$

and the total payment over 20 years will be $78,103.20. You'll pay about $11,000 more for the consolidated loan ($78,103.20 – $67,444.20 = $10,659), but your monthly payments will be lower for the first ten years ($325.43 versus $95.57 + $130.17 + $158.34 = $384.08). If, as a recent graduate, your budget is tight, it may be worth it to consolidate the loans. It also means you'll have to keep track of only one loan instead of three, though with automatic withdrawals offered by most banks, this isn't as much of an issue today as it might have been 15 years ago.

52. a. You'll owe 22% × $2000 = $440.

b. You'll pay $440 × 12 = $5280.

c. The monthly payment for the loan would be

$$PMT = \frac{\$2000\left(\dfrac{0.10}{12}\right)}{1-\left(1+\dfrac{0.10}{12}\right)^{-12\times3}} = \$64.53.\quad \text{This is}$$

significantly lower than the amount owed to the car-title lender.

53. a. The annual (*n* = 1) payment is $8718.46; the monthly (*n* = 12) payment is $716.43, the bi-monthly (*n* = 26) payment is $330.43, and the weekly (*n* = 52) payment is $165.17. The weekly payment is computed below; the others are done in a similar fashion.

$$PMT = \frac{\$100,000\left(\dfrac{0.06}{52}\right)}{1-\left(1+\dfrac{0.06}{52}\right)^{-52\times20}} = \$165.17.$$

b. The total payout for each scenario is as follows: $174,369.20 (*n* = 1); $171,943.20 (*n* = 12);

$$\frac{\$165.17}{\text{week}} \times \frac{52\text{ weeks}}{\text{year}} \times 20\text{ years} = \$171,776.80.$$

c. The total payout decreases as *n* increases.

54. a. The monthly payment is $716.43 (see 53a).

b. If each year you send 13 payments of $716.43 to the bank, you will be making annual payments of $716.43 × 13 = $9313.59. This is equivalent to making monthly payments of $9313.59/12 = $776.13. Using that amount as *PMT* in the loan payment formula yields

$$\$776.13 = \frac{\$100,000\left(\dfrac{0.06}{12}\right)}{1-\left(1+\dfrac{0.06}{12}\right)^{-12\times Y}}.$$

To find out how long it will take to pay off the loan, we must solve for *Y*. The trick is to realize this is an exponential equation, and solving such equations requires the use of logarithms (discussed later in the text). Recall that the exponential expression must be isolated before taking the logarithm of both sides. The steps are shown below (with units of dollars omitted; it is understood that *Y* is measured in years in the loan payment formula). Begin by cross-multiplying.

$$776.13\left[1-\left(1+\frac{0.06}{12}\right)^{-12Y}\right] = 100000\left(\frac{0.06}{12}\right)$$

$$776.13\left[1-(1.005)^{-12Y}\right] = 500 \ \text{(simplify)}$$

$$1-(1.005)^{-12Y} = \frac{500}{776.13} \ \text{(divide by 776.13)}$$

$$-(1.005)^{-12Y} = -0.355... \ \text{(subtract 1)}$$

$$(1.005)^{-12Y} = 0.355... \ \text{(divide by }-1)$$

$$-12Y\log(1.005) = \log(0.355...) \ \text{(take logs)}$$

$$Y = \frac{\log(0.355...)}{-12\log(1.005)} = 17.3 \text{ years}.$$

Another way to set up the problem is to imagine that the 13 payments are sent to the bank at equal time intervals over the course of the year. As with the savings plan formula, the loan formula used in the text assumes the compounding period is equal to the payment period (that is, if you send payments in 13 times per year, the bank compounds interest 13 times per year). With these assumptions, the problem boils down to solving the following equation for *Y*:

$$\$716.43 = \frac{\$100,000\left(\dfrac{0.06}{13}\right)}{1-\left(1+\dfrac{0.06}{13}\right)^{-13\times Y}}.$$

You can solve it following the same procedure as before, and you should find an answer that is virtually the same (it differs in the thousandths-place).

TECHNOLOGY EXERCISES

65. a. PMT(0.09/12,12*10,7500) = $95.01

b. PMT(0.09/12,12*20,7500) = $67.48. The payment decreases

c. PMT(0.045/12,12*10,7500) = $77.73. The payment decreases.

66. a.

Month	Interest	Principal	Balance
			7500
1	56.25	38.76	7461.24
2	55.9593	39.0507	7422.189
3	55.66642	39.34358	7382.846
4	55.37134	39.63866	7343.207
5	55.07405	39.93595	7303.271
6	54.77453	40.23547	7263.036
7	54.47277	40.53723	7222.498
8	54.16874	40.84126	7181.657
9	53.86243	41.14757	7140.51
10	53.55382	41.45618	7099.053

b. The interest paid in the first month of the loan is $56.25 and $38.76 is paid towards the principle.

c. The interest paid in the last month of the loan is $0.70 and $94.31 is paid towards the principle.

UNIT 4E

TIME OUT TO THINK

Pg. 268. The marginal tax rates have not changed. The boundaries on the tax brackets have all increased slightly.

Pg. 270. They pay different taxes because of their different filing statuses, which determine the amounts of their deductions and their tax rates. In Robert's case, he also has extra exemptions for his two children. Opinions will vary on the question of whether the outcome is fair. This would be a good topic for a discussion either during or outside of class.

Pg. 271. Among the many factors are maintenance cost of the house versus the apartment; utilities cost; whether you have the savings necessary for the home down payment; whether you plan to live in the house short or long-term; whether you think the house is a good investment; etc.

Pg. 272. Opinions will vary. This would be a good topic for a discussion either during or outside of class.

Pg. 273. This guide was completed before congress acted on changing capital gains tax rates. They are currently scheduled to increase to 20% in 2011.

Pg. 274. Serena pays more tax, but her tax rate is lower. With this example in mind, you can have fun debating the fairness of the capital gains tax rates either during or outside of class.

Pg. 275. This guide was completed before the tax reform panel has made its report, but you should able to find its recommendations at the White House web site.

QUICK QUIZ

1. **a.** Gross income is defined as the total of all income you receive.

2. **c.** The first portion of your income is taxed at 10% (the portion being determined by your filing status – see Table 4.10), the next at 15%, and only the last portion is taxed at 25%.

3. **a.** A tax credit reduces your tax bill by the dollar amount of the credit, so your tax bill will be reduced by $1000.

4. **b.** A tax deduction reduces your taxable income, so if you have a deduction of $1000, and you are in the 15% tax bracket, your bill will be reduced by 15% of $1000, or $150. This answer assumes you are far enough into the 15% tax bracket so that reducing your taxable income by $1000 means you remain in the 15% bracket.

5. **b.** You can claim deductions of $4000 + $2000 = $6000 as long as you itemize deductions.

6. **a.** If you chose to itemize your deductions, the only thing you can claim is the $1000 contribution, and as this is less than your standard deduction of $5700, it won't give relief to your tax bill (in fact, you'd pay more tax it you were to itemize deductions in this situation – take the standard deduction).

7. **c.** FICA taxes are taxes levied on income from wages (and tips) to fund the Social Security and Medicare programs.

8. **a.** Joe will pay 7.65% of his income for FICA taxes. Kim pays 7.65% of only her first $94,200; she pays 1.45% of her remaining salary, for a total FICA tax of 0.0765($94,200) + 0.0145($150,000 – $94,200) = $8015.40, which is 5.3% of her income. David pays nothing at all in FICA taxes because income from capital gains is not subject to FICA taxes.

9. **b.** Assuming all are of the same filing status, Jerome pays the most because his FICA taxes will be highest, followed by Jenny, and then Jacqueline.

10. **c.** Taxes on money deposited into tax-deferred accounts are *deferred* until a later date: you don't have to pay taxes on that money now, but you will when you withdraw the money in later years.

DOES IT MAKE SENSE?

11. Does not make sense. We know nothing of the rest of the picture for these two individuals – they may have very different deductions, and thus different tax bills.

12. Does not make sense. If you care for a dependent child, you earn the child tax credit, whether you itemize deductions or not.

13. Makes sense. You can deduct interest paid on the mortgage of a home if you itemize deductions, and for many people, the mortgage interest deduction is the largest of all deductions.

14. Does not make sense. The $12,000 mortgage interest deduction would be greater than the standard deduction coming to these people (whether they file separately or jointly), and thus there would be a tax benefit.

15. Makes sense (in some scenarios). Bob and Sue might be hit with the "marriage penalty" when they file taxes, and if they postpone their wedding until the new year, they could avoid the penalty for at least the previous tax year.

16. Makes sense. The top rate for dividends is 15%, no matter how much you earn in dividends.

17. Makes sense. Those who are self-employed must pay both the employee and employer ends of the FICA tax, and for any profit up to $94,200, the rate is 7.65%. Self-employed people must pay twice that rate, or 15.3%.

18. Makes sense. The tax break that one enjoys with tax-deferred investments results in a tax savings that ultimately affects take-home pay.

BASIC SKILLS & CONCEPTS

19. Antonio's gross income was $47,200 + $2400 = $49,600. His AGI was $49,600 – $3500 = $46,100. His taxable income was $46,100 – $3300 – $5150 = $37,650.

20. Marie's gross income was $28,400 + $95 = $28,495, and her AGI was the same as she had no adjustments to income. Her taxable income was $28,495 – $3300 – $5150 = $20,045.

21. Isabella's gross income was $88,750 + $4900 = $93,650. Her AGI was $93,650 – $6200 = $87,450. Her taxable income was $87,450 – $3300 – $9050 = $75,100.

22. Lebron's gross income was $3,452,000 + $54,200 = $3,506,200. His AGI was $3,506,200 – $30,000 = $3,476,200. His taxable income was $3,476,200 – $674,500 = $2,801,700. Lebron needs a good tax lawyer.

23. Your itemized deductions total to $8600 + $2700 + $645 = $11,945, and since this is larger than the standard deduction of $11,400, you should itemize your deductions.

24. Your itemized deductions total to $3700 + $760 = $4460, and since this is less than the standard deduction of $5700, you should claim the standard deduction.

25. Suzanne's gross income is $33,200 + $350 = $33,550, her AGI is $33,550 − $500 = $33,050, and her taxable income is $33,050 − $3650 − $5700 = $23,700. She should claim the standard deduction because it is much higher than her itemized deduction of $450.

26. Malcolm's gross income and AGI are both $23,700, and his taxable income is $23,700 − $3650 − $5700 = $14,350. He should claim the standard deduction because it is higher than his itemized deduction of $4500.

27. Wanda's gross income was $35,400 + $500 = $35,900, her AGI was the same, and her taxable income was $35,900 − $3650 × 3 − $5700 = $19,250. She should claim the standard deduction because it is higher than her itemized deduction of $1500.

28. Emily and Juan had a gross income of $75,300 + $2000 + $1650 = $78,950, their AGI was $78,950 − $3240 = $75,710, and their taxable income was $75,710 − $3650 × 4 − $11,400 = $49,710. They should claim the standard deduction of $11,400 for married couples because it's higher than their itemized deductions.

29. Gene owes 10% × ($8350) + 15% × ($33,950 − $8350) + 25% × ($35,400 − $33,950) = $5038 (taxes are rounded to the nearest dollar).

30. Sarah and Marco owe 10% × ($16,700) + 15% ($67,900 − $16,700) + 25% × ($87,500 − $67,900) = $14,250.

31. Bobbi owes 10% × ($8350) + 15% × ($33,950 − $8350) + 25% × ($68,525 − $33,950) + 28% × ($77,300 − $68,525) = $15,776.

32. Abraham owes 10% × ($8350) + 15% × ($23,800 − $8350) = $3152.

33. Paul owes 10% × ($11,950) + 15% × ($45,500 − $11,950) + 25% × ($89,300 − $45,500) − $1000 = $16,178.

34. Pat owes 10% × ($10,750) + 15% × ($41,050 − $10,750) + 25% × ($57,000 − $41,050) − $1000 = $8608.

35. Winona and Jim owe 10% × ($16,700) + 15% × ($67,900 − $16,700) + 25% × ($105,500 − $67,900) − $2000 = $16,750.

36. Chris owes 10% × ($8350) + 15% × ($33,950 − $8350) + 25% × ($68,525 − $33,950) + 28% × ($104,425 − $68,525) + 33% × ($127,300 − $104,425) = $30,920.

37. Their bill will be reduced by $500.

38. Her bill will be reduced by $500.

39. Her taxes will not be affected because she is claiming the standard deduction, and a $1000 charitable contribution must be itemized.

40. His tax bill will be reduced by 15% of $1000, or $150, provided he is far enough into the 15% tax bracket that his $1000 contribution does not drop him into the lower bracket.

41. His tax bill will be reduced by 28% of $1000, or $280, provided he is far enough into the 28% bracket that his $1000 contribution does not drop him into the lower bracket.

42. Her tax bill will be reduced by 35% of $1000, or $350, provided she is far enough into the 35% bracket that her $1000 contribution does not drop her into the lower bracket.

43. The $1800 per month of your payment that goes toward interest would be deductible, which means you'd save 33% × $1800 = $594 each month in taxes. Thus your $2000 mortgage payment would effectively be only $2000 − $594 = $1406, which is less than your rent payment of $1600. Buying the house is cheaper. This solution assumes that the $1800 × 12 = $21,600 interest deduction would not drop you into the 28% bracket (if it did, the solution would be more complicated).

44. The $600 per month of your payment that goes toward interest would be deductible, which means you'd save 15% × $600 = $90 each month in taxes. Thus your $675 mortgage payment would effectively be only $675 − $90 = $585, which is less than your rent payment of $600. Buying the house is cheaper. This solution assumes that the $600 × 12 = $7200 interest deduction would not drop you into the 10% tax bracket (if it did, the solution would be more complicated).

45. Maria saves 33% of $10,000, or $3300 in taxes, which means the true cost of her mortgage interest is $6700. Steve saves 15% of $10,000, or $1500 in taxes, which means the true cost of his mortgage interest is $8500. This solution assumes their deductions do not drop them into the lower tax bracket.

46. Yolanna saves 35% of $4000, or $1400 in taxes, which means the true cost of her contribution is $2600. Alia saves 10% of $4000, or $400 in taxes, which means the true cost of her contribution is $3600. This solution assumes Yolanna does not drop into the 33% bracket as a result of her contribution.

47. Luis will pay 7.65% × $28,000 = $2142 in FICA taxes. His taxable income is $28,000 − $3650 − $5700 − $2500 = $16,150. He will pay 10% × ($8350) + 15% × ($16,150 − $8350) = $2005 in income taxes, and thus his total tax bill will be $2142 + $2005 = $4147. This is $4147/$28,000 = 14.8% of his gross income, so his effective tax rate is 14.8%.

48. Carla will pay 7.65% × $34,500 = $2639 in FICA taxes. Her gross income is $34,500 + $750 = $35,250, and her taxable income is $35,250 − $3650 − $5700 − $3000 = $22,900. She will pay

10% × ($8350) + 15% × ($22,900 − $8350) = $3018 in income taxes, and thus her total tax bill will be $2639 + $3018 = $5657. This is $5657/$35,250 = 16.0% of her gross income, so her effective tax rate is 16.0%.

49. Jack will pay 7.65% × $44,800 = $3427 in FICA taxes. His gross income is $44,800 + $1250 = $46,050, and his taxable income is $46,050 − $3650 − $5700 − $2000 = $34,700. He will pay 10% × ($8350) + 15% × ($33,950 − $8350) + 25% × ($34,700 − $33,950) = $4863 in income taxes, and thus his total tax bill will be $3427 + $4863 = $8290. This is $8290/$46,050 = 18.0% of his gross income, so his effective tax rate is 18.0%.

50. Alejandro will pay 7.65% × ($106,800) + 1.45% × ($115,200 − $106,800) = $8292 in FICA taxes. His gross income is $115,200 + $4450 = $119,650, and his taxable income is $119,650 − $3650 − $5700 − $9500 = $100,800. He will pay 10% × ($8350) + 15% × ($33,950 − $8350) + 25% × ($82,250 − $33,950) + 28% × ($100,800 − $82,250) = $21,944 in income taxes, and thus his total tax bill will be $8292 + $21,944 = $30,236. This is $30,236/$119,650 = 25.3% of his gross income, so his effective tax rate is 25.3%.

51. Brittany will pay 7.65% × $48,200 = $3687 in FICA taxes. Her taxable income is $48,200 − $3650 − $5700 = $38,850. She will pay 10% × ($8350) + 15% × ($33,950 − $8350) + 25% × ($38,850 − $33,950) = $5900 in income taxes, and thus her total tax bill will be $3687 + $5900 = $9587. This is $9587/$48,200 = 19.9% of her gross income, so her effective tax rate is 19.9%.

52. Larae will pay 7.65% × $21,200 = $1622 in FICA taxes. Her taxable income is $21,200 − $3650 − $5700 = $11,850. She will pay 10% × ($8350) + 15% × ($11,850 − $8350) = $1360 in income taxes, and thus her total tax bill will be $1622 + $1360 = $2982. This is $2982/$21,200 = 14.1% of her gross income, so her effective tax rate is 14.1%.

53. Pierre will pay 7.65% × ($106,800) + 1.45% × ($120,000 − $106,800) = $8336 in FICA taxes, and because his taxable income is $120,000 − $3650 − $5700 = $110,650, he will pay 10% × ($8350) + 15% × ($33,950 − $8350) + 25% × ($82,250 − $33,950) + 28% × ($110,650 − $82,250) = $24,702 in income taxes. His total tax bill is $8336 + $24,702 = $33,038, so his overall tax rate is $33,038/$120,000 = 27.5%. Katarina will pay nothing in FICA taxes, and her income taxes will be 0% × ($33,950) + 15% × ($110,550 − $33,950) = $11,505 – like Pierre, her taxable income is $110,650, but she is taxed at the special rates for dividends and long-term capital

gains. Her overall tax rate is $11,505 /$120,000 = 9.6%.

54. Deion will pay 7.65% × $60,000 = $4590 in FICA taxes, and because his taxable income is $60,000 − $3650 − $5700 = $50,650, he will pay 10% × ($8350) + 15% × ($33,950 − $8350) + 25% × ($50,650 − $33,950) = $8850 in income taxes. His total tax bill is $4590 + $8850 = $13,440, so his overall tax rate is $13,440/$60,000 = 22.4%. Josephina will pay nothing in FICA taxes, and her income taxes will be 0% × ($33,950) + 15% × ($50,650 − $33,950) = $2505 – like Deion, her taxable income is $50,650, but she is taxed at the special rates for dividends and long-term capital gains. Her overall tax rate is $2505/$60,000 = 4.2%.

55. Because you are in the 15% tax bracket, every time you make a $400 contribution to your tax-deferred savings plan, you save 15% × $400 = $60 in taxes. Thus your take-home pay is reduced not by $400, but by $340.

56. Because you are in the 25% tax bracket, every time you make a $600 contribution to your tax-deferred savings plan, you save 25% × $600 = $150 in taxes. Thus your take-home pay is reduced not by $600, but by $450.

57. Because you are in the 25% tax bracket, every time you make an $800 contribution to your tax-deferred savings plan, you save 25% × $800 = $200 in taxes. Thus your take-home pay is reduced not by $800, but by $600.

58. Because you are in the 28% tax bracket, every time you make an $800 contribution to your tax-deferred savings plan, you save 28% × $800 = $224 in taxes. Thus your take-home pay is reduced not by $800, but by $576.

FURTHER APPLICATIONS

59. Gabriella's taxable income is $44,500 − $3650 − $5700 = $35,150, so her income tax is 10% × ($8350) + 15% × ($33,950 − $8350) + 25% × ($35,150 − $33,950) = $4975. Roberto's taxable income is $33,400 − $3650 − $5700 = $24,050, so his income tax is 10% × ($8350) + 15% × ($24,050 − $8350) = $3190. If they delay their marriage, they will pay $4975 + $3190= $8165 in taxes. If they marry, their combined AGI will be $44,500 + $33,400 = $77,900, and their taxable income will be $77,900 − $3650 × 2 − $11,400 = $59,200. Their income taxes will be 10% × ($16,700) + 15% × ($59,200 − $16,700) = $8045, which is lower than the taxes they would pay as individuals, and thus they will not face a marriage penalty (in fact, they'll benefit from becoming married).

60. Joan's taxable income is $32,500 – $3650 – $5700 = $23,150, so her income tax is 10% × ($8350) + 15% × ($23,150– $8350) = $3055. Paul's taxable income is $29,400 – $3650 – $5700 = $20,9050, so his income tax is 10% × ($8350) + 15% × ($20,950 – $8350) = $2590. If they delay their marriage, they will pay $3055 + $2590 = $5645 in taxes. If they marry, their combined AGI will be $32,500 + $29,400 = $61,900, and their taxable income will be $61,900 – $3650 × 2 – $11,400 = $43,200. Their income taxes will be 10% × ($16,700) + 15% × ($43,200 – $16,700) = $5645, which is the same amount they would pay as individuals, and thus they will not face a marriage penalty.

61. Steve's taxable income is $185,000 – $3650 – $5700 = $175,650, so his income tax is 10% × ($8350) + 15% × ($33,950 – $8350) + 25% × ($82,250 – $33,950) + 28% × ($171,550 – $82,250) + 33% × ($175,650– $171,550) = $43,107. Mia's tax is, of course, the same, so if they delay their marriage, they will pay $86,214. If they marry, their combined AGI will be $185,000 × 2 = $370,000, and their taxable income will be $370,000 – $3650 × 2 – $11,400 = $351,300. Their income taxes will be 10% × ($16,700) + 15% × ($67,900 – $16,700) + 25% × ($137,050 – $67,900) + 28% × ($208,850 – $137,050) + 33% × ($351,300 – $208,850) = $93,750, which is more than the taxes they would pay as individuals, and thus they will face a marriage penalty.

62. Lisa's taxable income is $85,000 – $3650 – $5700 = $75,650, so her income tax is 10% × ($8350) + 15% × ($33,950 – $8350) + 25% × ($75,650 – $33,950) = $15,100. Patrick pays no income tax, so if they delay their marriage, they will pay $15,100. If they marry, their combined AGI will be $85,000, and their taxable income will be $85,000 – $3650 × 2 – $11,400 = $66,300. Their income taxes will be 10% × ($16,700) + 15% × ($66,300– $16,700) = $9110, which is lower than the taxes they would pay as individuals, and thus they will not face a marriage penalty (in fact, they'll benefit from becoming married).

UNIT 4F

TIME OUT TO THINK

Pg. 281(1ˢᵗ). Answers will vary. When this guide was published, some companies had already paid back their loans. Opinions will vary on the overall success of the stimulus package.

Pg. 281(2ⁿᵈ). For most people, the answer depends on whether they own a home. For homeowners, who generally owe most of the value of their home to a bank, $30,000 is usually small in comparison. For others, including students, their share of the national debt generally is larger than personal debts.

Pg. 282. Rising debt means a greater likelihood that the company won't succeed, so getting further loans will depend on convincing lenders that the company will eventually become profitable and be able to pay back the loans.

Pg. 283. This is a political question and opinions will vary, but clearly Example 4 shows that the projections must be taken with a large grain of salt. Moreover, remember that if other economic assumptions hold true while taxes are cut or spending is increased, then the surplus will be reduced by the amount of the tax cut or spending.

Pg. 289. Opinions will vary. This would be a good topic for a discussion either during or outside of class.

QUICK QUIZ

1. **b**. Bigprofit.com had more outlays (expenses) than receipts (income) by $1 million, so it ran a deficit for 2009 of $1 million. Its debt is the total amount owed to lenders over the years; this is $7 million.

2. **c**. The federal debt is about $13 trillion dollars, and when divided evenly among all 300 million U.S. citizens, it comes to about $43,000 per person.

3. **c**. The error in predicting the budget is around 10%, and 10% of $2.5 trillion is $250 billion. Thus if receipts were 10% below what was predicted, the deficit would be $350 billion, and if receipts were 10% above what was predicted, there would be a surplus of $150 billion.

4. **b**. Discretionary outlays differ from mandatory outlays in that Congress passes a budget every year that spells out where the government will spend its discretionary funds.

5. **a**. Interest on the debt must be paid so that the government does not default on its loans, and Medicare is an entitlement program that is part of mandatory spending. On the other hand, all money spent on defense is considered discretionary spending.

6. **a**. Mandatory expenses include money spent on Social Security, Medicare, interest on the debt, government pensions, and Medicaid, and together these programs constitute almost 60% of the budget (see Figure 4.13).

7. **b**. The $100 billion is supposed to be deposited into an account used to pay off future Social Security recipients, but instead, the government

spends the money at hand, and essentially writes IOUs to itself, and places these in the account.

8. **b.** Publicly held debt is the money the government owes to those who have purchased Treasury bills, notes, and bonds.

9. **b.** The gross debt is the sum of all of the money that the government owes to individuals who have purchased bonds, and the money it owes to itself.

10. **c.** The amount of money set aside for education grants is miniscule in comparison to the billions of dollars the government will be required to spend on Social Security in 2030.

DOES IT MAKE SENSE?

9. Makes sense. Each U.S. citizen would have to spend about $43,000 to retire the federal debt, and it's certainly true that this exceeds the value of most new cars.

10. Does not make sense. In 2009, outlays were about $3.52 trillion (Table 4.10), and 8% of that (Figure 4.13) went toward the government's annual interest payment on the debt, which means around $282 billion was spent on interest for the debt. Divide that by 305 million U.S. citizens, and you get about $925 – this is not enough to buy a new car.

11. Does not make sense. The financial health of the government is very much dependent upon what happens with Social Security and the FICA taxes collected to fund it. The term "off-budget" is nothing more than a label that separates the Social Security program from the rest of the budget.

12. Makes sense. When receipts are more than outlays, the government ran a surplus for that year, but the debt may increase anyway, for a variety of reasons. Among them: the government claims to be running a surplus when the on-budget net income is positive even though it also spends off-budget (i.e. Social Security) funds; and the total debt may increase because of the huge amount of interest owed to holders of Treasury bills.

13. Does not make sense. The government has a difficult time predicting deficits or surpluses even one year out – it cannot predict what will happen with any level of accuracy in ten years.

14. Does not make sense. Despite the fact that the government collects more in FICA taxes than it owes to Social Security recipients (and due to demographics, this trend is expected to continue for some time), it spends all of that money on other programs even though it is supposed to deposit it into the Social Security trust fund.

BASIC SKILLS & CONCEPTS

15. a. Your receipts are $38,000, and your outlays are $12,000 + $6000 + $1200 + $8500 = $27,700, so you have a surplus.

b. A 3% raise means your receipts will be $38,000 + 3% × $38,000 = $39,140, and your outlays will be $27,700 + $8500 = $36,200, so you'll still have a surplus, though it will be smaller.

c. Your receipts will be $39,140 (see part **b**), and your outlays will be $27,700 × 1.01 + $7500 = $35,477, so you will be able to afford it.

16. a. Your receipts are $28,000, and your outlays are $8,000 + $4500 + $1600 + $10,400 = $24,500, so you have a surplus.

b. A 2% raise means your receipts would be $28,000 + 2% × $28,000 = $28,560, and your outlays would be $24,500 + $5200 = $29,700, so you could not afford to pay off all of the debt.

c. Your receipts will be $28,560 (see part **b**), and your outlays will be $24,500 × 1.01 + $3500 = $28,245, so you will be able to afford it.

17. $\dfrac{\$1.3 \times 10^{13}}{160 \times 10^6 \text{ workers}} = \dfrac{\$81,250}{\text{worker}}$.

18. $\dfrac{\$1.3 \times 10^{13}}{120 \times 10^6 \text{ families}} = \dfrac{\$108,333}{\text{family}}$.

19. a. The interest on the debt will be 8.2% × $773,000 = $63,000 (rounded to the nearest thousand dollars).

b. The total outlays are $600,000 + $200,000 + $250,000 + $63,000 = $1,113,000, so the year-end deficit is $1,050,000 – $1,113,000 = –$63,000, and the year-end accumulated debt is –$773,000 – $63,000 = –$836,000.

c. The interest on the debt in 2011 will be 8.2% × $836,000 = $69,000 (rounded to the nearest thousand dollars).

d. The total outlays are $600,000 + $200,000 + $69,000 = $869,000, so the year-end surplus is $1,100,000 – $869,000 = $231,000, and the year-end accumulated debt is –$836,000 + $231,000 = –$605,000, assuming all surplus is devoted to paying down the debt.

20. a. The interest on the debt will be 8.2% × $773,000 = $63,000 (rounded to the nearest thousand dollars).

b. The total outlays are $850,000 + $290,000 + $210,000 + $63,000 = $1,413,000, so the year-end deficit is $975,000 – $1,413,000 = –$438,000, and the year-end accumulated debt is –$773,000 – $438,000 = –$1,211,000.

c. The interest on the debt in 2011 will be 8.2% × $1,211,000 = $99,000 (rounded to the nearest thousand dollars).

d. The total outlays are $850,000 + $290,000 + $99,000 = $1,239,000, so the year-end deficit is $1,050,000 – $1,239,000 = –$189,000, and the year-end accumulated debt is –$1,211,000 – $189,000 = –$1,400,000.

21. A 1% decrease in total receipts in 2009 would result in a 99% × $2100 billion = $21 billion increase in the deficit. A 0.5% increase in total outlays would result in a 0.5% × $3520 billion = $18 billion increase in the deficit.

22. A 0.5% decrease in total receipts in 2009 would result in a 0.5% × $2100 billion = $11 billion increase in the deficit. A 1% increase in total outlays would result in a 1% × $3520 billion = $35 billion increase in the deficit.

23. Individual income taxes were 47% of $2100 billion = $987 billion, or just under $1 trillion.

24. Social insurance taxes were 35% of $2100 billion = $735 billion.

25. Excise taxes were 2% of $2100 billion = $42 billion.

26. Social Security expenses were 20% of $3520 = $704 billion.

27. Medicare expenses were 13% of $3520 = $458 billion.

28. Defense and Homeland Security expenses were 21% of $3520 = $739 billion.

29. Because *unified net income – off-budget net income = on-budget net income*, we have $40 billion – $180 billion = –$140 billion. In other words, despite the fact that the government proclaimed a surplus of $40 billion for this year, it actually ran a deficit of $140 billion due to the fact that the money earmarked for the Social Security trust fund was never deposited there (it was spent on other programs).

30. Because *unified net income – off-budget net income = on-budget net income*, we have –$220 billion – $205 billion = –$425 billion. In other words, despite the fact that the government proclaimed a deficit of $220 billion for this year, it actually ran a deficit of $425 billion due to the fact that the money earmarked for the Social Security trust fund was never deposited there (it was spent on other programs).

31. The government could cut discretionary spending, it could borrow money by issuing Treasury notes, or it could raise taxes (of course, a combination of these three would also be an option).

32. The government could cut discretionary spending, it could borrow money by issuing Treasury notes, or it could raise taxes (of course, a combination of these three would also be an option).

FURTHER APPLICATIONS

33. $\$1.3 \times 10^{13} \times \dfrac{1\text{ s}}{\$1} \times \dfrac{1\text{ hr}}{3600\text{ s}} \times \dfrac{1\text{ d}}{24\text{ hr}} \times \dfrac{1\text{ yr}}{365\text{ d}} = 412{,}227$ yr. It would take about 412,000 years.

34. The dimensions of a dollar bill are about 6.5 cm by 16.5 cm, so its area is around 100 cm^2. Convert $13 trillion into square kilometers:

$$\$1.3 \times 10^{13} \times \frac{100\text{ cm}^2}{\$1} \times \left(\frac{1\text{ km}}{100{,}000\text{ cm}}\right)^2 =$$

$130{,}000\text{ km}^2$.

This is $\dfrac{130{,}000\text{ km}^2}{10{,}000{,}000\text{ km}^2} = 1.3\%$ of the area of the United States. A more careful estimate (using $6.5\text{ cm} \times 16.5\text{ cm} = 107.25\text{ cm}^2$) gives an answer closer to $140{,}000\text{ km}^2$, or 1.4% of the land area.

35. In ten years, the debt will be
$$\$1.3 \times 10^{13}(1+0.01)^{10} = \$1.436 \times 10^{13},$$
or about $14.36 trillion. In 50 years, it will be
$$\$1.3 \times 10^{13}(1+0.01)^{50} = \$2.138 \times 10^{13},$$
or about $21.38 trillion.

36. In ten years, the debt will be
$$\$1.3 \times 10^{13}(1+0.02)^{10} = \$1.585 \times 10^{13},$$
or about $15.85 trillion. In 50 years, it will be
$$\$1.3 \times 10^{13}(1+0.02)^{50} = \$3.499 \times 10^{13},$$
or about $34.99 trillion.

37. The projected outlays are $2685 billion + $929 billion = $3614 billion. If the outlays were higher by 5%, they would be 105% × $3614 billion = $3795 billion, and if the receipts were lower by 5%, they would be 95% × $2685 billion = $2551 billion. This would result in a deficit of $2551 billion – $3795 billion = –$1244 billion.

38. The projected outlays are $2685 billion + $929 billion = $3614 billion. If the outlays were higher by 10%, they would be 110% × $3614 billion = $3975 billion, and if the receipts were lower by 10%, they would be 90% × $2685 billion = $2417 billion. This would result in a deficit of $2417 billion – $3975 billion = –$1558 billion.

39. $PMT = \dfrac{\$8 \times 10^{12}\left(\dfrac{0.04}{1}\right)}{1-\left(1+\dfrac{0.04}{1}\right)^{-1\times10}} = \$9.86 \times 10^{11}$, which is $986 billion per year.

40. $PMT = \dfrac{\$8 \times 10^{12}\left(\dfrac{0.02}{1}\right)}{1 - \left(1 + \dfrac{0.02}{1}\right)^{-1 \times 15}} = \$6.23 \times 10^{11}$, which

   is $623 billion per year.

41. $\$1.3 \times 10^{13} \times \dfrac{1\,\text{wk}}{\$150 \times 10^{6}} \times \dfrac{1\,\text{yr}}{52\,\text{wk}} = 1667$ years.

42. The annual revenue required from the lottery would be $13 trillion/50 = $260 billion, though this means annual lottery sales would need to be $520 billion (because only half of the proceeds go toward reduction of the debt). Divide $520 billion by 310 million citizens to find that each citizen would need to spend $1677 per year in lottery tickets. An interesting result of such a massive lottery is that there would be a number of very rich people at the end of the 50-year lottery experiment: roughly $13 trillion in prize money would be distributed. In fact, if a random citizen were chosen every day (for 50 years) to be the lottery winner for the day, that person would win about $700 million.

UNIT 5A

TIME OUT TO THINK

Pg. 302. The networks would be biased toward high ratings for their own shows, so no one would believe their own studies even if they did them carefully. Nielsen is an independent company, so in principle is not biased and is more likely to deliver fair ratings.

Pg. 303. Assign each participant a value from 0 to 100, then use the program to select enough random numbers (ignoring repeated values) to assign half the of participants to either the treatment or control group. The remaining participants would be assigned the other group.

Pg. 307. In this case the confidence interval is all above 50% (52% to 58%), so she can be (at least) 95% confident of winning.

QUICK QUIZ

1. **a**. The population is the complete set of people or things that are being studied.

2. **c**. Those who donated money to the governor's campaign are much more likely to approve of his job.

3. **a**. A representative sample is one where the characteristics of the sample match those of the population.

4. **b**. Those who do not receive the treatment (in this case, a cash incentive) are in the control group. Note that the teacher could also randomly select a third group of students who don't even know they are part of the experiment – she could study their attendance rates, and this would be another control group.

5. **c**. The experiment is not blind, because the participants know whether they are receiving money or not, and the teacher knows to which group each student belongs.

6. **a**. The purpose of a placebo is to control for psychological effects that go along with being a participant of the study.

7. **c**. A placebo effect results when participants of the study improve because they think they are receiving the treatment.

8. **c**. A single-blind experiment is one where the participants do not know whether they are part of the treatment group or the control group, but the person conducting the experiment does know.

9. **b**. With a margin of error of 3%, both Poll X and Poll Y have predictions that overlap (in that Poll X predicts Powell will receive 46% to 52% of the vote, and Poll Y predicts he will receive 50% to 56% of the vote), and so they are consistent in their predictions.

10. **b**. The confidence interval is simply the results of the poll plus-or-minus the margin of error.

DOES IT MAKE SENSE?

9. Does not make sense. A sample is a subset of the population, and thus it cannot exceed the size of the population.

10. Makes sense. Due to the random nature of the selection process, it certainly may happen that a sample, though well chosen, does not reflect the characteristics of the population.

11. Does not make sense. The control group should no treatment, not a different treatment than that given to the treatment group.

12. Makes sense. In an experiment where the results are derived from interviews conducted by those running the experiment, a bias may be present if the interviewers know who belongs to the control and treatment groups, and thus it is reasonable to doubt the results.

13. Makes sense. The poll makes a prediction about the outcome of the election, and though we can place a reasonable level of confidence in the results of the poll, it cannot tell the future for us.

14. Makes sense. As long as the sample is chosen carefully, a small sample can often provide good estimates about the population from which it was drawn.

BASIC SKILLS & CONCEPTS

15. The population is all Americans, and the sample was the set of 1001 Americans surveyed. The population parameters are the opinions of Americans on Iran, and the sample statistics consist of the opinions of those who were surveyed.

16. The population is the set of stars in the galaxy, and the sample is the set of stars selected for measurement. The population parameter is the average distance from Earth of all of the stars in the galaxy, whereas the sample statistic is the average distance from Earth of just those stars in the sample.

17. The population is the set of all Americans, and the sample is the set of 998 people who were surveyed. The population parameter is the percent Americans who believe there has been progress in finding a cure for cancer in the last 30 years, and the sample statistic is the 60% of those surveyed that believe there has been progress in finding a cure for cancer in the last 30 years.

18. The population is the set of American adults, and the sample is the set of 1051 American adults

surveyed. The population parameter is the percent of those who have been spending less in recent months, while the sample statistic is the 27% of those surveyed who have been spending less in recent months.

19. The population is the set of Americans, and the sample is the set of 1027 Americans surveyed. The population parameter is the percent of those who believe there should be an investigation of anti-terror tactics used during the Bush administration, while the sample statistic is the 62% of those surveyed who believe there should be an investigation of anti-terror tactics used during the Bush administration.

20. The population is the 1.4 million first-year college students, and the sample is the 241,000 students surveyed. The population parameters are the attitudes of all first-year students, and the sample statistics are the attitudes of those surveyed.

21. *Step 1*: The goal is to determine the average number of hours spent per week talking on cell phones among a population of ninth graders. *Step 2*: Randomly select (from a list of all students at the school) a sample from the population. *Step 3*: Determine cell phone use, in hours per week, from those in the sample, either with an interview, a survey, or a device that measures more precisely when the cell phone is in use. *Step 4*: Conclude that cell phone use among all ninth-graders is similar to cell phone use among the sample. *Step 5*: Assess the results and formulate a conclusion.

22. *Step 1:* The goal of the study is to determine customers' shopping needs and whether the store's variety meets those needs among a population of all customers of the store. *Step 2*: Randomly select a representative sample of customers to participate in the study. *Step 3*: Interview or survey those in the sample to determine the need. *Step 4*: Infer that the needs of the sample is the same for all customers. *Step 5*: Assess the results and draw conclusions from your study.

23. *Step 1*: The population of this study is American male college students, and the goal is to determine the percentage of the population that plays chess at least once per week. *Step 2*: Choose a representative sample of male college students. *Step 3*: Survey students and determine the percentage of those in the sample who play chess at least once a week. *Step 4*: Infer the percentage of the population who play chess from the results of the study. *Step 5*: Assess the results and draw conclusions.

24. *Step 1*: The goal is to determine the average tip (as a percentage of the total bill) that is left at restaurants among a population of those that go to restaurants. *Step 2*: Select a representative sample

of people who go to restaurants. *Step 3*: Determine the average tip among those in the sample. *Step 4*: Conclude that the average tip for those in the sample is the same for those in the population. *Step 5*: Assess the results and formulate a conclusion.

25. *Step1*: The population in the study is all batteries in a particular model of laptop, and the goal is to find the average time to failure of those batteries. *Step 2*: Select a representative sample of laptops. *Step 3*: Formulate a method to determine lifetimes of batteries, and compute the average lifetime. *Step 4*: Infer the average lifetime found in *Step 3* is the same for all batteries. *Step 5*: Assess the results and formulate a conclusion.

26. *Step1*: The goal is to determine the percentage of vegetarians among a population of all high school students. *Step 2*: Choose a representative sample of high school students. *Step 3*: Determine the percentage of students among those in the sample who are vegetarians. *Step 4*: Infer the percentage of vegetarians among all high school students. *Step 5*: Assess the results and formulate a conclusion.

27. The first 100 first-year students met in the student union is the most representative sample for first-year students at a particular school because they are a more random sample of students at that school. The other samples are not likely to be representative since they would be biased towards subgroups within the population.

28. The group of students enrolled in a required class is going to be the most representative group among those at the college because presumably all students must be enrolled in this class, and thus a random sample of students would be found in such a class. Those in a single dormitory will be influenced by the culture at that particular dorm, which may not be representative of the entire student body, (especially if this is a college where upperclassmen move out of the dorms into apartments, and are responsible for cooking their own meals). Students majoring in public health will be more educated about the benefits of a healthy diet, and thus it's likely a bias exists regarding their eating habits. Finally, the students who participate in sports probably eat differently than a random student.

29. This is an example of stratified sampling as the sample of taxpayers is broken in several categories (or strata).

30. This is an example of convenience sampling, because the sample is the set of people who voluntarily respond to a survey.

31. This is an example of stratified sampling as the participants are divided into groups based on age.

32. This is a systematic sampling: a rule (or simple system) is used to select each chip.

33. This is a simple random sampling because the people are selected at random.

34. This is an example of convenience sampling because the sample is made up of those who happen to show up at a particular supermarket.

35. This is an observational study, with a case-control element, where the cases are those who have a tendency to lie, and the controls are those who do not lie.

36. This is an observational study, with a case-control element, where the cases are patients with melanoma, and the controls are cancer-free patients.

37. This is an observational study, with no case-control component.

38. This is an observational study, with a case-control component, where the cases are participants who exercised regularly, and the controls are participants who do not exercise regularly.

39. This is an experiment where the treated group consists of patients who received ginkgo biloba extract, and the control group consists of those who received a placebo. Double-blinding would be necessary.

40. This is an observational study with no case-control.

41. An experiment would answer this question best. Recruit people to participate in the study, and ask one group to use magnet therapy, another group to use aspirin, while a third group receives a placebo. Observe the results among each group to determine the effect of magnet therapy versus aspirin and the placebo.

42. An observational study would be sufficient to determine which of eight airlines has the lowest percentage of delayed flights.

43. An observational study would be sufficient to determine which National Football League has the lineman with the greatest average weight.

44. To answer this question, an experiment would work best: give each group a different brand of insect repellent and one group a placebo. Observe if one brand offers more protection than the others.

45. An experiment would answer this question best. Recruit people to participate in the study, and ask one group to take a multi-vitamin every day, while the other group receives a placebo. Observe the rate of strokes among each group to determine the effect of multi-vitamins.

46. To answer this question, one should use an experiment to determine whether the Sunday horoscope is more accurate than the weekday horoscopes.

47. The confidence interval is 50.5% to 55.5%, and because there are only two candidates, it is likely (though not guaranteed) the Republican will win, so a victory party is called for.

48. The confidence interval is 48.6% to 57.4%, and thus it is not possible to claim that a majority of Americans support the weapons ban.

49. The confidence interval for the most recent data shows that 43% to 49% of Americans support legalized abortion, so 51% to 57% oppose legalized abortion, so you can claim that a majority of Americans oppose legalized abortion.

50. The confidence interval is 67% to 73%. The fact that the poll does not agree with the voting records percentage of 61% does not necessarily imply people were lying. It may be that the sample was not representative of the population of voters.

FURTHER APPLICATIONS

51. Because a significantly larger percentage of those who received the drug showed improvement compared to those who did not receive the drug, there is good evidence that the treatment is effective (or at least more effective than no treatment at all).

52. There is no difference in rates of improvement between the treatment group and the control group, so there is no evidence that suggests the treatment is effective.

53. Because a significantly larger percentage of those who received the drug showed improvement compared to those who did not receive the drug, there is good evidence that the treatment is effective.

54. There is no evidence that the drug treatment is effective – in fact, it may be harmful, as a larger percentage of those who did not receive treatment showed improvement.

55. a. The population is all North American HIV patients who have undergone drug treatment. The population parameters are the survival rates and times at which treatment began.
    b. The sample is the 17,517 asymptomatic North American patients with HIV. The sample statistics are the survival rates and times at which treatment began for those in sample.
    c. This is on observational study.
    d. The actual points in the progression of the disease

56. a. The population is all Americans. The population parameters are the percentages of men and women who regift.

b. The sample is 900 registered voters. The sample statistics are the percentages of men and women who regift.

c. This is on observational study.

d. How the sample was selected.

57. a. The population is all people over 60. The population parameters are the test scores for all elderly people, categorized by whether or not each individual was given a suggestion.

b. The sample is 100 people in the 60–70 and 71–82 age categories. The sample statistics are the test scores categorized by whether or not each individual was given a suggestion.

c. This is an experiment.

d. How the sample was selected and how cognitive performance was measured

58. a. The population is all adult Americans. The population parameter is the percentage of Americans who respond yes to the question.

b. The sample is 1546 people surveyed. The sample statistic is the percentage of people in the sample who respond yes to the question.

c. This is on observational study.

d. How the sample was selected and what the other options for answers were.

59. a. The population is all adolescents in 36 states. The population parameters are the percentages of students in each state who became regular smokers.

b. The sample is 16,000 adolescents in 36 states. The sample statistics are the percentages of students in the samples in each state who became regular smokers.

c. This is on observational study.

d. How the sample was selected and how many 10th-graders were in the sample

60. a. The population is all Americans. The population parameters are the percentages of Americans who responded yes and no to the survey questions.

b. The sample is 973 Americans. The sample statistics are the percentages of people in the sample who responded yes and no to the survey questions.

c. This is on observational study.

d. How the sample was selected

TECHNOLOGY EXERCISES

72. Answers will vary.

73. a. Answers will vary

b. Answers will vary.

c. The average of a large number of random numbers should be near ½.

UNIT 5B

TIME OUT TO THINK

Pg. 313. The primary difficulties involve what constitutes "resting." Does it mean sleeping? If so, does it depend on whether you are dreaming when heart rate is measured? And so on…

QUICK QUIZ

1. **c.** When the wrong technique is used in a statistical study, one should put little faith in the results.

2. **b.** While it is possible that an oil company can carry out legitimate and worthy research on an environmental problem it caused, the opportunity (and temptation) for bias to be introduced should make you wary of the results.

3. **a.** The fact that the researchers interviewed only those living in dormitories means the sample chosen may not be representative of the population of all freshmen, some of whom don't live on campus.

4. **b.** The poll that determines the winner suffers from participation bias, as those who vote choose to do so. Also true is that those who vote almost certainly watch the show, while the vast majority of Americans do not watch it, nor do they care who wins.

5. **b.** The quantities that a statistical study attempts to measure are called variables of interest, and this study is measuring the weights of 6-year-olds.

6. **a.** The quantities that a statistical study attempts to measure are called variables of interest, and this survey is measuring the number of visits to the dentist.

7. **c.** It's reasonable to assume that people who use sunscreen do so because they spend time in the sun, and this can lead to sunburns.

8. **c.** The availability error is best avoided by carefully choosing the order in which answers to a survey are presented, and in this case, it's best to switch the order for half of the people being polled.

9. **b.** A self-selected survey suffers from participation bias, where people make the choice to participate (that is, they select themselves, rather than being randomly selected by a polling company).

10. **b.** Carefully conducted statistical studies give us good information about that which is being studied, but it's always possible for unforeseen problems (such as confounding variables) to arise, and the "95% confidence" that was spoken of in Unit 5A (and expanded upon in Unit 6D) can always come into play.

DOES IT MAKE SENSE?

5. Does not make sense. A TV survey with phone-in responses suffers from participation bias, whereas a survey carried out by professional pollsters more likely than not will give better results.

6. Makes sense. A survey about religious beliefs (in general) will suffer from selection bias if the sample consists only of Catholics.

7. Does not make sense. Statistical studies can rarely (if ever) make the claim that the results are proven beyond all doubt.

8. Does not make sense. A careful study that makes the claim "this training regimen will increase your jogging speed by 1%" is essentially meaningless – a very small change in jogging speed may result from any number of factors, and attributing the change to the training regimen is putting too much faith in the study.

BASIC SKILLS & CONCEPTS

9. You should not put much faith in the study because the sample is not likely to be representative of the population (SATs are taken before the teachers go to college, which will not be a good indication of the teachers' academic preparation.

10. Because the study was double-blind, precautions have been taken to assure quality information, and thus there is no reason to doubt the veracity of the results.

11. A study done by a liberal group to determine opinions about a Republican tax cut plan could easily include biases, so you should doubt the results.

12. Because this study found results that positively impact the company conducting the study, there is reason to doubt the results. Had the company found their product was not superior, you would do well to think otherwise.

13. You should doubt a poll that suffers from participation bias, as this one does.

14. This study suffers from selection bias, and thus you should put little trust in the results.

15. It is very difficult to quantify or even define happiness, and thus this study is essentially meaningless (and you should not trust it, unless you believe happiness was correctly defined and measured).

16. There is no reason to doubt the results of this study based on the information given.

17. You should doubt the results of this study because there is no control group to which results might be compared.

18. Based on the information given, this observational study appears to be one that you can trust.

19. You should doubt the results of this study because it uses self reporting, which is not always accurate (especially in cases of sensitive issues, like abuse.)

20. The wording of the question in this study is poorly chosen if its purpose is to determine whether people would support a flag-burning amendment. There is ample reason to doubt the results.

21. Since the affect of inflation was not addressed, you should doubt this claim.

22. Saying the average weight loss was 24.3 does not mean all participants showed significant weight loss. The mean could be skewed by a few participants losing a large amount of weight. You should at least doubt the claim that "the program works for anyone with enough discipline."

23. Without knowing the relationship between cell phone use and traffic fatalities, you should doubt the claim.

24. Since several independent organizations were involved in conducting the poll, there is no reason to doubt this claim.

25. There is no reason to doubt this claim.

26. Assuming that the sampling was done correctly, the claim is believable.

FURTHER APPLICATIONS

27. The survey will suffer from a selection bias in that this group of shoppers is not representative of the entire population of people with colds.

28. This survey may suffer from selection bias if the sample is not representative of all Americans, but most likely does not.

29. A potential selection bias exists in this survey because the people who vote from 7:00 to 7:30 a.m. may not be a representative sample of the voting population (those in the sample are more likely to be working people who vote on the way to their jobs).

30. The state of New York tends to vote in favor of Democratic candidates (it's more often than not a "blue state" in recent times), and thus the exit poll will suffer from selection bias.

31. This survey will suffer from a selection bias due to the fact that the National Guard is charged with protecting the borders, and thus their views on immigration won't be representative of the entire country.

32. The study will be influenced by a selection bias, as only those who choose to return the survey will be counted in the final tally.

33. Planned Parenthood members have different views on the issue of contraceptives for high school students than the population of American adults (that is, they are not a representative sample), and thus this survey is influenced by the selection bias.

34. By just sampling from registered voters, the sample may not be representative of all Americans. The poll will suffer from a selection bias.

35. – 36. Answers will vary.

37. There is no mention of how the respondents were selected or what questions was asked that had 60% of adults avoiding visits to the dentist because of fear.

38. There is no mention of how the respondents were selected. Also, did the question only ask whether the respondents preferred "Merry Christmas" to "Happy Holidays" or were other greetings (or no greeting) also included in the question?

39. The way in which the question was asked may have influenced responses, and we know nothing of the sample or its size.

40. What question was asked that had 60% of Americans in favor of repealing estate taxes? (In particular, are they made aware that only 2% paid estate taxes, and that this 2% likely constituted those with large estates?) We don't know how large the sample was, nor whether it was representative of the population.

41. We don't know what question was asked to obtain the responses (did the question just ask for a favorite vegetable, or were potatoes one of a list of options?) We also don't know how the sample was selected.

42. We don't know what conditions qualify for intensive care in the U.S., and we don't know how the information concerning babies in India was obtained.

43. A headline like this implies "illegal drugs" to most readers, and the government study includes smoking and drinking (both of which are legal and largely acceptable practices in many segments of society). The study is based upon top movie rentals, and yet the headline implies all movies. It's a misleading headline.

44. The difference between the percentages (82% versus 79%) is not statistically significant, so the headline may be overstating its case. Also true is that the term "sex" used in the headline has a different connotation to most readers than a "satisfying sex life," which has a more wholesome feel to it.

45. The headline might have some truth to it (and to the credit of the headline writer, the word "may" is included in the claim), but the study is based upon a small sample, and there's a potential conflict of interest as Welch Foods (think Welch Grape Juice) has an interest in a favorable outcome for the study.

46. a. There were 1185 + 158 = 1343 people who completed the study.

b.

	Exercise	No Exercise	Total
Dementia	106	52	158
No Dementia	912	273	1185
Total	1018	325	1343

c. Following is one of four possible Venn diagrams.

UNIT 5C

TIME OUT TO THINK

Pg. 321. The relative frequency for each category represents its fraction of the total. Thus, when all categories are included, the total relative frequency must be the whole of 1.

Pg. 322. Star ratings at restaurants, numbers on player uniforms, social security numbers, telephone numbers, etc.

Pg. 326. The countries are not in the same order since the bars in the graph are drawn by descending height. China is the world's most populous country (though India is quite close), so its per capita emissions are much lower than those of the US and other more developed countries. India's per capita emissions are even lower. On a graph of per capita emissions, the U.S. still ranks first, but Canada is very close. China and India are the lowest in per capita emissions. This has important implications to efforts to slow global warming: the less developed countries have an economic interest in development, but if their per capita emissions rise to the level of current developed countries the world will have far more carbon dioxide going into the atmosphere.

Pg. 327. One possible advantage is the pie chart makes it obvious that the total of all the listed categories is 100%, whereas the bar graph does not. Generally, however, most people find it easier to interpret bar graphs than pie charts.

QUICK QUIZ

1. **b.** The relative frequency of a category expresses its frequency as a fraction or percentage of the total, and thus is 25/100 = 0.25.

2. **c.** We would need to know the number of As assigned before being able to compute the cumulative frequency.

3. **b**. Qualitative data describe non-numerical categories.

4. **c**. The sizes of the wedges are determined by the percentage of the data that corresponds to a particular category, and this is the same as the relative frequency for that category.

5. **a**. Depending on how you want to display the data, you could actually use any of the three options listed. However, a line chart is used for numerical data, which means you would have to suppress the names of the tourist attractions (your categories would become bins, such as "0-2 million"). For a pie chart, you would need to compute the relative frequencies of the data, and while that's not terribly difficult, it requires an extra step. It would be most appropriate to use a bar graph, with the various tourist attractions as categories (e.g. Disney World, Yosemite National Park, etc.), and the annual number of visitors plotted on the y-axis.

6. **c**. The ten tourist attractions are the categories for a bar graph, and these belong on the horizontal axis.

7. **a**. With 100 data points, each precise to the nearest 0.001, it would be best to bin the data into several categories.

8. **c**. A line chart is often used to represent time-series data.

9. **c**. A histogram is a bar graph for quantitative data categories.

10. **b**. For each dot in a line chart, the horizontal position is the center of the bin it represents.

DOES IT MAKE SENSE?

7. Does not make sense. A frequency table has two columns, one of which lists the frequency of the various categories.

8. Makes sense. A relative frequency of 0.3 means 30% of the grades were Bs, which is reasonable.

9. Does not make sense. The width of the bars in a bar chart is not important (though they should all be of the *same* width in a histogram, and even for those bar charts that are not histograms, even-width bars look better).

10. Makes sense. As long as the teacher's key is correct, the frequencies should be the same in both charts.

11. Does not make sense. The position of the wedges in a pie chart is immaterial.

12. Makes sense. The total of all frequencies in a pie chart should always be 100% (or very near to that – sometimes the total does not add up to 100% due to rounding).

13. Does not make sense. Bar charts can be used for qualitative data: the categories are the qualities of concern, and the vertical axis shows the frequency of each category (or the relative frequencies).

14. Does not make sense. Histograms are used for quantitative data, and they have a natural order imposed by the numbers used (usually these are listed smallest-to-largest, corresponding to left-to-right).

BASIC SKILLS & CONCEPTS

15.

Grade	Freq.	Rel. freq.	Cum. freq.
A	2	0.10	2
B	5	0.25	7
C	8	0.40	15
D	3	0.15	18
F	2	0.10	20
Total	20	1.00	20

16.

Rating	Freq.	Rel. freq.	Cum. freq.
5-star	5	0.09	5
4-star	10	0.18	15
3-star	20	0.36	35
2-star	15	0.27	50
1-star	5	0.09	55
Total	55	0.99*	55

*Due to rounding.

17. Birth month is qualitative data, even if listed numerically.

18. The responses to the question are qualitative data because they are non-numerical responses.

19. The yes/no responses on the ballot are qualitative data because it describes a non-numerical quality of opinion.

20. The amount of rainfall is quantitative data because rainfall measures are numerical data.

21. Flavors of ice cream are qualitative data because they are non-numerical choices in the poll.

22. Breed of dog is qualitative data because they are non-numerical choices in the poll.

23. Annual salaries are quantitative data because it is a numerical measurement of money.

24. The gold medal count is quantitative data because it is a numerical measurement.

25.

Bin	Freq.	Rel. freq.	Cum. freq.
95–99	3	0.15	3
90–94	2	0.10	5
85–89	3	0.15	8
80–84	2	0.10	10
75–79	4	0.20	14
70–74	1	0.05	15
65–69	4	0.20	19
60–64	1	0.05	20
Total	20	1.00	20

26.

Bin	Freq.	Rel. freq.	Cum. freq.
90–99	5	0.25	5
80–89	5	0.25	10
70–79	5	0.25	15
60–69	5	0.25	20
Total	20	1.00	20

27.

28.

29.

30.

31.

32.

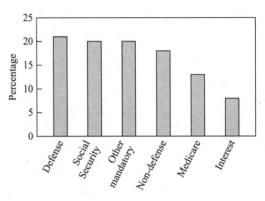

33.

Bin	Frequency
20–29	1
30–39	8
40–49	9
50–59	4
60–69	2
Total	24

34. Male performers tend to win Oscars at older ages than female performers.

35. Answers will vary.

36. Answers will vary.

FURTHER APPLICATIONS

37. a. The ages are quantitative categories.

b.

c. People who win the Nobel Prize (in literature) do so rather late in their career.

38. a. The companies are qualitative categories.

b.

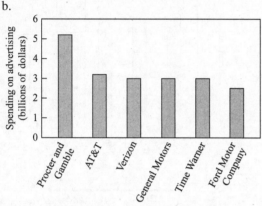

c. Proctor and Gamble spends much more than any of the other companies.

39. a. The data are quantitative.

b.

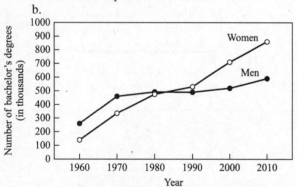

c. The number of bachelor's degrees conferred on both men and women have been increasing and more women than men now earn bachelor's degrees.

40. a. The artists are qualitative categories.

b.

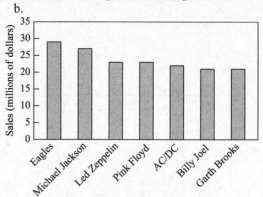

c. Wow! That's a lot of albums sold.

41. a. The data are quantitative.

b.

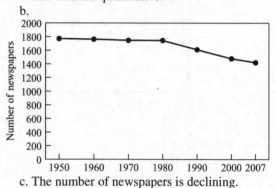

c. The number of newspapers is declining.

42. a. The energy sources are qualitative categories.

b.

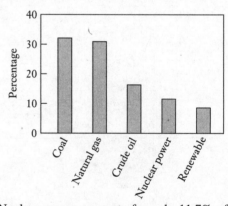

c. Nuclear power accounts for only 11.7% of the energy produced in the U.S.

43. a. The religions are qualitative categories.
    b.

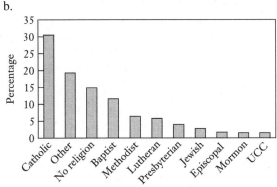

c. Catholics outnumber every category by a significant percentage.

44. a. The age groups are quantitative categories.
    b.

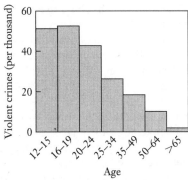

c. Victims of violent crimes are much more likely to be young (12–24 years old).

45. a. The years are quantitative categories.
    b.

c. Families are getting smaller in the U.S.

46. a. There were about 26,000 alcohol related fatalities in 1982, and about 15,000 in 2007.
    b. The percent change is (15,000 – 26,000)/26,000 = –42%.
    c. In 1982, the percent of auto fatalities that involved alcohol was about 26,000/43,945 = 59%. The percent in 2007 was about 15,000/41,059 = 37%.
    d. There are likely many variables that contributed to the trend, among them: people are better educated about the dangers of driving under the influence of alcohol (due to educational efforts on the part of many organizations); law enforcement agencies have increased patrols that deal exclusively with drunk driving (especially on certain weekends and holidays); and cars have become safer with the addition of airbags.

47. a.

b. The presidents that could have said that they were the *youngest* president (or the same age in years as the youngest) at the time they took office are 1, 3, 4, 6, 8, 10, 11, 14, 18, and 26.
c. The presidents could have said that they were the *oldest* president (or the same age in years as the oldest) at the time they took office are 1, 2, 7, 9, and 40.
d. Answers will vary.

TECHNOLOGY EXERCISES

56. a

Category of Car	Frequency	Relative Frequency	Cumulative Frequency
American cars	30	37.5%	30
Japanese cars	25	31.25%	55
English cars	5	6.25%	60
Other European cars	12	15%	72
Motorcycles	8	10%	80
Total	80	100%	80

b. 80
c. 100%
d. 80

57.

Car Data

(bar chart: American cars 30, Japanese cars 25, English cars 5, Other European cars 12, Motorcycles 8)

58.

59.

60.

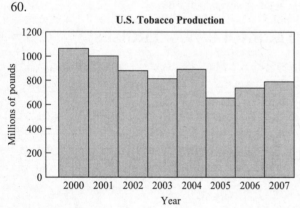

UNIT 5D

TIME OUT TO THINK

Pg. 339. Answers will vary depending on the map chosen, but the main ideas are that contours connect points with the same value and the spacing of contours provides information about the change in values (tightly spaced contours imply greater changes in value).

Pg. 341. The large rise in recent times has been bringing women toward parity (50% of the competitors). It certainly seems reasonable to think that this parity will be achieved within a few years. However, since it is unlikely that the percentage of men will ever fall much below 50%,

the upward trend should slow as parity is approached.

Pg. 343. The graph shows the speed increasing by a factor of 10 every 5 years, which means a factor of 100 in 10 years. Thus speed is predicted to increase from 10^{11} calculations per second to about 10^{13} calculations per second. The steep slope of Figure 5.24b makes it very difficult to make the same prediction with this graph.

QUICK QUIZ

1. **c**. The fact that the red segment starts higher up in the second bar indicates the sum of the values represented by the segments below it are greater than those in the first bar.
2. **b**. The height of the Tuberculosis wedge at 1950 is about 20 years.
3. **a**. The color of Oregon corresponds to the 200 – 299 million BTUs category.
4. **c**. Iowa is contained between contour lines that are marked 30°F and 40°F, so the temperature there is between these values.
5. **b**. The tan regions lie between contour lines marked by 40°F and 50°F, and thus the temperature there is between those values.
6. **c**. When contour lines are close together, the data they represent change more rapidly compared to areas where the lines are far apart.
7. **c**. The height of the center of the pie charts corresponds to the number of women attending, and the height of the 1948 pie chart is about 450.
8. **b**. Because the scale on the y-axis is exaggerated, the changes appear to be larger than they really were.
9. **c**. Each tick mark represents another power of ten.
10. **b**. For all of the years shown in the figure, there is a positive percent change, which means the cost of college was increasing; it increases at a smaller rate when the graph is decreasing.

DOES IT MAKE SENSE?

9. Does not make sense. Using three-dimensional bars for two-dimensional data is a cosmetic change; it adds no information.
10. Makes sense. When the spread of your data values is very large, it is sometimes difficult to draw a reasonable linear scale on the y-axis. An exponential scale overcomes this difficulty.
11. Makes sense. Experimenting with different scales on the axes of graphs allows you to highlight certain aspects of the data.
12. Makes sense. As long as the graph shows a positive rate of increase, then the number of users is rising.

BASIC SKILLS & CONCEPTS

13. a. China, India and Russia all had to import grain because their net grain production is negative.
b. China, India, and Russia are all expected to need grain imports because their projected 2030 net grain production is negative.
c. The graph shows that both China and India will require significant grain imports, and thus (based only on the information shown in the graph), it's likely world grain production will need to increase.

14. a. Earnings increase with level of education.
b. The unemployment rate decreases with level of education.
c. ($1522 − $978)/$978 = 56%
d. Since 9.0/2.8 = 3.333..., a high school dropout will be more than three times more likely to be unemployed than someone with a bachelor's degree.
e. In 45 years, the average college graduate would earn $52 \times 45 \times \$978 - 52 \times 45 \times \$591 = \$906,000$ more than the average high school graduate.

15. a. The death rate for pneumonia, cardiovascular disease (cardiovascular disease increased and then decreased, for an overall decrease), and tuberculosis decreased from 1900 to 2004; it increased for cancer.
b. The death rate was the greatest around 1950, where it was about 500 deaths per 100,000.
c. The death rate for cancer in 2000 was about 196 deaths per 100,000.
d. If the lines of the graph were extended, cancer would overtake cardiovascular disease as the leading cause of death in 2050.

16. a. Tuition and fees vary the most; they are more than ten times greater at private 4-year colleges than at public 2-year colleges..
b. Books and supplies vary the least, probably because students at all types of colleges need the same number of books and other supplies on average, and these don't vary much in cost.
c. Transportation, because commuters must spend more to get to and from school, while students at private colleges probably spend more time on campus.

17. a. In 1930, about 75,000 degrees were awarded to men, and about 40,000 were awarded to women. In 2010, a little around 590,000 degrees were awarded to men, and around 860,000 degrees were awarded to women.
b. Men earned slightly more degrees in 1980, and women earned more degrees in 2010.
c. The steepest portion of the upper line occurred in the 1960s, and the upper line can be interpreted as the total number of degrees awarded.

d. In 1950, about 450,000 degrees were awarded, and in 2010, about 1.45 million degrees were awarded.
e. A multiple bar graph would probably be easier to read, and to answer questions of the sort from steps **a** through **d**.

18. a. About 15% of the budget went to net interest in 1990 and 1995; it dropped to about 8% in 2005.
b. In 1960, about 52% of the budget went to defense. The percentage dropped to about 23% in 1980, and dropped again in 2005, to about 20%.
c. In 1980, about 47% of the budget went to payments to individuals. This figure was about 57% in 2000, and about 54% in 2005.

19. There are significant regional differences: the probability that a black student had white classmates is much higher in the northern states. It's difficult to make a blanket statement about the differences between urban and rural areas, but it certainly appears that the probability is lower in many urban areas (look at San Francisco/Oakland, Los Angeles and San Diego, Chicago, Detroit, Miami, and the larger cities along the eastern seaboard, and compare these with adjoining rural areas).

20. a. Since points A and B correspond to summits, you would walk downhill from A to C.
b. Since there are more contour lines between B and D, your elevation would change more between those two points.
c. Since both points lie in the same contour, there would be no change in elevation if you walk directly from E to F.
d. Since you return to your original location, there would be no net change in elevation.

21. a. In 2010, the over-65-year-old group constituted 12% of the population. By 2050, this figure is projected to increase to about 20%.
b. The percentage of 45 to 54-year-olds was about q15% in 2010, and is projected to decrease to about 10% in 2050.
c. The under-25-year-old group decreases in size between 2010 and 2050 since the percentages of each subgroup either decreases or remains constant during that time interval.
d. The 45 to 54-year-old group was the largest percentage of the population in 2010. (In that year, its bar is higher than all others)
e. The population is aging as evidenced by the increase in the over-65 category, and the decrease in the under-5 category.

22. a. (6.0 − 4.9)/4.9 = 0.22 = 22%.
b. (6.9 − 1.9)/1.9 = 2.6 = 260%.
c. China overtook the United States in 2008.
d. Russia has not seen a steady increase. Its CO_2 emissions declined and then increased.

23. a. Happiness is qualitative. The meaning of zero is not clear, because the happiness scale is not explained in the display.

b. Since there are no points in the lower right of the graph, no countries with good economic strength have a low happiness index

c. They are mostly European and North American countries.

d. They are mostly Central and South American countries.

e. This graph does not support the claim. Happiness is not clearly defined and per capita G.N.P. is not a good indicator or individual wealth.

24. a. The color of the country indicates the continent in which it is located. Benin is in Africa.

b. Approximately 5 million people in South Africa live with HIV. The per capita income is about $9000.

c. Approximately 1 million people in India live with HIV. The per capita income is about $3000.

d. With some exceptions, HIV incidence decreases with the wealth of the country.

e. South Africa

25. The area of the screen on the 2008 TV is larger than the area of the 1980 TV by a factor of about 25, and the volume of the 2008 TV is larger than the volume of the 1980 TV by a factor of about 125, and yet the actual number of homes with cable in 2008 is larger than the 1980 level by a factor of over 5 (98/18 = 5.44).

26. In a flat pie chart, a wedge with central angle of, say, 60° represents 1/6 of the total area of the circle, no matter where it is located in the circle. In the distorted version shown, the face of the pie is an ellipse, and 60° wedges in ellipses don't necessarily have equal areas, and thus they won't correspond to the percentages they are attempting to depict.

27. The zero point for earnings is not on the graph, and thus it appears that women earn about 25% of what men earn. A fairer graph (not shown) would start from zero.

28. Note that the zero point for braking distance is not on the graph, and because of this, it looks like the breaking distance of a Lexus is about half that of a Lincoln. In reality, the breaking distance of the Lincoln is about 10% greater than the breaking distance of the Lexus. A fairer graph (not shown) would start from zero.

29. Ordinary vertical scale

Exponential vertical scale

Answers will vary on which scale is more useful as neither scale hides details of the data, although it may be claimed that the ordinary vertical scale may make it appear that the number of subscribers has been increasing linearly.

30. a. Public college costs rose by about 13% in the 2003–04 academic year.

b. The percentage increase in private college costs in the 2003–04 year was about 5%.

c. Private college costs rose more in dollars, because 5% of the 2003–2004 costs for private colleges is more than 13% of the 2003–2004 costs for public colleges.

31. Most of the growth occurred after 1950.

FURTHER APPLICATIONS

32. a. The total wealth increased from 2003 through later 2007 and then decreased through the end of 2008.

b. Since ($78 − $65)/$78 = −0.17 = −17%, total wealth fell by 17%.

c. Real estate represents the greatest share of total wealth. It is $22/$65 = 0.34 = 34%.

d. Since ($6.9 – $11)/$11 = –0.37 = –37%, It declined approximately 37%.

e. Total wealth has most likely declined, with real estate and assets connected to the stock market falling the most.

f. Answers will vary.

33. a. The change from one month to the next looks less significant when zero is included.

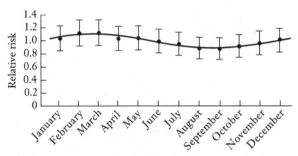

Month of birth

b. The claim is not justified because the error bars are large enough that the true values of relative risk may form a straight line across all months (which would mean the risk does not vary with season).

34. Two graphs work best for this data. Both men and women are waiting much longer to get married for the first time.

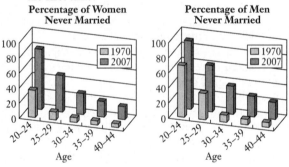

35. A simple line plot works well for this data.

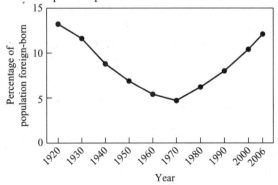

36. A simple stack plot with stacked lines works well for this data.

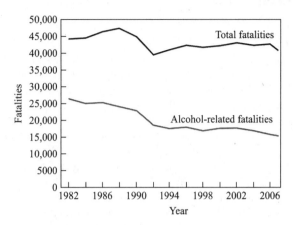

37. A simple multiple bar graph or a line graph would work well for this data.

38. Combing the ideas of a stack plot with a bar graph allows all of the data to be displayed in a way that makes comparisons easy.

Annual Deaths Due to Firearms (excluding U.S., which has 30 times more deaths than Germany and Canada)

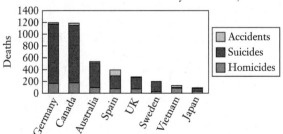

UNIT 5E

TIME OUT TO THINK

Pg. 353. If a gene makes people prone to both smoking and lung cancer, then this gene would cause them to smoke and also cause them to get lung cancer. In that case, it is the gene, not the smoking, that caused the lung cancer. Note that this question foreshadows discussion, in Section 5E, of possible explanations for correlations by asking how a common underlying cause (the gene) might have led to the observed correlation between smoking and lung cancer.

Pg. 354. The point below Prince Caspian represents The Golden Compass. The labels of the remaining points can be found by matching their values on the horizontal and vertical axes with the production costs and the U.S. gross receipts, respectively, from Table 5.6.

Pg. 359. Answers will vary, but students should ability to argue their points clearly. Possible topics could include the medical benefits of animal experiments, whether animals have inherent rights, or people have an inherent responsibility to treat animals humanely.

Pg. 361. Students should check the global warming discussion against the principles for establishing causality, which are which should help them understand why the scientific consensus strongly supports the idea that this is a serious issue for humanity.

Pg. 362. Answers will vary, but be aware the scientific consensus is now clearly in the category of "beyond reasonable doubt."

QUICK QUIZ

1. **c**. When one variable is correlated with another, an increase in one goes with either increasing values of the other, or decreasing values of the other.
2. **b**. The dot representing Russia has a horizontal coordinate of about 63 years.
3. **a**. When points on a scatter diagram all lie near a line, there is a strong correlation between the variables represented. We call it a positive correlation when an increase in one variable goes along with an increase in another (and this is what produces a positive slope).
4. **b**. A negative correlation exists between two variables when an increase in one goes with a decrease in the other, and this is what produces a negative slope. That the points described fall in a broad swath, rather than a tight configuration that more closely resembles a line, means the correlation between the variables is weak.
5. **a**. Correlation is a necessary condition for causation.
6. **c**. When wages (adjusted for inflation) go higher, there's more incentive for people to work, which leads to lower unemployment. Or, looking at it from the other side, when unemployment rates fall, employers are forced to offer higher wages to attract good people from the small pool of available labor.
7. **a**. When establishing causation, look for evidence that larger amounts of the suspected cause produce larger amounts of the effect.
8. **c**. Values before humans peaked at a little less than 300 ppm, while values today are a little less than 400 ppm, and this is a 30% change.
9. **b**. From 1960 to 2000 (a span of 40 years), CO_2 concentration increased by about 50 ppm, and if that trend continues for another 40 years, to the year 2040, we can expect another increase of about 50 ppm, which will result in CO_2 levels near 420 ppm.
10. **c**. The courts have proclaimed that a member of the jury should find the defendant guilty when the jury member is firmly convinced the defendant is guilty of the crime charged.

DOES IT MAKE SENSE?

7. Makes sense. A strong negative correlation means that a decrease in the price goes along with an increase in the number of tickets sold.
8. Makes sense. A strong positive correlation means that an increase in time spent studying goes along with higher grades.
9. Does not make sense. Despite the fact that A and B are strongly correlated, we cannot be sure that A causes B (there may be an underlying effect that causes both A and B).
10. Does not make sense. A strong negative correlation between C and D does not mean that C must be the cause for D (there may be an underlying effect that causes the correlation between C and D).
11. Makes sense. If it were true that an increase in E caused a decrease in F, then a negative correlation would exist.
12. Does not make sense. It is very difficult to establish absolute proof, but if we find that increasing helmet use tends to decrease injury rates (and you agree that kids should wear helmets in situations where helmet use decreases injury rates), then you should support the requirement that kids wear helmets.

BASIC SKILLS & CONCEPTS

13. We seek a correlation between a car's *weight* and its *city gas mileage*.

    a. The diagram shows a moderately strong negative correlation.

    b. Heavier cars tend to get lower gas mileage.

14. We seek a correlation between *unemployment rate* and *voter turnout* during a presidential election.

    a. It appears that there is no correlation between the variables.

    b. There's not much regarding the relationship between the two variables that we can conclude from this diagram, as no correlation exists. We could reasonably conclude that unemployment ranged from 4% to 8% between the years of 1964 to 2004, and that voter turnout was between 50% and 70% for those years, though we have only a sample of the years (every fourth year, to be specific).

15. We seek a correlation between *Percent of AGI* and *Average AGI* for 11 states.

    a. At first glance, there's no correlation (which is a reasonable answer), though one could also argue for a very weak positive correlation based on the slight increasing trend of the data points.

    b. Higher AGI may imply slightly higher charitable giving as a percentage of AGI.

16. We seek a correlation between *number of farms* and *size of farms in acres*.

    a. There is a strong negative correlation.

    b. As the number of farms has decreased, the size of the farms has increased..

17. Use degrees of latitude and degrees of temperature as units. There is a strong negative correlation, because as you move north from the equator, the temperatures in June tend to decrease.

18. Use inches and number of attendances as units. It's likely no correlation between height and attendance at religious services.

19. Use years and hours as units. There is probably a negative correlation because older people most likely do not spend as much time on social networking sites..

20. Use feet and pounds per square inch as units. There is a strong negative correlation because air pressure decreases as one increases altitude.

21. Use years and square miles as units. There is probably a positive correlation because states that joined the union later are usually larger than those that joined earlier. (Compare Alaska to Rhode Island, for example.)

22. Use pounds and shoe size as units. There is a positive correlation, heavier people are more likely to be older, which means they would have larger feet.

23. Use children per woman and years as units. There is a strong negative correlation, because an increase in the life expectancy of a country goes along with a decrease in the number of children born.

24. Use dollars and dollars as units. There is likely a positive correlation, because districts with higher property taxes will have more funds available to pay teachers.

FURTHER APPLICATIONS

25. a.

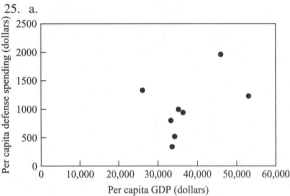

    b. There is a strong positive correlation.

    c. In those countries where per capita GNP is high, there's more money available to spend on various government programs, and thus the per capita expenditure on defense increases.

26. a.

    b. There does not appear to be any correlation.

    c. Hitting a home run and getting a hit are different skills, and thus some players who are able to hit for power don't have particularly impressive batting averages, and some players (e.g. Ichiro Suzuki) are very good at getting a hit, but aren't as able to send one out of the park.

27. a.

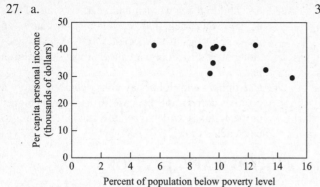

b. There is no correlation between the variables.

c. Per capita income will be skewed high (in the direction of wealthier residents of a state), so there will not be correlation with the percent of the population below the poverty level.

28. a.

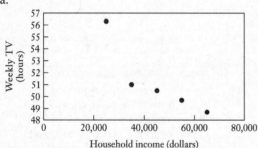

b. There is a strong negative correlation between the variables.

c. As people work more and earn more money, they have less time to spend in front of the TV.

29. a.

b. There is a strong positive correlation.

c. The per pupil expenditure almost certainly includes teacher salaries (that is, salaries are part of the cost of educating the students), and thus in those districts where the teacher salaries are high, the per pupil expenditure is also high.

30. a.

b. There is a strong negative correlation.

c. Countries where the literacy is low are generally poorer countries, so not only are its inhabitants lacking in the basic needs, but also in advanced health care.

31. There is a positive correlation between the crime rate and the number of tourists. There may be direct cause and effect here: with more tourists, there is a greater need for taxis and also more targets for opportunistic crimes against them.

32. There is a positive correlation between the number of miles of freeway in Los Angeles and the amount of traffic congestion. There is likely a common underlying cause here: an increase in population.

33. There is a negative correlation between the cost of gas and the number of SUVs sold. There may be a direct cause at work here, because when gas prices increase, people are more conscious about the gas mileage for the car they purchase.

34. Sales of ice cream are positively correlated with sales of swimming suits. The common underlying cause is most likely a change in season.

35. Gas mileage is positively correlated with tire pressure. This is a direct cause: when tire pressure goes down, gas mileage also goes down.

36. The number of ministers and priests is positively correlated with movie ticket sales. There is a common underlying cause: an increase in population.

37. a. When the suspected cause (bad air in the building in which you work) is removed, the afternoon headaches go away. This is guideline 2.

b. Even when you vary other factors, such as drinking Coke, the headaches are still present, suggesting that Coke isn't the cause, but rather bad air in the building is to blame. This is guideline 1.

c. When the suspected cause is decreased, the headaches are less frequent. This is guideline 3.

d. The observations suggest that your headaches are caused by bad air at your work environment.

38. The causes of cancer are often random. A cancer cell is produced when the growth control mechanisms of a normal cell are altered by a random mutation. Smoking may increase the chance of such a mutation occurring, but the mutation will not occur in all individuals. Therefore, by chance, some smokers escape cancer.

39. People do not decide to become conductors until relatively late in life, say, 30 years of age or over. Having already survived this many years, a person has a longer-than-average life expectancy.

40. You cannot conclude that the high-voltage line is the cause of cancer because a mechanism for the cause must be established. There may be an underlying cause.

41. A plausible explanation is that many youth soccer leagues around the world use age divisions. Those children born earlier in a given year are slightly older than others born in the same year. Being slightly stronger and better developed, they survive and move on to more advanced leagues.

TECHNOLOGY EXERCISES

50. a.

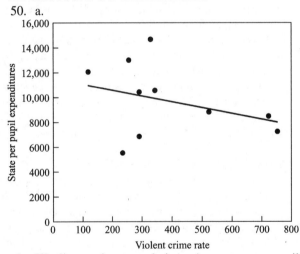

b. Weak negative correlation. As state per pupil expenditures decrease, the violent crime rate increases.

c. See graph above

d. The correlation coefficient is –0.36, indicating a weak negative correlation.

UNIT 6A

TIME OUT TO THINK

Pg. 373. In this case, saying that the average contract offer is zero also seems a bit misleading (just as did saying it is $700,000 if we used the mean).

Pg. 375. Assuming the administration uses 12 faculty members to teach the 12 classes, they could simply redistribute assignments so that each of the 3 courses uses 4 faculty teaching sections of 25 students each. The advantages and disadvantages of such a change are a matter of opinion, but a few factors to consider: redistributing means students will have fairly small classes all around, which is generally a good thing, but will not have the benefit of the extra small class that they now have in one case. Other factors may also be involved, such as having only one qualified faculty member for one of the courses.

Pg. 377(1st). In either a right-skewed or left-skewed distribution, the mean is further away from the mode (center) than the median, which shows that the mean is affected by outliers and the median is not.

Pg. 377(2nd). In statistics, it refers to a distortion away from symmetry.

QUICK QUIZ

1. **b**. The mean of a data set is the sum of all the data values divided by the number of data points.
2. **b**. The median of a data set is the middle value when the data are placed in numerical order.
3. **c**. Outliers are data values that are much smaller or larger than the other values.
4. **a**. Outliers that are larger than the rest of the data set tend to pull the mean to the right of the median, and this is the case for all possible data sets that satisfy the conditions given.
5. **c**. Because the mean is significantly higher than the median, the distribution is skewed to the right, which implies some students drink considerably more than 12 sodas per week. Specifically, it can be shown that at least one student must drink more than 16 sodas per week.
6. **c**. The high salaries of a few superstars pull the tail of this distribution to the right.
7. **a**. High outliers tend to pull the mean to the right of the median, and thus you would hope to get a salary near the mean. There are data sets with high outliers that can be constructed where the median is higher than the mean, but these are rare.
8. **a**. In general, data sets with a narrow central peak typically have less variation than those with broad, spread out values (the presence of outliers can confound the issue).
9. **c**. Driving in rush hour can go quickly on some days, but is agonizingly slow on others, so the time it takes to get downtown has high variation.
10. **b**. The mayor would like to see a high median and low variation because that means there's a tight, central peak in the distribution that corresponds to support for her.

DOES IT MAKE SENSE?

7. Makes sense. The two highest grades may be large enough to balance the remaining seven lower grades so that the third highest is the mean.
8. Does not make sense. The median for this exam is, by definition, the mean of the two middle scores (the fifth and sixth scores), and thus it could not be the third highest score.
9. Makes sense. When very high outliers are present, they tend to pull the mean to the right of the median (right-skewed).
10. Does not make sense. The word "average" has several meanings in mathematics, and the management and employees may be using different measures of the average (the mean and the median, for example).
11. Does not make sense. When the mean, median, and mode are all the same, it's a sign that you have a symmetric distribution of data.
12. Makes sense. Suppose the mean age of the general population is 32 years. There's no reason why a college extension class (which typically attracts older students) could not share the same mean.

BASIC SKILLS & CONCEPTS

13. The mean and median are 5.68 and 5.685, respectively. Because there is an even number of data points, the median is calculated by taking the mean of the middle two values (add 5.67 and 5.70, and divide by 2). Since no value occurs more than once, there is no mode.
14. The mean, median, and mode are 98.44, 98.4, and 98.4, respectively. Because there is an even number of data points, the median is calculated by taking the mean of the middle two values (add 98.4 and 98.4, and divide by 2).
15. The mean and median are 201.14 and 200, respectively. Since no value occurs more than once, there is no mode.
16. The mean and median are 78.4 and 79, respectively. This is a multi-modal data set, with modes of 70, 73, 76, and 81.
17. The mean and median are 1.18 and 1.05, respectively. Since no value occurs more than once, there is no mode.

18. The mean and median are 0.9194 and 0.920, respectively. There is no mode.

19. The mean and median are 0.81237 and 0.8161, respectively. The outlier is 0.7901, because it varies from the others by a couple hundredths of a pound, while the rest vary from each other only by a few thousandths of a pound. Without the outlier, the mean is 0.81608, and the median is 0.8163.

20. The mean is 11.125 years, and the median is 7 years. 27 is an outlier. Eliminating 27, the mean and median are 5.83 and 3, respectively.

21. The median would be a better representation of the average. A small number of households with high earnings skew the distribution to the right, affecting the mean.

22. This distribution is probably skewed to the right by a small percentage of men who marry (for the first time) very late in life. Therefore the median would do a better job representing the average age (the outliers affect the mean).

23. This distribution is probably skewed to the right by a small percentage of people who change jobs many times. Thus the median would do a better job of representing the average, as the outliers affect the mean.

24. More likely than not, this distribution is skewed to the right by a few flights where many pieces of luggage were lost. Because of this, the mean is probably higher than the median, and thus the airline would want to use the median as the best representation of the average. Customers of the airline might argue that the mean is a better descriptor for the average.

25. This is a classic example of a symmetric distribution, and thus the mean and the median are almost identical (in a perfectly symmetric distribution, they are identical) – either the mean or the median could be used.

26. This distribution is probably skewed to the right by those times when the wait is long, and therefore the median is a better representation of the average (certainly from the view of an advertisement for the bank – customers might claim the mean is a more honest way of describing the average wait time).

27. a. There is one peak on the far left due to all the people who scored low.
    b. The distribution is right-skewed because the scores tail off to the right.
    c. The variation is large.

28. a. There would be two peaks, one representing the figure skaters who use the rink in the morning, who would have lower weights, and the other representing the professional hockey players who would have higher weights.
    b. This distribution would be symmetric, as each peak would be close to the same shape, centered around a point in the middle of the data.
    c. The variation would be moderate, since the variation within the weights of hockey players and within the weights of the figure skaters would not be great.

29. a. There are likely two peaks in such a distribution, one for the women, and one for the men.
    b. The distribution is symmetric because one would find a tail on the left representing the lightest people on the team, and a tail on the right representing the heaviest people on the team.
    c. Relative to a single-gendered set of athletes, the variation would be large.

30. a. The distribution would not have a peak since all digits, 0–9, have nearly the same frequency in the case where the last digit is selected randomly.
    b. This is a symmetric distribution because it is uniform.
    c. The data values are spread out evenly across the distribution, so there is large variation.

31. a. Consider a typical data set for the monthly sales: we expect the sales to be high in the winter months, with very low sales (or even no sales) in the summer. The number of shovels sold each month, beginning in January, might look like this: {25, 20, 15, 3, 0, 0, 0, 0, 0, 3, 15, 20}. To picture this data set as a distribution, we create a frequency histogram.

Monthly Shovel Sales

This histogram has two peaks, the second not as dramatic as the first. Realize that although the histogram would look different if we varied the bin sizes or the hypothetical sales data, its basic shape is captured in the diagram above. This is due to the fact that a majority of the monthly sales figures are expected to be low (corresponding to the left peak), and the winter monthly sales figures would be high (corresponding to the right peak).

b. The histogram shown in part **a** is right-skewed.

c. The variation is large because of the difference between low sales in the summer, and high sales in the winter.

32. a. There are likely two peaks in such a distribution, one for the compact cars, and one for the sports utility vehicles.

b. The frequency histogram in part **a** would be symmetric.

c. The variation in car weights would be moderate because the weights of compact cars and sports utility vehicles would differ greatly, but there would be little variation among the weights of compact cars and among the weights of sports utility vehicles.

33. a. There would be one peak in the distribution, corresponding to the average price of detergent.

b. More likely than not, there would be no extreme outliers in this data set, and it would be symmetric.

c. There would be moderate variation in the data set because we don't expect outliers. (The detergent may not sell well next to 19 other brands if its price is radically different. Of course this begs the question, "But what if it's much cheaper than the other brands?" That's not too likely to happen for a commodity like detergent, because once one company begins selling its detergent at a low price, the others would be forced to lower their prices to compete).

34. a. There would be one peak to the left, corresponding to the ages of children, who would visit the amusement parks in larger numbers than adults.

b. The distribution is right-skewed because the ages of adults visiting the amusement park would tail off to the right.

c. The variation would be large, since there could be infants and senior citizens visiting the amusement park.

FURTHER APPLICATIONS

35. The distribution has two peaks (bimodal), with no symmetry, and large variation. For tourists who want to watch the geyser erupt, it means they may have to wait around for a while (most likely between 25 and 40 minutes, though perhaps as long as 50 to 90 minutes, depending on when they arrive at the site).

36. The distribution has one peak, and is right-skewed. Most of the data is clustered around its peak, though it has considerable spread, so it has moderate variation. The histogram tells us that if a computer chip is going to fail, it will most likely fail soon, rather than late.

37. This distribution has one peak, is symmetric, and has moderate variation. The graph says that weights of rugby players are usually near the mean weight, but that there are some light and some heavy players.

38. a. As shown, the graph is not symmetric (though the idea it represents – uniform distribution of randomly chosen numbers – is symmetric).

b. No, the peaks appear randomly (though, again, the smooth distribution one envisions when numbers are chosen randomly could be described as a distribution with no peaks).

c. No, the distribution would look different because the numbers are chosen at random, and the ups and downs of the graph would appear at random (and different) locations.

d. The histogram would get smoother, approaching a uniform distribution.

39. a. Sketches will vary. We cannot be sure of the exact shape of the distribution with the given parameters, as we don't have all the raw data. However, because the mean is larger than the median, and because the data set has large outliers, it would likely be right-skewed, with a single peak at the mode.

b. About 150 families (50%) earned less than $45,000 because that value is the median income.

c. We don't have enough information to be certain how many families earned more than $55,000, but it is likely a little less than half, simply because the mean is a measure of center for all distributions. (Note that it is a little less than half because the outliers tend to pull the mean right of the median).

40. a. Because the mode is 0 minutes, and the distribution is right skewed (its mean is right of the median, and there are high outliers), the graph would have a single peak at 0 and would decrease to the right. (Note that planes do not typically depart earlier than scheduled – it would be unwise to leave passengers behind – and thus there are no negative delays).

b. 50% of the flights were delayed less than the median time of 6 minutes due to the definition of the median.

c. 50% of the flights were delayed more than the median time of 6 minutes due to the definition of the median.

TECHNOLOGY EXERCISES

48. a. The mean, median and mode for team A are 134, 125, and 115 respectively. The mean and median for team B are 131 and 135, respectively. There is no mode for Team B.

b. The coach of team A can claim that his team has the greater mean weight.

c. The coach of team B can claim that his team has the greater median weight.

d. The mean weight of the teams combined is 132.5, which is equal to the mean of the two mean weights of the teams. This is true since both teams have the same number of players.

e. The median weight of the teams combined is 130, which is equal to the median of the two median weights of the teams. This result is not true in general.

UNIT 6B

TIME OUT TO THINK

Pg. 382. Examples and opinions will vary. Big Bank's three lines will have greater variation since customers entering the bank can choose the shortest line, change lines if the customer at the front of the line has a time consuming transaction to complete, and there is a chance that the person at the front of all three lines has a lengthy transaction.

Pg. 387. Students should notice the sense in which the standard deviation is an average of the individual deviations. Also, notice that the larger deviations are more heavily weighted in the calculation as a result of taking the squares.

QUICK QUIZ

1. **a**. The range is defined as the high value – low value.
2. **c**. The five-number summary includes the low value, the first quartile, median, and third quartile, and the high value. Unless the mean happens to be the same as the median, it would not be part of the five-number summary.
3. **a**. Roughly half of any data set is contained between the lower and upper quartiles ("roughly" because with an odd number of data values, one cannot break a data set into equal parts).
4. **b**. Consider the set {0, 0, 0, 0, 0, 0, 0, 0, 0, 0, 100}. Its mean is 10, which is larger than the upper quartile of 0.
5. **b**. You need the high and low values to compute the range, and you need all of the values to compute the standard deviation, so the only thing you can compute is a single deviation.
6. **b**. The standard deviation is defined in such a way that it can be interpreted as the average distance of a random value from the mean.
7. **c**. The standard deviation is defined as the square root of the variance, and thus is always non-negative.

8. **a**. Using the range rule of thumb, we see that the range is about four times as large as the standard deviation. (The worst-case scenario is when the range and standard deviation are both zero).
9. **b**. Newborn infants and first grade boys have similar heights, whereas there is considerable variation in the heights of all elementary school children.
10. **c**. Because the standard deviation for Garcia is the largest, the data are more spread out, so Professor Garcia must have had very high grades from more students than the other two.

DOES IT MAKE SENSE?

7. Does not make sense. The range depends upon only the low and high values, not on the middle values.
8. Makes sense. The upper quartile includes the highest score.
9. Makes sense. Consider the case where the 15 highest scores were 80, the next score was 68, and the lowest 14 scores were 40. There are numerous such cases that satisfy the conditions given.
10. Makes sense. Using the range rule of thumb, the range is approximately four times as large as the standard deviation. The only instance where the range would not be larger than the standard deviation is the case where both were 0.
11. Makes sense. The standard deviation describes the spread of the data, and one would certainly expect the heights of 5-year old children to have less variation than the heights of children aged 3 to 15.
12. Does not make sense. The standard deviation carries the same units as the mean.

BASIC SKILLS & CONCEPTS

13. The mean waiting time at Big Bank is (4.1 + 5.2 + 5.6 + 6.2 + 6.7 + 7.2 + 7.7 + 7.7 + 8.5 + 9.3 + 11.0) ÷ 11 = 79.2 ÷ 11 = 7.2. Because there are 11 values, the median is the sixth value = 7.2.
14. The mean waiting time at Best Bank is (6.6 + 6.7 + 6.7 + 6.9 + 7.1 + 7.2 + 7.3 + 7.4 + 7.7 + 7.8 + 7.8) ÷ 11 = 79.2 ÷ 11 = 7.2. Because there are 11 values, the median is the sixth value = 7.2.
15. a. For the East Coast, the mean, median, and range are 134.97, 123.45, and 117.8, respectively. For the West Coast, the mean, median, and range are 145.82, 150.3, and 69.2, respectively.
    b. For the East Coast, the five-number summary is (98.2, 108.7, 123.45, 140.0, 216.0). For the West Coast, it is (113.2, 122.7, 150.3, 156.0, 182.4). The boxplots are not shown.
    c. The standard deviation for the East Coast is 42.86. For the West Coast, it is 25.06.

d. For the East Coast, the standard deviation is approximately 117.8 ÷ 4 = 29.45, which is a far cry from the actual value of 42.86. This is due, in part, to the outlier of New York City (216.0). For the West Coast, the standard deviation is approximately 69.2 ÷ 4 = 17.3, which is also well off the mark.

e. The cost of living index is smaller, on average, for the East Coast cities shown, though the variation is higher (due in part to the outlier of New York City).

16. a. For the coastal cities, the mean, median, and range are 7943.6, 7832, and 5614, respectively. The mean, median, and range for the non-coastal cities are 6468.2, 6699, and 5358, respectively.

b. For the coastal cities, the five-number summary is (4876, 7488, 7832, 8923, 10,490). For the non-coastal cities, it is (2899, 5683, 6699, 7434, 8257). The boxplots are not shown.

c. The standard deviation for the coastal cities is 1593.4. It is 1533.9 for the non-coastal cities.

d. The standard deviation for the coastal cities is approximately 5614 ÷ 4 = 1403.5, which underestimates the actual value of 1593.4. For the non-coastal cities, the standard deviation is approximately 5358 ÷ 4 = 1339.5, which also underestimates the actual value of 1533.9.

e. The mean and median taxes for non-coastal cities are considerably smaller than the taxes paid in coastal cities, though the variation is slightly larger.

17. a. For the no treatment group, the mean, median, and range are 0.184, 0.16, and 0.35, respectively. For the treatment group, the mean, median, and range are 1.334, 1.07, and 2.11, respectively.

b. The five-number summary for the no treatment group is (0.02, 0.085, 0.16, 0.295, 0.37). It is (0.27, 0.595, 1.07, 2.205, 2.38) for the treatment group. The boxplots are not shown.

c. The standard deviation for the no treatment group is 0.127; for the treatment group, it is 0.859.

d. The standard deviation for the no treatment group is approximately 0.35 ÷ 4 = 0.0875, which underestimates the actual value of 0.127. For the treatment group, the standard deviation is approximately 2.11 ÷ 4 = 0.5275, which is underestimates the actual value of .859.

e. The average weight and standard deviation of trees in the treatment group are higher that those of the no treatment group.

18. a. The mean, median, and range for Beethoven's symphonies are 38.8, 36, and 42 minutes, respectively. For Mahler, these numbers are 75, 80, and 44 minutes.

b. Beethoven's five-number summary is (26, 29, 36, 45, 68). Mahler's is (50, 62, 80, 87.5, 94). The boxplots are not shown.

c. The standard deviation for Beethoven's symphonies is 13.13 minutes. It is 15.44 for Mahler's symphonies.

d. The standard deviation for Beethoven's symphonies is approximately 42 ÷ 4 = 10.5, which underestimates the actual value of 13.13. For Mahler, the standard deviation is approximately 44 ÷ 4 = 11, which underestimates the actual value of 15.44.

e. Mahler wrote symphonies that were significantly longer, on average, than Beethoven's, and the variation is slightly larger for Mahler's symphonies.

FURTHER APPLICATIONS

19. a.

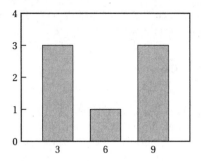

b. The five-number summaries for each of the sets shown are (in order): (9, 9, 9, 9, 9); (8, 8, 9, 10, 10); (8, 8, 9, 10, 10); and (6, 6, 9, 12, 12). The boxplots are not shown.

c. The standard deviations for the sets are (in order): 0.000, 0.816, 1.000, and 3.000.

d. Looking at just the answers to part **c**, we can tell that the variation gets larger from set to set.

20. a.

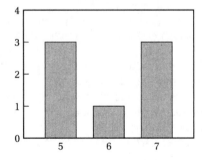

b. The five-number summaries for each of the sets shown are (in order): (6, 6, 6, 6, 6); (5, 5, 6, 7, 7); (5, 5, 6, 7, 7); and (3, 3, 6, 9, 9). The boxplots are not shown.

c. The standard deviations for the sets are (in order): 0.000, 0.816, 1.000, and 3.000.

d. Looking at just the answers to part **c**, we can tell that the variation gets larger from set to set.

21. The first pizza shop has a slightly larger mean delivery time, but much less variation in delivery time when compared to the second shop. If you want a reliable delivery time, choose the first shop. If you don't care when the pizza arrives, choose the shop that offers cheaper pizza (you like them equally well, so you may as well save some money).

22. While Skyview Airlines runs a little ahead of schedule (on average), it can also have long delays (late arrivals). SkyHigh Airlines on average runs slightly behind schedule, but it tends to have smaller delays. If you want to avoid the possibility of long delays, SkyHigh might be the better choice.

23. A lower standard deviation means more certainty in the return, and a lower risk.

24. Factory A has the lower average defect rate per day, but on some days, it can be expected to produce more defective chips than Factory B. The process in Factory B is more uniform and consistent, and thus one might argue that it is more reliable.

25. Batting averages are less varied today than they were in the past. Because the mean is unchanged, batting averages above .350 are less common today.

TECHNOLOGY EXERCISES

30. a. The mean, median, and standard deviation of the data are 91.25, 93.5, and 8.85, respectively.

b. The mean, median, and standard deviation of the data are 99.55, 94, and 31.3, respectively. The mean and standard deviation are both greater.

c. The mean, median, and standard deviation of the new data are 91.25, 93, and 8.48, respectively.

The mean remains the same. The median and standard deviation are smaller.

UNIT 6C

TIME OUT TO THINK

Pg. 396. No; the 100th percentile is defined as a score for which 100% of the data values are less than or equal to it. Thus it must be the highest score, so no one can score ABOVE the 100th percentile.

Pg. 397. The most likely explanation is that a minimum height is thought necessary for the army. If there is any maximum height, it must be taller than most men (since men make up much of the army), which means it is much taller than most women. Opinions will vary on the issue of fairness. This would be a good topic for a discussion either during or outside of class.

QUICK QUIZ

1. **b**. A normal distribution is symmetric with one peak, and this produces a bell-shaped curve.
2. **a**. The mean, median and mode are equal in a normal distribution.
3. **a**. Data values farther from the mean correspond to lower frequencies than those close to the mean, due to the bell-shaped distribution.
4. **c**. Since most of the workers earn minimum wage, the mode of the wage distribution is on the left, and the distribution is right-skewed.
5. **a**. Roughly 68% of data values fall within one standard deviation of the mean, and 68% is about 2/3.
6. **c**. In a normally distributed data set, 99.7% of all data fall within 3 standard deviations of the mean.
7. **a**. Note that 43 mpg is 1 standard deviation above the mean. Since 68% of the data lies within one standard deviation of the mean, the remaining 32% is farther than 1 standard deviation from the mean. The normal distribution is symmetric, so half of 32%, or 16%, lies above 1 standard deviation.
8. **c**. The *z*-score for 84 is $(84 - 75)/6 = 1.5$.
9. **b**. Table 6.3 shows that the percentile corresponding with a standard score of –0.60 is 27.43%.
10. **c**. If your friend said his IQ was in the 75th percentile, it would mean his IQ is larger than 75% of the population. It is impossible to have an IQ that is larger than 102% of the population.

DOES IT MAKE SENSE?

5. Makes sense. Physical characteristics are often normally distributed, and college basketball players are tall, though not all of them, so it makes sense that the mean is 6'3", with a standard deviation of 3" (this would put approximately 95% of the players within 5'9" to 6'9").
6. Makes sense. Physical characteristics are often normally distributed, and these statistics say that approximately 95% of babies born at Belmont are between 4.4 and 9.2 pounds (which is reasonable).
7. Does not make sense. With a mean of 6.8 pounds, and a standard deviation of 7 pounds, you would expect that a small percentage of babies would be born 2 standard deviations above the mean. But this would imply that some babies weigh more than 20.8 pounds, which is much too heavy for a newborn.
8. Does not make sense. The standard score is computed for an individual data value, not for an entire set of exams scores. Furthermore, a standard score of 75 for a particular data value would mean that value is 75 standard deviations away from the mean, which is virtually impossible (almost all data in a normally distributed data set is within 3 standard deviations of the mean).
9. Makes sense. A standard score of 2 or more corresponds to percentiles of 97.72% and higher, so while this could certainly happen, the teacher is giving out As (on the final exam) to only 2.28% of the class
10. Makes sense. If Jack is in the 50th percentile, he is taller than half of the population (to which he is being compared), and by definition, he is at the median height.

BASIC SKILLS & CONCEPTS

11. Diagrams **a** and **c** are normal, and diagram **c** has a larger standard deviation because its values are more spread out.
12. Diagrams **b** and **c** are normal, and diagram **b** has a larger standard deviation because its values are more spread out.
13. Most trains would probably leave near to their scheduled departure times, but a few could be considerably delayed, which would result in a right-skewed (and non-normal) distribution.
14. This distribution would be normal because a machine fills the bags with approximately 40 pounds of lawn fertilizer, and the variation in these weights would be random, which typically results in normal distributions.
15. Random factors would be responsible for the variation seen in the distances from the bull's-eye, so this distribution would be normal.
16. Distributions that measure athletic ability tend to be normal.

17. Easy exams would have scores that are left-skewed, so the scores would not be normally distributed.

18. Performances in athletic events are often normally distributed.

19. a. Half of any normally distributed data set lies below the mean, so 50% of the scores are less than 100.

   b. Note that 120 is one standard deviation above the mean. Since 68% of the data lies within one standard deviation of the mean (between 80 and 120), half of 68%, or 34%, lies between 100 and 120. Add 34% to 50% (the answer to part **a**) to find that 84% of the scores are less than 120.

   c. Note that 140 is two standard deviations above the mean. Since 95% of the data lies within two standard deviations above the mean (between 60 and 140), half of 95%, or 47.5%, lies between 100 and 140. Add 47.5% to 50% (see part **a**) to find that 97.5% of the scores are below 140.

   d. Note that 60 is two standard deviations below the mean. Since 95% of the data lies within two standard deviations of the mean (between 60 and 140), 5% of the data lies outside this range. Because the normal distribution is symmetric, half of 5%, or 2.5%, lies in the lower tail below 60.

   e. A sketch of the normal distribution would show that the amount of data lying above 60 is equivalent to the amount of data lying below 140, so the answer is 97.5% (see part **c**).

   f. Note that 160 is three standard deviations above the mean. Since 99.7% of the data lies within three standard deviations of the mean (between 40 and 160), 0.3% of the data lies outside this range. Because the normal distribution is symmetric, half of 0.3%, or 0.15%, lies in the upper tail above 160.

   g. A sketch of the normal distribution shows that the percent of data lying above 80 is equivalent to the percent lying below 120, so the answer is 84% (see part **b**).

   h. The percent of data between 60 and 140 is 95%, because these are each two standard deviations from the mean.

20. a. A heart rate of 55 is one standard deviation below the mean. Since 68% of the data lies between 55 and 85, 32% lie outside that range, which implies 16% lies below 55 (due to symmetry).

   b. A heart rate of 40 is two standard deviations below the mean. Since 95% of the data lies between 40 and 100, 5% lie outside that range, which implies 2.5% lies below 40 (due to symmetry).

   c. Half of 68% (or 34%) lies between 70 and 85, 50% lies below the mean of 70, so 84% of the data is less than 85.

   d. Half of 95% (or 47.5%) lies between 70 and 100, and 50% lies below the mean of 70, so 97.5% of the data lies below 100.

   e. This portion of the distribution is equal to the portion less than 55 because of symmetry, so the answer is 16% (see part **a**).

   f. The portion of the distribution greater than 55 is equal to the portion less than 85 because of symmetry, so the answer is 84% (see part **c**).

   g. The portion of the distribution more than 40 is equal to the portion less than 100 because of symmetry, so the answer is 97.5% (see part **d**).

   h. Both 55 and 85 are one standard deviation from the mean, and thus 68% of the data lies between them.

21. A score of 59 is one standard deviation below the mean. Since 68% of normally distributed data lies within one standard deviation of the mean, half of 68%, or 34%, lies between 59 and 67 due to symmetry. The percent of data lying above 67 is 50%, so we add these two results to find that 84% of the scores lie above 59.

22. A score of 83 is two standard deviations above the mean. Since 95% of normally distributed data lies within two standard deviations of the mean (between 51 and 83), 5% lies outside this range. Half of 5%, or 2.5%, will be in the upper tail, above 83, so 100% − 2.5% = 97.5% of the scores lie below 83.

23. Subtract two standard deviations from the mean to get the cutoff score of 67 − 16 = 51. Since 95% of the data lies within two standard deviations of the mean, 5% lies outside this range. Half of 5%, or 2.5%, will be below 51, and will fail the exam.

24. A score of 75 is one standard deviation above the mean. Since 68% of the data lies within one standard deviation of the mean (between 59 and 75), 32% of the data is outside this range. Half of 32%, or 16%, will be in the lower tail of the distribution. Since 68% + 16% = 84%, 84% × 500 = 420 of the students will score below 75.

25. The standard score for 67 is $z = (67 − 67)/8 = 0$.

26. The standard score for 59 is $z = (59 − 67)/8 = −1$.

27. The standard score for 55 is $z = (55 − 67)/8 = −1.5$

28. The standard score for 88 is $z = (88 − 67)/8 = 2.625$.

29. a. $z = 1$. The corresponding percentile is 84.13%.

   b. $z = 0.5$, and the corresponding percentile is 69.15%.

   c. $z = −1.5$, and the corresponding percentile is 6.68%.

30. a. $z = −0.5$, and the corresponding percentile is 30.85%.

   b. $z = −2$, and the corresponding percentile is 2.28%.

c. $z = 1.2$, and the corresponding percentile is 88.48%.

31. a. The 20th percentile corresponds to a standard score of about $z = -0.83$, which means the data value is about 0.83 standard deviations below the mean.

    b. The 80th percentile corresponds to a standard score of about $z = 0.84$, which means the data value is 0.84 standard deviations above the mean.

    c. The 63rd percentile corresponds to a standard score of about $z = 0.33$, which means the data value is 0.33 standard deviations above the mean.

32. a. The 10th percentile corresponds to a standard score of about $z = -1.28$, which means the data value is 1.28 standard deviations below the mean.

    b. The 35th percentile corresponds to a standard score of about $z = -0.38$, which means the data value is 0.83 standard deviations below the mean.

    c. The 88th percentile corresponds to a standard score of about $z = 1.18$, which means the data value is 1.18 standard deviations above the mean.

FURTHER APPLICATIONS

33. About 68% of births occur within 15 days of the mean, because this range is one standard deviation from the mean.

34. Within one month of the due date corresponds to two standard deviations on either side of the mean, which implies 95% of the births occur within one month of the mean.

35. Since 68% of births occur within 15 days of the due date, 32% occur outside this range, and half of 32%, or 16%, occur more than 15 days after the due date.

36. Since 95% of births occur within 30 days of the due date, 5% occur outside this range, and half of 5%, or 2.5%, occur more than 30 days after the due date.

37. a. The standard score is $z = (66 - 63.6)/2.5 = 0.96$, which corresponds to an approximate percentile of 83%.

    b. $z = (62 - 63.6)/2.5 = -0.64$, which corresponds to an approximate percentile of 26%.

    c. $z = (61.5 - 63.6)/2.5 = -0.84$, which corresponds to an approximate percentile of 20%.

    d. $z = (64.7 - 63.6)/2.5 = 0.44$, which corresponds to an approximate percentile of 67%.

38. a. The standard score is $z = (22 - 26.2)/4.7 = -0.89$, which corresponds to an approximate percentile of 19%.

    b. $z = (28 - 26.2)/4.7 = 0.38$, which corresponds to an approximate percentile of 65%.

    c. For a BMI of 25, $z = (25 - 26.2)/4.7 = -0.26$, which corresponds to an approximate percentile of 40%, so 60% of American men are overweight. For a BMI of 30, $z = (30 - 26.2)/4.7 = 0.81$, which

corresponds to an approximate percentile of 79%, so 21% of American men are obese.

39. It is not likely because heights of eighth-graders would be normally distributed, and a standard deviation of 40 inches would imply some of the eighth graders (about 16%) are taller than 95 inches, which is preposterous.

40. Assuming the scores are out of 100, it is not likely. A standard deviation of 50 would imply some of the scores are higher than 100.

41. The 90th percentile corresponds to a z-score of about 1.3, which means a data value is 1.3 standard deviations above the mean. For the verbal portion of the GRE, this translates into a score of $462 + 1.3(119) = 617$. For the quantitative portion, it translates into a score of $584 + 1.3(151) = 780$.

42. The standard score for 600 is $z = (600 - 462)/119 = 1.16$, which corresponds to about the 87th percentile. This is the percent of students who score below 600, so the percent that score above 600 is 13%.

43. The standard score for 600 is $z = (600 - 584)/151 = 0.106$, which corresponds to about the 54th percentile. This is the percent of students who score below 600, so the percent that score above 600 is 46%.

44. The standard score for 700 is $z = (700 - 584)/151 = 0.77$, which is 0.77 standard deviations above the mean. Your verbal score would also need to be 0.77 standard deviations above the mean to be in the same percentile, which translates to a score of $462 + 0.77(198) = 554$.

45. The z-score for an 800 on the quantitative exam is $z = (800 - 584)/151 = 1.43$, or about 1.4. This corresponds to the 91.92 percentile, so about 92% score below 800, which means 8% score 800.

46. The z-score for an 800 on the verbal exam is $z = (800 - 462)/119 = 2.84$, which corresponds to an approximate percentile of 99.7%. Since 99.7% score below 800, about 0.3% score 800.

47. For the verbal exam, $z = (400 - 462)/119 = -0.52$. , which corresponds to an approximate percentile of 30%. Thus about 30% score below 400. For the quantitative exam, $z = (400 - 584)/151 = -1.22$, which corresponds to an approximate percentile of 11%. Thus about 11% score below 400.

TECHNOLOGY EXERCISES

53. a. $z = (72 - 69.7)/2.7 = 0.85$, which, from table 6.3, corresponds to an approximate percentile of 80%.

    b. $z = (65 - 69.7)/2.7 = -1.74$; NORMDIST(64,69.7,2.7,TRUE) gives the percentile as 4.0865%, which corresponds to an approximate percentile of 4%.

c. 6'4" = 76"; NORMDIST(76,69.7,2.7,TRUE), gives the percentile as 99.0185%, so approximately 1% of American adult males are taller than 6'4".

d. 5'4" = 64"; NORMDIST(64,69.7,2.7,TRUE), gives the percentile as 1.7381%, so approximately 1.7% of American adult males are shorter than 5'4".

e. 6'7" = 79"; NORMDIST(79,69.7,2.7,TRUE), gives the percentile as 99.97139%, so approximately (100% – 99.97139%) × 115,000,000 = 33,000 of American adult males are as tall as Kobe Bryant.

UNIT 6D

TIME OUT TO THINK

Pg. 403. The probability is 0.01, or 1 in 100, that the results occurred by chance. This is certainly strong evidence in support of the herbal remedy, but by no means does it constitute proof.

Pg. 405. Opinions will vary, but 95% confidence seems reasonable for most surveys, which have no need to be perfect. However, for something of great importance, such as deciding an election, it is far too low. That is why elections must be decided by letting everyone vote, not through statistical sampling.

Pg. 407. The null hypothesis is "the suspect is innocent." A guilty verdict means rejecting the null hypothesis, concluding that the suspect is NOT innocent. A "not guilty" verdict means not rejecting the null hypothesis, in which case we continue to assume that the suspect is innocent.

QUICK QUIZ

1. **c**. A divorce rate of 60% is statistically significant because such large variation from the national rate of 30% is not likely to occur by chance alone.

2. **b**. In order to determine whether a result is statistically significant, we must be able to compare it to a known quantity (such as the effect on a control group in this case).

3. **a**. Statistical significance at the 0.01 level means an observed difference between the effectiveness of the remedy and the placebo would occur by chance in fewer than 1 out of 100 trials of the experiment.

4. **c**. If the statistical significance is at the 0.05 level, we would expect that 1 in 20 experiments would show the pill working better than the placebo by chance alone.

5. **b**. The confidence interval is found by subtracting and adding 3% to the results of the poll (65%).

6. **c**. The central limit theorem tells us that the true proportion is within the margin of error 95% of the time.

7. **c**. The margin of error is approximately $\frac{1}{\sqrt{n}}$. Set this equal to 4% (0.04), and solve for n to find that the sample size was 625. If we quadruple the sample size to 2500, the margin of error will be approximately $\frac{1}{\sqrt{2500}} = 0.02$, or 2%.

8. **a**. The null hypothesis is often taken to be the assumption that there is no difference in the things being compared.

9. **c**. If you cannot reject the null hypothesis, the only thing you can be sure of is that you don't have evidence to support the alternative hypothesis.

10. **b**. If the difference in gas prices can be explained by chance in only 1 out of 100 experiments, you've found a result that is statistically significant at the 0.01 level.

DOES IT MAKE SENSE?

9. Makes sense. If the number of people cured by the new drug is not significantly larger than the number cured by the old drug, the difference could be explained by chance alone, which means the results are not statistically significant.

10. Does not make sense. While results significant at the 0.05 level offer some evidence that the Magic Diet Pill works, we cannot remove all doubt that the results came about by chance alone.

11. Does not make sense. The margin of error is based upon the number of people surveyed (the sample size), and thus both Agency A and B should have the same margin of error.

12. Makes sense. The margin of error is based upon the number of people surveyed (the sample size), and because it is approximately $\frac{1}{\sqrt{n}}$, it decreases as n increases.

13. Makes sense. The alternative hypothesis is the claim that is accepted if the null hypothesis is rejected.

14. Does not make sense. One cannot prove the null hypothesis – it can be rejected, in which case there is evidence for the alternative hypothesis, or we can not reject it, which only means we do not have evidence to support the alternative hypothesis.

BASIC SKILLS & CONCEPTS

15. Most of the time you would expect around 10 sixes in 60 rolls of a standard die. It would be very rare to get only 2 sixes, and thus this is statistically significant.

16. Most of the time you would expect around 50 heads in 100 tosses of a coin, and since 48 is well within the bounds of what would be expected by chance alone, this is not statistically significant.

17. Note that 11/200 is about 5% – this is exactly what you would expect by chance alone from an airline that has 95% of its flights on time.

18. It is very unlikely that a basketball player that makes 92% of free throws would miss 18 in a row. This is statistically significant. (In chapter 7, you will learn that probability of this occurring is practically zero.)

19. There aren't many winners in the Power Ball lottery, and yet there are a good number of 7-11 stores. It would be very unlikely that ten winners in a row purchased their tickets at the same store, so this is statistically significant.

20. The likelihood of 42 people in a group of 45 all sharing the same birthday is extremely small, so this is statistically significant.

21. The result is significant at far less than the 0.01 level (which means it is significant at both the 0.01 and 0.05 level), because the probability of finding the stated results is less than 1 in 1 million by chance alone. This gives us good evidence to support the alternative hypothesis that the accepted value for temperature is wrong.

22. This result is significant at the 1/10,000 = 0.0001 level, so it is significant at both the 0.01 and 0.05 levels. Because chance alone does not do a good job of explaining the difference found in length of hospital stays, it would be reasonable to conclude that seat belts reduce the severity of injuries (assuming that the severity of injury is directly correlated with length of hospital stay).

23. The results of the study are significant at neither the 0.05 level nor the 0.01 level, and thus the improvement is not statistically significant.

24. The difference found in the weights would be expected by chance alone in only 1 out of 100 such surveys.

25. The margin of error is $1/\sqrt{1012} = 0.03$, or 3%, and the 95% confidence interval is 29% to 35%. This means we can be 95% confident that the actual percentage is between 29% and 35%.

26. The margin of error is $1/\sqrt{65,000} = 0.004$, or 0.4%, and the 95% confidence interval is 8.5% to 9.3%. This means we can be 95% confident that the actual percentage is between 8.5% and 9.3%.

27. The margin of error is $1/\sqrt{540} = 0.043$, or 4.3%, and the 95% confidence interval is 59.7% to 68.3% for the satisfied group, and 59.7% to 68.3% for the dissatisfied group. This means we can be 95% confident that the actual percentage is between and 59.7% and 68.3%.

28. The margin of error is $1/\sqrt{1110} = 0.03$, or 3%, and the 95% confidence interval is 56% to 62%. This means we can be 95% confident that the actual percentage is between and 56% and 62%.

29. The margin of error is $1/\sqrt{1003} = 0.03$, or 3%, and the 95% confidence interval is 45% to 51%. This means we can be 95% confident that the actual percentage is between and 45% and 51%.

30. The margin of error is $1/\sqrt{2818} = 0.02$, or 2%, and the 95% confidence intervals are 71% to 75% and 49% to 53%. This means we can be 95% confident that the actual percentage is between and 71% and 75%.

31. The margin of error is $1/\sqrt{1100} = 0.03$, or 3%, and the 95% confidence intervals are 38% to 44% and 12% to 16%. This means we can be 95% confident that the actual percentage is between and 38% and 44%.

32. The margin of error is $1/\sqrt{1229} = 0.03$, or 3%, and the 95% confidence intervals are 25% to 31% and 12% and 18%.

33. a. Null hypothesis: percentage of high school graduates = 85%. Alternative hypothesis: percentage of high school students > 85%.
    b. Rejecting the null hypothesis means there is evidence that the percentage of high school graduates exceeds 85%. Failing to reject the null hypothesis means there is insufficient evidence to conclude that the percentage of high school graduates exceeds 85%.

34. a. Null hypothesis: vitamin C in tablets = 500 mg. Alternate hypothesis: vitamin C in tablets < 500 mg.
    b. Rejecting the null hypothesis means that there is evidence that the tablets contain less than 500 mg. Failing to reject the null hypothesis means there is insufficient evidence to conclude that the tablets contain less than 500 mg.

35. a. Null hypothesis: mean teacher salary = $47,750. Alternative hypothesis: mean teacher salary > $47,750.
    b. Rejecting the null hypothesis means there is evidence that the mean teacher salary in the state exceeds $47,750. Failing to reject the null hypothesis means there is insufficient evidence to conclude that the mean teacher salary exceeds $47,750.

36. a. Null hypothesis: water usage = 1675 gallons per month. Alternative hypothesis: water usage > 1675 gallons per month.
    b. Rejecting the null hypothesis means there is evidence that the water usage exceeds 1675 gallons per month. Failing to reject the null hypothesis means there is insufficient evidence to

conclude that water usage exceeds 1675 gallons per month.

37. a. Null hypothesis: percentage of underrepresented students = 20%. Alternative hypothesis: percentage of underrepresented students < 20%.
b. Rejecting the null hypothesis means there is evidence that the percentage of underrepresented students is less than 20%. Failing to reject the null hypothesis means there is insufficient evidence to conclude that the percentage of underrepresented students is less than 20%.

38. a. Null hypothesis: pollution levels = EPA minimum. Alternative hypothesis: pollution levels < EPA minimum.
b. Rejecting the null hypothesis means there is evidence that the pollution levels are less than the EPA minimum. Failing to reject the null hypothesis means there is insufficient evidence to conclude that the pollution levels are less than the EPA minimum.

39. Null hypothesis: mean annual mileage of cars in the fleet = 11,725 miles. Alternative hypothesis: mean annual mileage of cars in the fleet > 11,725. The result is significant at the 0.01 level, and provides good evidence for rejecting the null hypothesis.

40. Null hypothesis: proportion of supporting voters = 0.5. Alternative hypothesis: proportion of supporting voters > 0.5. The result is not significant at the 0.05 level, and there are no grounds for rejecting the null hypothesis.

41. Null hypothesis: mean stay = 2.1 days. Alternative hypothesis: mean stay > 2.1 days. The result is not significant at the 0.05 level, and there are no grounds for rejecting the null hypothesis.

42. Null hypothesis: mean bounce height = 90.10 inches. Alternative hypothesis: mean bounce height < 90.10 inches. The result is significant at the 0.05 level, and provides evidence for rejecting the null hypothesis.

43. Null hypothesis: mean income = $50,000. Alternative hypothesis: mean income > $50,000. The result is significant at the 0.01 level, and provides good evidence for rejecting the null hypothesis.

44. Null hypothesis: mean ownership = 7.5 years. Alternative hypothesis: mean ownership < 7.5 years. The result is not significant at the 0.05 level, and there are no grounds for rejecting the null hypothesis.

FURTHER APPLICATIONS

45. The margin of error is $1/\sqrt{13,000} = 0.009$, or 0.9%, and the 95% confidence interval is 64.1% to 65.9%. This means we can be 95% confident that the actual percentage of viewers who watched *American Idol* was between 64.1% and 65.9%.

46. Null hypothesis: mean birth weight = 3.38 kg. Alternative hypothesis: mean birth weight > 3,38 kg. The result is significant at the 0.01 level, and provides good evidence for rejecting the null hypothesis.

47. The margin of error is approximately $1/\sqrt{n}$. If we want to decrease the margin of error by a factor of 2, we must increase the sample size by a factor of 4, because $\dfrac{1}{\sqrt{4n}} = \dfrac{1}{2\sqrt{n}} = \dfrac{1}{2} \cdot \dfrac{1}{\sqrt{n}}$.

48. The margin of error is approximately $1/\sqrt{n}$. If we want to decrease the margin of error by a factor of 10, we must increase the sample size by a factor of 100, because $\dfrac{1}{\sqrt{100n}} = \dfrac{1}{10\sqrt{n}} = \dfrac{1}{10} \cdot \dfrac{1}{\sqrt{n}}$.

49. The margin of error, 3%, is consistent with the sample size because $1/\sqrt{1019} = 0.03 = 3\%$.

UNIT 7A

TIME OUT TO THINK

Pg. 417. Birth orders of BBG, BGB, and GBB are the outcomes that produce the event of two boys in a family of 3. We can represent the probability of two boys as P(2 boys). This problem is covered later in Example 3.

Pg. 419. The only change from the Example 2 solution is that the event of a July 4 birthday is only 1 of the 365 possible outcomes, so the probability is 1/365.

Pg. 421. (Should be covered only if you covered Unit 6D). The experiment is essentially a hypothesis test. The null hypothesis is that the coins are fair, in which case we should observe the theoretical probabilities. The alternative hypothesis is that the coins are unfair. The results in this case do not differ significantly from the results expected under the null hypothesis. Therefore we do NOT reject the null hypothesis, so we lack sufficient evidence for claiming that the coins are unfair.

Pg. 423. Four coins have $2^4 = 16$ possible outcomes, but only five possible events: 0 heads, 1 head, 2 heads, 3 heads, and 4 heads.

QUICK QUIZ

1. **b**. HHT is a different outcome than HTH due to the order in which the heads appear, but both are the same event because each has two heads.

2. **b**. This is a probability based on observations about the number of free throws Shawna attempted and made, and so it is empirical.

3. **a**. This is a theoretical probability because we are assuming each outcome is equally likely, and no experiment is being carried out to determine the probability.

4. **c**. If the probability of an event is $P(A)$, the probability it does not occur is $1 - P(A)$.

5. **c**. The most likely outcome when a coin is tossed several times is that half of the time heads will appear.

6. **b**. Table 7.3 shows that the probability Mackenzie wins is 5/36, whereas the probability that Serena wins is 4/36.

7. **c**. There are six possible outcomes for each of the four dice, and the multiplication principle says we multiply these outcomes together to get the total number of outcomes when all four dice are rolled.

8. **b**. The lowest sum that could occur when four dice are rolled is 4, and the highest is 24, and every sum in between is possible.

9. **a**. The sum of all the probabilities for a probability distribution is always 1.

10. **a**. If Triple Treat's probability of winning is 1/4, then the probability he loses is 3/4. This implies the odds that he wins is $(1/4) \div (3/4)$, or 1 to 3, which, in turn, means the odds against are 3 to 1.

DOES IT MAKE SENSE?

7. Makes sense. The outcomes are HTTT, THTT, TTHT, TTTH.

8. Does not make sense. The probability of any event is always between 0 and 1.

9. Makes sense. This is a subjective probability, but it's as good as any other guess one might make.

10. Does not make sense. The two outcomes in question are not equally likely.

11. Does not make sense. The sum of $P(A)$ and $P(\text{not } A)$ is always 1.

12. Makes sense. This is the method we use to compute empirical probabilities.

BASIC SKILLS & CONCEPTS

13. There are $15 \times 3 = 45$ choices.

14. There are $9 \times 8 \times 12 = 864$ packages.

15. There are $3 \times 6 \times 5 = 90$ three-course meals.

16. Assuming each district elects exactly one representative, there are $2 \times 3 \times 4 = 24$ possible commissions.

17. There are $28 \times 4 = 112$ combinations.

18. There are $4 \times 3 \times 5 \times 2 \times 3 = 360$ sets.

19. There are $7 \times 9 \times 11 = 693$ systems.

20. There are $2 \times 2 \times 2 \times 8 = 64$ versions.

21. There are 4 queens in a standard deck, so the probability is $4/52 = 1/13$. We are assuming that each card is equally likely to be chosen.

22. There are 26 black cards, so the probability is $26/52 = 1/2$. We are assuming each card is equally likely to be chosen.

23. The probability is $2/6 = 1/3$. We are assuming equally likely outcomes.

24. There are $6 \times 6 = 36$ possible outcomes, and 3 of these sum to 4 (see Table 7.3), so the probability is $3/36 = 1/12$. It is assumed that each outcome is equally likely to occur.

25. There are 12 royalty cards, so the probability is $12/52 = 3/13$. It is assumed that each card is equally likely to be chosen.

26. There are 3 even numbers on a die, so the probability is $3/6 = 1/2$. We are assuming equally likely outcomes.

27. The probability is $2/52 = 1/26$ because there are 2 red aces. We are assuming equally likely outcomes.

28. There are 6 ways to get the same number on both dice, and 36 possible outcomes, so the probability

is 6/36 = 1/6. It is assumed that all outcomes are equally likely.

29. There are ten possible outcomes for the last digit in a phone number, and two of these is are 1 or 2, so the probability is 2/10 = 1/5. It is assumed that each digit is equally likely to occur at the end of a phone number.

30. The probability is 1/7, assuming that births are uniformly distributed over the days of the week.

31. Assuming that people are equally likely to be born during any hour of the day, the probability is 1/24.

32. There are 12 months in the year, so the probability is 2/12 = 1/6, assuming births are uniformly distributed across the months of the year. If using the number of days in the months, there are 30 + 31 = 61 total days in April and October, so the probability is 61/365, assuming births are uniformly distributed across the days of the year.

33. There are 4 possible outcomes with a 2-child family (BB, BG, GB, GG), and 2 of these have one boy and one girl, so the probability is 2/4 = 1/2. This assumes each outcome is equally likely to occur.

34. There are 8 possible outcomes with a 3-child family (BBB, BBG, BGB, GBB, GGB, GBG, BGG, GGG), and 3 of these have exactly two girls, so the probability is 3/8. This assumes each outcome is equally likely to occur.

35. There are 8 possible outcomes with a 3-child family (BBB, BBG, BGB, GBB, GGB, GBG, BGG, GGG), and 1 of these has exactly three girls, so the probability is 1/8. This assumes each outcome is equally likely to occur.

36. There are 22 pairs of socks, and 8 are white, so the probability is 8/22 = 4/11, assuming that each pair of socks is equally likely to be chosen.

37. Your address ends in one of ten digits, and the probability that a randomly selected person has the same ending digit is 1/10. This assumes that each digit is as likely as the others to be at the end of an address, and it assumes that addresses end in digits.

38. You will wait longer than 15 minutes if you arrive at any of the first 15 minutes of a given half hour (30 minutes), so the probability is 15/30 = 1/2. This assumes your arrival times are uniformly distributed across any given half-hour.

39. The probability is 18/30 = 3/5 = 0.6.

40. The probability is 1/200 = 0.005.

41. The probability is 72% = 0.72.

42. The probability of a head is 42/100, so the probability of a tail is 58/100 = 0.58.

43. The probability is 225/250 = 0.9.

44. The probability is 0.3.

45. Answers will vary.

46. Answers will vary.

47. The probability is 5/6, because there are 5 outcomes that aren't 2s. It is assumed that each outcome is equally likely.

48. There are 8 possible outcomes when 3 heads are tossed (HHH, HHT, HTH, THH, TTH, THT, HTT, TTT), and only one of them consists of all 3 tails. Thus the probability of tossing 3 tails is 1/8, and the probability of not tossing 3 tails is 1 – 1/8 = 7/8. Equally likely outcomes are assumed.

49. The probability he will make the next free throw is 75% = 0.75, so the probability he will miss is 1 – 0.75 = 0.25, or 25%. The probabilities computed here are based on his past performance.

50. The probability that the next person you meet was born on in July is 1/12 (assuming each month is equally likely), so the probability that the person was not born In July is 1 – 1/12 = 11/12.

51. The probability of rolling a sum of 7 is 6/36 (see Table 7.3), so the probability of not rolling a sum of 7 is 1 – 6/36 = 30/36 = 5/6. Equally likely outcomes are assumed.

52. The probability is 100% – 30% = 70% = 0.7. This answer assumes that "not rain" means "sunny day" (rather than, say, a cloudy day with no rain), and it assumes the subjective/empirical probability of rain is a reasonable prediction.

53. The probability of having a 100-year flood is 1/100, so the probability of not having one is 1 – 1/100 = 99/100 = 0.99. This assumes that each year the probability of a 100-year flood is 1/100.

54. The probability of meeting someone born in May or June is 2/12, so the probability that this does not occur is 1 – 2/12 = 10/12 = 5/6. This assumes births are uniformly distributed across the year.

55.

Result	Probability
0 H	1/16
1 H	4/16
2 H	6/16
3 H	4/16
4 H	1/16

56.

Sum	Probability
2	1/16
3	2/16
4	3/16
5	4/16
6	3/16
7	2/16
8	1/16

57. The probability of getting a 1 or a 2 is 2/6 = 1/3, and the probability of not getting a 1 or a 2 is 2/3. Thus the odds for the event are $(1/3) \div (2/3) = 1$ to 2, and the odds against are 2 to 1.

58. The probability of getting two tails is 1/4, so the probability of not getting two tails is 3/4. Thus the odds for the event are $(1/4) \div (3/4) = 1$ to 3, and the odds against are 3 to 1.

59. This problem is similar to exercise 57, except that we are focusing on getting a 5 or a 6 (instead of a 1 or a 2) – the probabilities and odds remain the same. Thus the odds for the event are 1 to 2, and odds against are 2 to 1.

60. The probability of getting a head and a tail is 2/4 = 1/2, and the probability of not getting a head and a tail is 1/2. Thus the odds for the event are $(1/2) \div (1/2) = 1$ to 1, and the odds against are 1 to 1.

61. Since the odds on your bet are 3 to 4, you'll win $3 for every $4 you bet. A $20 bet is five $4 bets, so you will gain $15.

62. Since the odds on your bet are 5 to 4, you'll win $5 for every $4 you bet. A $20 bet is five $4 bets, so you will gain $25.

FURTHER APPLICATIONS

63. a. There are 52 women at the convention, so the probability a random delegate is a woman is 52/100 = 0.52.
   b. There are 10 Independents, so the probability is 10/100 = 0.1.
   c. There are 41 Democrats, and thus 59 non-Democrats, which means the probability is 59/100 = 0.59.
   d. There are 21 female Republicans, so the probability is 21/100 = 0.21.
   e. There are 16 male Democrats, so the probability you meet one is 16/100 = 0.16. Thus the probability that you meet a someone who is not a male Democrat is 1 – 0.16 = 0.84.

64. The probability in 2010 is 40 million $\div$ 310 million = 0.13, and the probability in 2050 is 82 million $\div$ 439 million = 0.19. Thus the probability is greater in 2050.

65. The empirical probabilities for 0 heads, 1 head, 2 heads, and 3 heads are (respectively): 260/1000 = 0.26, 495/1000 = 0.495, 245/1000 = 0.245, and 0/1000 = 0.0. The 8 possible outcomes when 3 coins are tossed are (HHH, HHT, HTH, THH, TTH, THT, HTT, TTT), and thus the theoretical probabilities for 0 heads, 1 head, 2 heads, and 3 heads are (respectively): 1/8 = 0.125, 3/8 = 0.375, 3/8 = 0.375, and 1/8 = 0.125. The differences between the empirical and theoretical probabilities are large enough to suspect that the coins are unfair.

66. The probability, as shown in the table, is 4.5% = 0.045. The table already *is* a probability distribution: it shows the probabilities (expressed as percents) that a randomly selected person will be in each of the categories.

67. The odds for event *A* are $(0.99) \div (0.01) = 99$ to 1, and the odds for event *B* are $(0.96) \div (0.04) = 24$ to 1. The odds for *A* are much higher, even though the probabilities for *A* and *B* are relatively close to one another.

UNIT 7B

TIME OUT TO THINK

Pg. 428. The same reasoning suggests that the probability of rolling a 6 in 6 rolls is 6/6, or 1. But you're certainly not guaranteed getting a 6 in 6 rolls of a die, any more than you are guaranteed to get heads if you toss a coin twice. Thus the Chevalier's method for combined probability must be incorrect.

Pg. 430. Replacing the candy makes the events independent, so the probability is the same on each draw. In contrast, eating a chocolate on the first draw lowers the probability of chocolate on the second draw because there are (proportionally) fewer chocolates left in the box. Therefore the probability is greater when you replace the candy.

Pg. 434. Based on Example 7, there is more than a 1 in 3 chance that a 100-year flood will not occur during any 100-year period — a result that surprises many people. But given this substantial probability of no flood in 100 years, you should not be surprised if a 100 year flood has not occurred in the past century. And you certainly should not use this fact to become complacent about the prospect of a flood in future years.

Pg. 435. The small change in probability has a big effect if the game is played often enough. Casinos can count on many games by many people. Therefore they can set the odds only slightly below even, which means almost half the people will feel "lucky" because they won, while still being assured of a tidy profit.

QUICK QUIZ

1. **c.** The probability of getting a double-1 on at least one of the rolls is $1 - (35/36)^2$.

2. **c.** The rule works only when *A* and *B* are independent events.

3. **b.** The probability of choosing a pink rose on the second pick is dependent upon what happens on the first pick (because there will be fewer roses in the vases).

4. **c.** Since these are dependent events, the rule $P(A$ and B and $C) = P(A)$ $P(B$ given $A)$ $P(C$ given A and $B)$ must be used.

5. **c.** A person can be born on both a Wednesday and in July, so the events are overlapping.

6. **c.** $P(5$ or 6 or 7 or $8) = P(5) + P(6) + P(7) + P(8) = 4/36 + 5/36 + 6/36 + 5/36 = 20/36 > 0.5$.

7. **a.** Since these events are independent, we have $P(sum\ of\ 3$ and $sum\ of\ 4) = P(sum\ of\ 3) \times P(sum\ of\ 4) = 2/36 \times 3/36$.

8. **b.** The probability of getting at least one success in ten trials of the experiment is $1 - [P(\text{not two heads})]^{10}$, so you need first to compute the probability of not two heads.

9. **c.** This answer shows the correct application of the *at least once* rule.

10. **c.** This answer shows the correct application of the *at least once* rule.

DOES IT MAKE SENSE?

5. Makes sense. You can't get both heads and tails on a single flip of a coin, but you must get one or the other.

6. Does not make sense. The events of flipping a coin several times in a row are independent, and thus the outcome of the first three do not affect the result of the fourth flip.

7. Does not make sense. The probability of drawing an ace or a spade is 16/52, but the probability of drawing the ace of spades is 1/52.

8. Does not make sense. The numbers in a lottery are randomly chosen, and each outcome is as equally likely (or equally unlikely) as the others.

9. Does not make sense. The chance of getting at least one 5 is $1 - (5/6)^3 \neq 3/6$.

10. Makes sense. The calculation described is a correct application of the *at least once* rule.

BASIC SKILLS & CONCEPTS

11. The events are most likely independent (there may be some situations where one could argue dependence, such as the case where a woman gives birth to quintuplets, and these happen to be the next five births – but we can't solve the problem without assuming independence). Assuming the probability of giving birth to a girl is 1/2, the answer is $(1/2)^4 = 1/16$.

12. The events are independent. The probability is $(1/12)^3 = 1/1728 = 0.00058$.

13. The events are independent. $P(2$ and 2 and $6) = P(2) \times P(2) \times P(6) = (1/6)^3 = 1/216$.

14. The events are independent. $P(queen$ and *queen* and *queen*$) = P(queen) \times P(queen) \times P(queen) = (4/52)^3 = 1/2197 = 0.0005$.

15. The events are dependent. $P(Q_1$ and Q_2 and $Q_3) = P(Q_1) \times P(Q_2$ given $Q_1) \times P(Q_3$ given Q_1 and $Q_2) = (4/52) \times (3/51) \times (2/50) = 0.0002$.

16. The events are dependent. This is similar to exercise 15, with an answer of $(13/52) \times (12/51) \times (11/50) = 0.0129$.

17. The events are independent. Because the probability of rolling an even result is the same on each throw (1/2), the probability of getting an odd result on all four dice is $(1/2)^4 = 1/16$.

18. The events are independent. Because the probability of rolling a 6 is the same on each throw (1/6), the probability of getting all 6s is $(1/6)^4 = 1/1296$.

19. The events are independent. This is similar to exercise 14, with an answer of $(13/52)^3 = 1/64 = 0.0156$.

20. The events are dependent. This is also similar to exercise 15, with an answer of $(26/52) \times (25/51) \times (24/50) \times (23/49) = 0.055$.

21. The events are independent. The probability of all four tickets being winners is $(1/10)^4 = 0.0001$.

22. The events are dependent. The probability is $(18/30) \times (17/29) \times (16/28) = 0.201$.

23. The events are dependent, and the probability is $(15/30) \times (14/29) \times (13/28) \times (12/27) \times (11/26) \times (10/25) = 0.0084$.

24. The events are independent for all practical purposes, because the batch from which the chips are chosen is large. The probability is $(0.95)^3 = 0.857$.

25. The events are independent for all practical purposes (as long as the student population is large). The probability is $(1/12)^3 = 1/1728$.

26. The events may be independent, and we'll have to assume as much to solve the problem. The probability is $(0.20)^4 = 0.0016$.

27. The events are non-overlapping. $P(red$ 6 or *black* $8) = P(red$ 6$) + P(black$ 8$) = 2/52 + 2/52 = 1/13$.

28. The events are non-overlapping. $P(6$ or $8) = P(6) + P(8) = 5/36 + 5/36 = 5/18 = 0.278$.

29. The events are overlapping. $P(J$ or *spade*$) = P(J) + P(spade) - P(J$ and *spade*$) = 4/52 + 13/52 - 1/52 = 16/52 = 4/13$.

30. The events are overlapping. $P(face\ card$ or *diamond*$) = P(face\ card) + P(diamond) - P(face\ card$ and *diamond*$) = 12/52 + 13/52 - 3/52 = 22/52 = 11/26$.

31. The events are non-overlapping. $P(10 \text{ or } 11 \text{ or } 12)$ $= P(10) + P(11) + P(12) = 1/36 + 2/36 + 3/36 =$ 1/6.

32. The events are non-overlapping. $P(J \text{ or } K) = P(J)$ $+ P(K) = 4/52 + 4/52 = 2/13 = 0.154.$

33. The events are overlapping. The probability is 1/6 $+ 3/6 - 1/6 = 3/6 = 1/2.$

34. The events are non-overlapping. The probability is $1/6 + 3/6 = 4/6 = 2/3.$

35. The events are overlapping. $P(W \text{ or } R) = P(W) +$ $P(R) - P(W \text{ and } R) = 140/200 + 120/200 - 80/200$ $= 180/200 = 9/10 = 0.9.$

36. The events are overlapping. $P(M \text{ or } A) = P(M) +$ $P(A) - P(M \text{ and } A) = 20/50 + 15/50 - 5/50 = 30/50$ $= 3/5 = 0.6.$

37. The events are non-overlapping. The easiest way to solve the problem is to look at the set of possible outcomes for a three child family, (GGG, GGB, GBG, BGG, BBG, BGB, GBB, BBB), and count the number of outcomes with either 1 or 2 boys. The probability is $6/8 = 3/4$. One could also use the formulas for *or* probabilities.

38. The events are overlapping, and the probability is $15/27 + 10/27 - 5/27 = 20/27.$

39. The probability of not getting a 6 on a single roll is 5/6, so $P(\text{at least one 6}) = 1 - (5/6)^4 = 0.518.$

40. The probability of not getting a 1 on a single roll is 5/6, so $P(\text{at least one 1}) = 1 - (5/6)^8 = 0.767.$

41. $P(\text{at least one 3}) = 1 - (5/6)^3 = 0.421.$

42. $P(\text{at least one } H) = 1 - (1/2)^6 = 0.984.$

43. $P(\text{at least one king}) = 1 - (48/52)^8 = 0.473.$

44. $P(\text{at least one ace}) = 1 - (48/52)^{20} = 0.798.$

45. $P(\text{rain at least once}) = 1 - (0.80)^6 = 0.738.$

46. $P(\text{high winds at least once}) = 1 - (0.90)^{20} = 0.878.$

47. $P(\text{at least one flu encounter}) = 1 - (0.96)^{12} = 0.387.$

48. $P(\text{at least one lefty}) = 1 - (0.89)^8 = 0.606.$

49. $P(\text{at least one ticket}) = 1 - (0.7)^5 = 0.832.$

50. $P(\text{at least one false test}) = 1 - (0.975)^5 = 0.119.$

FURTHER APPLICATIONS

51. a. $P(G \text{ or } P) = P(G) + P(P) - P(G \text{ and } P) =$ $956/1028 + 450/1028 - 392/1028 = 0.986.$
    b. $P(NG \text{ or } NP) = P(NG) + P(NP) - P(NG \text{ and } NP) = 72/1028 + 578/1028 - 14/1028 = 0.619.$

52. a. The probability is $100/340 + 120/340 = 220/340$ $= 0.647.$

b. The probability is $120/340 + 165/340 - 70/340$ $= 215/340 = 0.632.$
c. The probability is $70/340 = 0.206.$
d. The probability is $70/165 = 0.424.$
e. The probability is $70/120 = 0.583.$
f. Yes, the drug appears to have some effect because the improvement rate for people who took the drug (70/120) is greater than both the improvement rate for the placebo group (55/100) and the control group (40/120).

53. a. These events are dependent because there are fewer people to choose from on the second and subsequent calls, and this affects the probability that a Republican is chosen.
    b. $P(R_1 \text{ and } R_2) = P(R_1) \times P(R_2 \text{ given } R_1) =$ $(25/45) \times (24/44) = 0.303.$
    c. If the events are treated as independent, then the pollster is selecting a person from random and not crossing that person off the list of candidates for the second call. The probability of selecting two Republicans is then $P(R_1 \text{ and } R_2) = P(R_1) \times P(R_2)$ $= (25/45) \times (25/45) = 0.309.$
    d. The probabilities are nearly the same. This is due to the fact that the list of names is large, and removing one person from the list before making the second call doesn't appreciably change the probability that a Republican will be chosen.

54. $P(\mathbf{AA}) = 1/4$; $P(\mathbf{Aa}) = 1/2$; $P(\mathbf{aa}) = 1/4$. The probability that the child will have the dominant trait is 3/4, and the probability for the recessive trait is 1/4.

55. The probability of winning would be $1 - (35/36)^{25} = 0.506$. Since this is larger than 50%, he should come out ahead over time.

56. a. These events are non-overlapping, so the probability is $1/10 + 1/50 + 1/500 = 0.122$. This is not much larger than the probability of getting only a \$2 winner (1/10) because the other probabilities are so low they don't contribute much to the overall probability.
    b. $P(\text{at least one \$5 winner}) = 1 - (49/50)^{50} = 0.636.$
    c. $P(\text{at least one \$10 winner}) = 1 - (499/500)^{500} = 0.632.$

57. a. The probability is 1/20.
    b. $P(H_1 \text{ and } H_2) = P(H_1) \times P(H_2) = (1/20) \times (1/20) = 1/400 = 0.0025.$
    c. $P(\text{at least one hurricane}) = 1 - (19/20)^{10} = 0.401.$

58. a. $P(\text{at least one STI}) = 1 - (0.8)^{10} = 0.89.$
    b. $P(\text{at least one STI}) = 1 - (0.8)^{20} = 0.99.$

UNIT 7C

TIME OUT TO THINK

Pg. 440. Expected values depend on large enough numbers for the law of averages to be relevant. On a single policy, we can only state a probability, not an expectation. For a probability of 1/500, even 1,000 policies is too small to count on the law of averages. But by a million policies, the expected value ought to be a good approximation of reality.

Pg. 441. Opinions will vary. This would be a good topic for a discussion either during or outside of class.

Pg. 442. No. This is the gambler's fallacy in action. As long as the chance of rain on one day is independent of the chance on another, the prior drought has no effect on the probability of rain the next day. Some students will point out that the climate is complex, and one day's weather is not fully independent of prior days weather. However, for the purposes of this question, this subtlety can be ignored...

Pg. 444. The casino can lose money on gambling only if the number of bets placed is too small for the law of averages to come into play. For popular casinos, this is a near-impossibility; that is, the casino is virtually guaranteed to win overall — and win by almost precisely the house edge — on the thousands or millions bets made daily. Of course, a casino can still lose money on other operations, such as its overhead expenses, restaurant operations, and so on.

QUICK QUIZ

1. **b**. The law of large numbers says that the proportion of years should be close to the probability of a hurricane on a single year (and $100/1000 = 0.1$).

2. **c**. The expected value is $-\$1 \times 1 + \$75$ million $\times 1/100,000,000 = -\$0.25$.

3. **c**. If you purchase 1/10 of the available number of lottery tickets, there's a 1 in 10 chance that you have the winning ticket. But this means that 90% of the time you have purchased 1 million losing tickets.

4. **c**. The expected value can be understood as the average value of the game over many trials.

5. **b**. The expected value of a $2000 fire insurance policy from the point of view of the insurance company is $\$2000 \times 1 + (-\$100,000) \times 1/50 = 0$, so they can expect to lose money if they charge less than $2000 per policy.

6. **a**. The shortcut saves 5 minutes 90% of the time, but it loses 20 minutes 10% of the time.

7. **c**. The results of the previous five games have no bearing on the outcome of the next game.

8. **c**. The results of the previous five games have no bearing on the next game.

9. **c**. In order to compute the probability of winning on any single trial, you would need to know the probability of winning on each of the various payouts.

10. **c**. 97% of $10 million is $9.7 million, which leaves $300,000 in profit for the casino (over the long haul).

DOES IT MAKE SENSE?

7. Makes sense. An organization holding a raffle usually wants to raise money, which means the expected value for purchasers of raffle tickets will be negative.

8. Does not make sense. The expected value comes into play for large increases in sales.

9. Does not make sense. Each of the 16 possible outcomes when four coins are tossed is equally likely.

10. Does not make sense. The slot machine doesn't remember what happened on the previous 25 pulls, and your probability of winning remains the same for each pull.

11. Does not make sense. The slot machine doesn't remember what happened on the previous 25 pulls, and your probability of winning remains the same for each pull.

12. Does not make sense. You lost $750 because roulette is a losing proposition (for players, and over the long haul). If you keep playing, it's most likely that you'll continue to lose.

BASIC SKILLS & CONCEPTS

13. You should not expect to get exactly 5000 heads (the probability of that happening is quite small), but you should expect to get a result near to 5000 heads. The law of large numbers says that the proportion of a large number of coin tosses that result in heads is near to the probability of getting heads on a single toss. Since the probability of getting heads is 1/2, you can expect that around one-half of the 10,000 tosses will result in heads.

14. The phrase means that over the long run, the person will most likely get a traffic citation. While it is true that the probability of getting a traffic citation for a single instance of speeding is low, it is also true that the probability of getting at least one citation (or perhaps several) is rather high over many instances of speeding.

15. The probability of tossing three heads is 1/8, and that of not tossing three heads is 7/8. Thus the expected value of the game is $\$5 \times 1/8 + (-\$1) \times$

7/8 = –$0.25. Though one can assign a probability to the outcome of a single game, the result cannot be predicted, so you can't be sure whether you will win or lose money in one game. However, over the course of 100 games, the law of averages comes into play, and you can expect to lose money.

16. The expected value is $9 × 1/8 + (–$1) × 7/8 = $0.25 (see exercise 15). The outcome of one game cannot be predicted, though over 100 games, you should expect to win.

17. The probability of rolling two even numbers is 9/36 = 1/4 (of the 36 possible outcomes, 9 are "two even numbers"), and the probability of not rolling two even numbers is 27/36 = 3/4. Thus the expected value is $2 × 1/4 + (–$1) × 3/4 = –$0.25. The outcome of one game cannot be predicted, though over 100 games, you should expect to lose.

18. The probability of rolling doubles is 6/36 = 1/6 (of the 36 possible outcomes, 6 are "doubles"), and the probability of not rolling doubles is 30/36 = 5/6. Thus the expected value is $8 × 1/6 + (–$1) × 5/6 = $0.50. The outcome of one game cannot be predicted, though over 100 games, you should expect to win.

19. The expected value for a single policy is $900 × 1 + (–$10,000) × 1/50 + (–$25,000) × 1/100 + (–$60,000) × 1/250 = $210. The company can expect a profit of $210 × 10,000 = $2.1 million.

20. The expected value for a single policy is $500 × 1 + (–$5000) × 1/50 + (–$10,000) × 1/100 + (–$30,000) × 1/200 = $150. The company can expect a profit of $150 × 10,000 = $1.5 million.

21. For the sake of simplicity, assume that you arrive on the half-minute for each minute of the hour (that is, you arrive 30 seconds into the first minute of the hour, 30 seconds into the second minute of the hour, etc.). The probability that you arrive in any given minute in the first half-hour is 1/30, and your wait times (in minutes) for the first 30 minutes are 29.5, 28.5, 27.5, … , 0.5. Thus your expected wait time is 29.5 × 1/30 + 28.5 × 1/30 + 27.5 × 1/30 + … + 0.5 × 1/30 = 15 minutes. Of course the same is true for the second half-hour. (Note for instructors: if you wanted to allow for arrival at *any* time during a given minute, you would need to use calculus in order to solve the problem with any level of rigor, because the wait time function is continuous).

22. a. The probability that you will arrive between noon and 12:20 is 1/3 (because 20 minutes is one-third of an hour). Using a process similar to exercise 21, the mean waiting time is 10 minutes. (This is also the expected value for the wait time in the first 20 minutes as expected value is just a weighted mean – when the weights, or probabilities, are all the same, it is the mean).

b. Similar to part **a** and exercise 21, the probability that you arrive between 12:20 and 1:00 is 2/3, and the mean waiting time is 20 minutes.

c. The expected value for the wait time over the entire hour is 10 × 1/3 + 20 × 2/3 = 16.67 minutes.

d. The expected waiting time would be shorter, as shown in exercise 21.

23. a. Heads came up 46% of the time, and you've lost $8.

b. Yes, the increase in heads is consistent with the law of large numbers: the more often the coin is tossed, the more likely the percentage of heads is closer to 50%. Since 47% of 300 is 141, there have been 141 heads and 159 tails, and you are now behind $18.

c. You would need 59 heads in the next 100 tosses (so that the total number of heads would be 200) in order to break even. While it's possible to get 59 heads in 100 tosses, a number nearer to 50 is more likely.

d. If you decide to keep playing, the most likely outcome is that half of the time you'll see heads, and half the time you'll see tails, which means you'll still be behind.

24. a. You have lost $10.

b. You lost $6 in the second one hundred rolls, so you have now lost $16.

c. In the next 300 rolls, you lose $4, which means you are down $20.

d. You would need to roll 60 even numbers in the next 100 rolls in order to break even, and this is not as likely as rolling a number of evens closer to 50.

e. The percentages were 45% (45/100), 46% (92/200), and 48% (240/500), and this illustrates the law of large numbers because the percentages are approaching 50% as the number of rolls increases.

25. a. The probability of getting heads is the same as the probability of getting tails.

b. The most likely outcome after 1000 more flips is 500 heads and 500 tails (in which case the difference would remain at 16). The distribution of the number of heads is symmetric so that any deviation from "500 heads/500 tails" is as likely to be in the upper tail as the lower tail.

c. Once you have fewer heads than tails, the most likely occurrence after additional coin tosses is that the deficit of heads remains.

26. Both sets are equally likely as each is one of many possible outcomes when six numbers are drawn.

27. The probability of getting ten heads in ten tosses is $(1/2)^{10} = 1/1024$. There are many ten-toss sequences in the 1000 tosses (991 to be precise), and you should expect, on average, one streak of ten heads in every 1024 ten-toss sequences.

28. The probability of getting three hits in a row (in three at-bats) is $(1/3)^3 = 1/27$. It's typical for a starting player to have 5 at-bats in a game, which means there are three 3-at-bat sequences in each game you play, and thus approximately 75 such 3-at-bat sequences over the course of a season. You should expect to get three hits in a row once every 27 "3-at-bat" sequences, so it's not at all unlikely to find yourself getting three hits in a row, even in a game where you come to bat only three times.

29. a. Suppose you bet $1. Then your expected value is $1 × 0.493 + (–$1) × 0.507 = –$0.014. In general, the expected value is –1.4% of your bet, which means the house edge is 1.4% (or 1.4¢ per dollar bet).
b. You should expect to lose 100 × $0.014 = $1.40.
c. You should expect to lose $500 × 1.4% = $7.
d. The casino should expect to earn 1.4% of $1 million, which is $14,000.

30. The casino earns 6¢ to the dollar, or 6%, so it will earn 6% of $100 million, which is $6 million.

FURTHER APPLICATIONS

31. The expected value is (–$1) × 1 + $30,000,000 × 1/195,249,054 + $200,000 × 1/5,138,133 + $10,000 × 1/723,145 + $100 × 1/19,030 + $100 × 1/13,644 + $7 × 1/359 + $7 × 1/787 + $4 × 1/23 + $3 × 1/62 = –$0.53. You can expect to lose 365 × $0.53 = $193

32. The expected value is (–$1) × 1 + $10,000,000 × 1/195,249,054 + $200,000 × 1/5,138,133 + $10,000 × 1/723,145 + $100 × 1/19,030 + $100 × 1/13,644 + $7 × 1/359 + $7 × 1/787 + $4 × 1/23 + $3 × 1/62 = –$0.63. You can expect to lose 365 × $0.63 = $230

33. The expected value is (–$1) × 1 + $5,000,000 × 1/175,711,536 + $250,000 × 1/3,904,701 + $10,000 × 1/689,065 + $150 × 1/15,313 + $150 × 1/13,781 + $10 × 1/844 + $7 × 1/306 + $3 × 1/141 + $2 × 1/75 = –$0.79. You can expect to lose 365 × $0.79 = $288

34. The expected value is (–$1) × 1 + $20,000,000 × 1/175,711,536 + $250,000 × 1/3,904,701 + $10,000 × 1/689,065 + $150 × 1/15,313 + $150 × 1/13,781 + $10 × 1/844 + $7 × 1/306 + $3 × 1/141 + $1 × 1/75 = –$0.70. You can expect to lose 365 × $0.79 = $255.

35. The expected value for 1-point kicks is 1 × 0.96 + 0 × 0.04 = 0.96 points. The expected value for 2-point attempts is 2 × 0.49 + 0 × 0.51 = 0.98 points. In most cases, it makes sense to take the almost certain extra-point, rather than risk a failed 2-point attempt. One situation where most coaches will go for a 2-point attempt: if your team is down by 8 points late in the game, and you score a touchdown (6 points), you don't benefit much by taking the extra point. You'll still need a field goal (3 points) to win the game. However, if you go for a 2-point attempt, you may tie the game, and send it into overtime. If you miss the 2-point attempt, you'll still be able to win the game with a field goal.

36. a. The expected value of a bet on 7 is (–$5) × (37/38) + $175 × (1/38) = –$0.26
b. The expected value of a bet on an odd number is (–$5) × (20/38) + $5 × (18/38) = –$0.26
c. Since the expected value of each bet is negative, the best option is to not bet.

37. The expected value for the number of people in a household is 1.5 × 0.57 + 3.5 × 0.32 + 6 × 0.11 = 2.6 people. The expected value is a weighted mean, and it is a good approximation to the actual mean as long as the midpoints are representative of the categories.

38. a. For decision 1, the expected value for option A is $1,000,000, and the expected value for option B is $2,500,000 × 0.1 + $1,000,000 × 0.89 + $0 × 0.01 = $1,140,000. For decision 2, the expected value for option A is $1,000,000 × 0.11 + $0 × 0.89 = $110,000, and the expected value for option B is $2,500,000 × 0.1 + $0 × 0.9 = $250,000.
b. The responses in decision 1 are not consistent with the expected values, whereas they are for decision 2.
c. For decision 1, people aren't willing to risk it all and earn nothing, and thus they chose option A – there is a huge guaranteed payback (especially for people in the 1950s) that isn't much different from the expected value of option B. For decision 2, people realize that there's little chance for gaining anything, so they may as well go for the bigger prize at the expense of a slightly lowered chance of winning it.

UNIT 7D

TIME OUT TO THINK

Pg. 450. Opinions will vary. Among many other common measures are fatalities per person, fatalities per trip, and fatalities per hour traveled. Because there are so many fewer airline fatalities per year, flying would appear safer in terms of fatalities per person (in the overall population). This would be a good topic for a discussion either during or outside of class.

Pg. 451. For the young, stroke is very rare, and the risk from accidents is much higher. For the old, stroke is indeed a greater risk than accidents.

Pg. 452. Women tend to have lower death rates at every age, which may be partly due to biological factors and partly due to environmental factors such as stress. Social policy is affected because we must recognize that women outnumber men in old age. Medical and life insurance rates, if they are adjusted by sex, should be lower for women since they tend to live longer.

Pg. 454. Opinions will vary, but clearly, longer life spans increase the problem for social security. This would be a good topic for a discussion either during or outside of class.

QUICK QUIZ

1. **a.** The accident rate will go down because the numerator of the "accident rate per mile" ratio is decreasing while the denominator is increasing.

2. **a.** The death rate per mile went down because the number of miles driven increased.

3. **b.** Though there has been some variation in the number of deaths, the number of miles driven has steadily increased, and thus the death rate has generally decreased.

4. **c.** The death rate per person is the number of deaths due to AIDS divided by the population.

5. **c.** The death rate per person is $\dfrac{121,599}{300 \text{ million}}$, and this needs to be multiplied by 100,000 to get the death rate per 100,000 people.

6. **a.** The chart shows that children in their younger years have a significant risk of death.

7. **c.** Your life expectancy decreases as you age because the number of years before you die is decreasing.

8. **c.** Current life expectancies are calculated for current conditions – if these change, life expectancies can also change.

9. **b.** The life expectancies of men are consistently below those of women (and from the graph, the gap has widened a bit in the last several decades).

10. **a.** If life expectancy goes up, people will live longer, and will draw Social Security benefits for a longer period of time.

DOES IT MAKE SENSE?

5. Does not make sense. Automobiles are successfully sold in huge quantities despite the risks involved.

6. Does not make sense. Far fewer people drive motorcycles, so one would expect the number of deaths attributed to them is smaller. The death rate per mile driven on a motorcycle is probably higher than the death rate per mile driven in a car.

7. Does not make sense. Your life expectancy is an average life expectancy for people born when you were. Much more important is your genetic makeup, and the choices you make throughout life (your diet, your line of work, the activities you choose to participate in, etc.).

8. Makes sense. A 60-year old has about 15–25 years left on the meter, whereas a 20-year old has about 60 years left (on average).

BASIC SKILLS & CONCEPTS

9. The per-mile death rate was $\dfrac{37,313}{2.9 \times 10^{12}} = 1.3 \times 10^{-8}$. Multiply by 100 million to get 1.3 deaths per 100 million vehicle-miles.

10. The per-person rate was $\dfrac{37,313}{3.04 \times 10^{8}} = 1.23 \times 10^{-4}$. Multiply by 100,000 to get 12.3 fatalities per 100,000 people.

11. The per-driver rate was $\dfrac{37,313}{2.08 \times 10^{8}} = 1.79 \times 10^{-4}$. Multiply by 100,000 to get 17.9 fatalities per 100,000 drivers.

12. In 1987, the per-person fatality rate was $\dfrac{46,390}{2.42 \times 10^{8}} = 1.92 \times 10^{-4}$. Multiply this by 100,000 to get 19.2 fatalities per 100,000 people. There were 28.6 fatalities per 100,000 drivers, and 2.4 fatalities per 100 million vehicle miles (the calculations are similar). In 2008, these figures were 1.3, 12.3, and 1.79, respectively. In all three measures, the death rates declined from 1987 to 2008.

13. There were $\dfrac{3}{1.93 \times 10^{7}} \times 10^{5} = 0.016$ death per 100,000 flight hours, $\dfrac{3}{7.8 \times 10^{9}} \times 10^{9} = 0.385$ death per 1 billion miles flown, and $\dfrac{3}{1.08 \times 10^{7}} \times 10^{5} = 0.028$ deaths per 100,000 departures. There were $\dfrac{28}{1.93 \times 10^{7}} \times 10^{5} = 0.15$ accident per 100,000 flight hours, $\dfrac{28}{7.8 \times 10^{9}} \times 10^{9} = 3.59$ accidents per 1 billion miles flown, and $\dfrac{28}{1.08 \times 10^{7}} \times 10^{5} = 0.259$ accident per 100,000 departures.

14. There were $\dfrac{495}{2.19\times10^7}\times10^5 = 2.3$ deaths per 100,000 flight hours, and $\dfrac{1559}{2.19\times10^7}\times10^5 = 7.12$ accidents per 100,000 flight hours. The risks in commercial aviation are significantly lower than in general aviation.

15. The probability of death by diabetes is 72,449 ÷ 304 million = 0.00024. Since 72,449 ÷ 34,243 = 2.1, death by diabetes is 2.1 times more likely than death by septicemia.

16. Since 121,599 ÷ 45,344 = 2.7, death by accident is 2.5 times more likely than death by kidney disease.

17. The death rate is $\dfrac{72,432}{3.04\times10^8}\times10^5 = 23.8$ deaths per 100,000 people.

18. The death rate due to heart disease is $\dfrac{631,636}{3.04\times10^8}\times10^5 = 207.8$ deaths per 100,000 people.

19. The death rate due to stroke is $\dfrac{137,119}{3.04\times10^8}\times10^5 = 45.1$ deaths per 100,000 people, so in a city of 500,000, you would expect 45.1 × 5 = 225 people to die from a stroke each year.

20. The death rate due to pulmonary disease is $\dfrac{124,583}{3.04\times10^8}\times10^5 = 41.0$ deaths per 100,000 people, so in a city of 500,000, you would expect 41 × 5 = 205 people to die from pulmonary disease each year.

21. The death rate for 60-year-olds is about 10 per 1000, and for 65-year-olds, it's about 14 per 1000, so the death rate for the category of 60- to 65-year-olds is about 12 deaths per 1000 people. Multiply 12.5/1000 by 13.4 million to find the number of people in this category expected to die in a year: $\dfrac{12.5}{1000}\times13.4\times10^6 = 167,500$ people.
    (Note: Answers will vary depending on values read from the graphs)

22. The death rate for 25- to 35-year-olds is about 1 per 1000. Multiply 1/1000 by 42 million to find the number of people in this category expected to die in a year: $\dfrac{1}{1000}\times42\times10^6 = 40,000$ people.
    (Note: Answers will vary depending on values read from the graphs)

23. The life expectancy for a 40-year-old is about 40 years, so the average 40-year-old can expect to live to age 80.

24. The life expectancy for an 80-year-old is about 9 years, so an average 80-year-old can expect to die at age 89.

25. The death rate for a 50-year-old is about 5 per 1000, which means the probability that a randomly selected 50-year-old will die in the next year is 5/1000. Those that don't die will file no claim; the beneficiaries of those that do will file a $50,000 claim. Thus the expected value of a single policy (from the point of view of the insurance company) is $200 × 1 + (–$50,000) × 5/1000 + ($0) × 995/1000 = –$50. The company insures 1 million 50-year-olds, and expects to lose $50 per policy, so it can expect a loss of $50 million.

26. The death rate is 3 per 1000, which means the probability that a randomly selected 40-year-old will die in the next year is 3/1000. Those that don't die will file no claim; the beneficiaries of those that do will file a $50,000 claim. Thus the expected value of a single policy (from the point of view of the insurance company) is $200 × 1 + (–$50,000) × 3/1000 + ($0) × 997/1000 = $50. The company insures 5000 people, and expects to gain $50 per policy, so it can expect a profit of $250,000.

FURTHER APPLICATIONS

27. a. In Utah, about 53,504 ÷ 365 = 147 people were born per day.
    b. In Vermont, about 6511 ÷ 365 = 18 people were born per day.
    c. The birth rate in Utah was $\dfrac{53,504}{2.6\times10^6}\times10^5 = 2058$ births per 100,000 people.
    d. The birth rate in Vermont was $\dfrac{6511}{620,000}\times10^5 = 1050$ births per 100,000 people.

28. a. In West Virginia, the death rate was $\dfrac{20,676}{1.81\times10^6}\times10^5 = 1142$ deaths per 100,000 people. In Colorado it was $\dfrac{29,519}{4.75\times10^6}\times10^5 = 621$ deaths per 1,000,000 people.
    b. In West Virginia, about 20,676 ÷ 365 = 57 people die per day.
    c. No, the death rates for various states are dependent upon not only the number of deaths, but also the population.

29. a. There were (14.3/1000) × 304 million = 4.35 million births in the U.S.

b. There were (8.0/1000) × 304 million = 2.43 million deaths in the U.S.

c. The population increased by 4.35 million – 2.43 million = 1.92 million people.

d. About 3.5 million – 1.92 million = 1.6 million people immigrated to the U.S. (this estimate neglects to account for emigration, though the number of people who emigrate from the U.S. is relatively low). The proportion of the overall population growth due to immigration was 1.6/3.5 = 46%.

30. The category of young children (ages 0–5) has had a steady ratio of boys to girls that is slightly larger than 1 – this is due to the fact that more boys are born than girls. The category of older people (ages 65+) has had a marked decline in the ration of men to women, falling well below 1 – this is due to the fact that the life expectancy for women is larger than that for men, and the gap between the two has grown over the century (see Figure 7.9). The category of "all ages" represents the happy medium between these other two categories.

31. a. The probability of giving birth to more than one baby is about (133,000 + 6118 + 355) ÷ 4,300,000 = 0.032.

b. We first need to calculate the total number of children born each year. There were 4,300,000 – 133,000 – 6118 – 355 = 4,160,527 single births, so there will be a total of 4,160,527 + 2 × 133,000 + 3 × 6118 + 4 × 355 = 4,446,301 children born each year. The probability that a randomly selected newborn is a twin is about (2 × 133,000) ÷ 4,446,301 = 0.060.

c. The probability that a randomly selected newborn is a twin, a triplet, or a quadruplet is about (2 × 133,000 + 3 × 6118 + 4 × 355) ÷ 4,446,301 = 0.064.

UNIT 7E

TIME OUT TO THINK

Pg. 458. Human population is about 6 billion, so both answers in Example 1 are larger by more than a factor of 10. For license plates, this effectively means the state will never run out of choices. For the passwords, the more relevant question is how long it would take a hacker to run through all 75 billion possibilities to get your password. With high-speed computers, this would not take that long, and 6-character passwords are considered inadequate for high-security applications.

Pg. 461. Instead of 15 players being selected 9 at a time, we have 25 players being selected 9 at a time. Therefore all the instances of "15" in the formula become 25 instead.

Pg. 463. All of the 2,598,960 possible five-card hands have precisely the same probability of 1 in 2,598,960. Thus, the probability of the particular hand described is the same as the probability of the royal flush of spades. The only difference is that the royal flush is defined to be "special" in the game of poker, whereas most hands are considered quite ordinary. But it's interesting to note that whatever hand you are dealt, you had only a 1 in 2.5 million probability of getting that particular hand. Of course, you were bound to get something.

QUICK QUIZ

1. **b.** This is an arrangement with repetition, with 36 choices at each selection.

2. **c.** Assuming each person gets one entrée, this is a permutation of 3 items taken 3 at a time, and $_3P_3 = 3!/0! = 6$.

3. **c.** The order of selection is important when counting the number of ways to arrange the roles.

4. **b.** Once the five children have been chosen, we are arranging just those five (and all five) into the various roles, and thus this is a permutation of 5 items taken 5 at a time, or $_5P_5$.

5. **b.** The number of permutation of n items taken r at a time is always at least as large as the number of combinations of n items taken r at a time (by a factor of $r!$), and $_{15}P_7 = 32,432,400$ is much larger than $_7P_7 = 5040$.

6. **c.** The variable n stands for the number of items from which you are selecting, and the variable r stands for the number of items you select. Here, $n = 9$, and $r = 4$, and thus $(n - r)! = 5!$.

7. **c.** The number of combinations of 9 items taken 4 at a time is $_9C_4 = \dfrac{9!}{(9-4)!4!} = \dfrac{9 \times 8 \times 7 \times 6}{4 \times 3 \times 2 \times 1}$.

8. **b.** If there is a drawing, the probability that one person is selected is 100%.

9. **c.** The probability that it will be you is 1/100,000 = 0.00001, so the probability it will not be you is 1 – 0.00001 = 0.99999.

10. **c.** As shown in Example 8b, the probability is about 57%.

DOES IT MAKE SENSE?

5. Makes sense. The permutations formula is used when order of selection is important.

6. Makes sense. The order in which you receive the various cards of a poker hand is immaterial (this is true, at least, for 5-card stud – there are some variations of poker where the order in which you receive your cards can affect your decision to bet, fold, etc., and thus one could argue that the order of the cards is important).

7. Makes sense. The number of such batting orders is $_{25}P_9 = 7.4 \times 10^{11}$, which is nearly 1 trillion ways. Clearly there is no hope of trying all of them.

8. Does not make sense. Perhaps it is your lucky day, but some coincidence is bound to happen – of the millions of poker hands dealt to people around the world over the last, say, 24 hours, it's likely that someone will be dealt a low-probability hand. That it happened to be you is just coincidence.

9. Makes sense. This illustrates the general principle that *some* coincidence is far more likely that a *particular* coincidence.

10. Does not make sense. The probability of winning a state lottery is so low (typically 1 in several million) that you should not expect to win, even if you played every week of your life (there are only 4171 weeks in the life span of someone who makes it to age 80).

BASIC SKILLS & CONCEPTS

11. $6! = 720$

12. $12! = 479,001,600$.

13. $5! \div 3! = 20$.

14. $10! \div 8! = 90$.

15. $\dfrac{12!}{4!3!} = 3,326,400$.

16. $\dfrac{9!}{4!2!} = 7560$.

17. $\dfrac{11!}{3!(11-3)!} = 165$.

18. $\dfrac{30!}{29!} = 30$.

19. $\dfrac{8!}{3!(8-3)!} = 56$.

20. $\dfrac{30!}{28!} = 870$.

21. $\dfrac{6!8!}{4!5!} = 10,800$.

22. $\dfrac{15!}{2!13!} = 105$.

23. This is an arrangement with repetition, where we have 10 choices (the digits 0–9) for each of 9 selections, and thus there are $10^9 = 100,000,000$ possible zip codes.

24. This is an arrangement with repetition, where there are 26 choices for each of 5 selections, and thus there are $26^5 = 11,881,376$ passwords.

25. This is a permutation of 26 items taken 5 at a time because the order in which the characters are arranged is important (a different order results in a different password). Thus there are $_{26}P_5 = 7,893,600$ passwords.

26. This is a permutation (of 9 items taken 4 at a time) because once four committee members are chosen, the offices which they are to hold must be determined (and different orders produce different people in the various offices). The number of such executive committees is $_9P_3 = 3024$.

27. This is a permutation of 9 items taken 9 at a time, and $_9P_9 = 362,880$.

28. The order of selection does not affect whether one is chosen for the committee, so this is a combination of 9 items taken 3 at a time, and $_9C_3 = 84$.

29. Because order of selection does not matter, this is a combination of 20 items taken 6 at a time, or $_{20}C_6 = 38,760$.

30. Since every player can be assigned to any position, the order of selection matters (perhaps it determines the position played, for example), and this is a permutation of 15 items taken 6 at a time. The number of such permutations is $_{15}P_6 = 3,603,600$.

31. This is an arrangement with repetition, where there are 2 choices for each of 5 selections, and thus there are $2^5 = 32$ birth orders.

32. Assuming that the order in which the card is dealt is immaterial to the hand, this is a combination of 52 items taken 5 at a time, so there are $_{52}C_5 = 2,598,960$ hands.

33. This is an arrangement with repetition, so use the multiplication principle to find that there are $26^2 \times 10^5 = 67,600,000$ such license plates.

34. If we assume that the order in which the balls are selected do not affect the count, this is a combination of 36 items taken 6 at a time, and there are $_{36}C_6 = 1,947,792$ groups of six balls.

35. This is an arrangement with repetition, so use the multiplication principle to get $9 \times 10 \times 10 \times 9 \times 10 \times 10 \times 10 \times 10 \times 10 \times 10 = 8,100,000,000$. Note that with the first digit and the fourth digit, there are only 9 choices.

36. This is a permutation of 9 items taken 9 at a time, so there are $_9P_9 = 362,880$ anagrams.

37. If we assume that the letters can be repeated, this is an arrangement with repetition, and there are 4 choices for each of the 3 selections, which implies there are $4^3 = 64$ different "words."

38. The order of selection does not matter, so this is the number of combinations of 15 items taken 5 at a time, which is $_{15}C_5 = 3003$ teams.

39. The order in which the songs appear matters, so this is a permutation of 12 objects taken 12 at a time, and thus there are $_{12}P_{12} = 479,001,600$ different ways to order the songs.

40. The order in which the dogs are selected does not affect the 4-dog family you bring home, so this is a combination of 15 items taken 4 at a time. There are $_{15}C_4 = 1365$ different dog families.

41. Following Example 8 in the text, the probability that no one has your birthday is $1 - \left(\frac{364}{365}\right)^{11} = 0.0297$. The probability that at least one pair shares a birthday is given by $1 - \frac{364 \times 363 \times \ldots \times 354}{365^{11}} = 1 - \frac{1.276 \times 10^{28}}{1.532 \times 10^{28}} = 0.167$.

42. Following Example 8 in the text, the probability that no one has your birthday is $1 - \left(\frac{364}{365}\right)^{19} = 0.0508$. The probability that at least one pair shares a birthday is given by $1 - \frac{364 \times 363 \times \ldots \times 346}{365^{19}} = 1 - \frac{2.8402 \times 10^{48}}{4.8257 \times 10^{48}} = 0.411$.

FURTHER APPLICATIONS

43. a. Use the multiplication principle to get $20 \times 8 = 160$ different sundaes.
    b. This is an arrangement with repetition, so there are $20^3 = 8000$ possible triple cones.
    c. Since you specify the locations of the flavors, the order matters, and you should use permutations. There are $_{20}P_3 = 6840$ possibilities.
    d. The order of the flavors doesn't matter, so use combinations. There are $_{20}C_3 = 1140$ possibilities.

44. a. Since there are 8 choices for the first and fourth digits, and 10 choices for every other digit, there are $8 \times 8 \times 10^8 = 6.4$ billion different 10-digit phone numbers. Since each area code represents 6.4 billion phone numbers, one area code is enough to serve a city with 2 million telephone numbers.
    b. A single three-digit exchange represents $10^4 = 10,000$ phone numbers, which would translate into 8 exchanges for a city of 80,000 if we assumed an average of one number for every person. However, given the enormous increase in the use of cell phones, fax lines, and the like the phone company probably uses more than 8 exchanges for such a city. Answers will vary.

45. This problem is best solved by trial and error. For Luigi, we know that 56 is the number of combinations of n items taken 3 at a time, and thus $_nC_3 = 56$. After a little experimentation, you will discover that $n = 8$; that is, Luigi uses 8 different toppings to create 56 different 3-topping pizzas. In a similar fashion, you can discover that Ramona uses 9 different toppings (solve $_nC_2 = 36$ for n).

46. a. As long as there are no rules that restrict the use of certain digits at various locations in the zip code, there are ten choices for each digit, and thus there are $10^5 = 100,000$ five-digit zip codes.
    b. There are $300,000,000 \div 100,000 = 3000$ people per zip code.
    c. There are $10^9 = 1$ billion nine-digit zip codes. Since there are only 300 million people in the U.S., everyone could have a personal zip code. In fact, in some sense, everyone already does: the Social Security number.

47. There are $_{36}C_6 = 1,947,792$ ways to choose the balls, and only one way to match all six numbers, so the probability is $1/1,947,792$.

48. There are $_{42}C_5 = 850,668$ ways to choose the balls, and only one way to match all five numbers, so the probability is $1/850,668$.

49. There are $_{52}C_5 = 2,598,960$ five-card hands. Four of those consist of the 10, J, Q, K, and A of the same suit, so the probability is $4/2,598,960 = 1/649,740$.

50. The order of selection matters, so there are $_{10}P_3 = 720$ ways to order the three top teams. There's only one way to pick the correct order, and thus the probability of doing so is $1/720$.

51. There are $_{15}C_3 = 455$ ways to choose the top three spellers, and only one way to guess the correct three, so the probability is $1/455$.

52. There are $_{16}C_3 = 560$ ways to choose any three students, but only $_7C_3 = 35$ ways to pick three students from Ohio. Thus the probability is $35/560 = 1/16$.

53. There are $_{52}C_5 = 2,598,960$ five-card hands. In order to get four-of-a-kind in, say, aces, you need to select all four aces, and then any of the other remaining 48 cards. Thus there are 48 ways to get a four-of-a-kind in aces. This is true for the other 12 card values as well, so there are $13 \times 48 = 624$ different four-of-a-kind hands. The desired probability is then $624/2,598,960 = 0.00024$.

54. The intuitive answer is $1/2$: half of the time you are in the first half of the program, and half of the time you are not. To prove it rigorously, count the number of ways to arrange the ten performers, and count the number of ways you could be in the first half of the program. There are $_{10}P_{10} = 3,628,800$ ways to arrange the ten performers. Now assume that you perform first: there are $_9P_9 = 362,880$ ways to arrange the other 9 performers, so there are 362,880 arrangements in the case where you go first. But there are also 362,880 arrangements in the case when you go second, third, fourth, or fifth. Thus there are $5 \times 362,880 = 1,814,400$

arrangements where you perform in the first half, and the probability of doing so is $1{,}814{,}400 \div 3{,}628{,}880 = 0.5$.

55. a. The probability of winning five games in a row is $0.48^5 = 0.025$, assuming you play only five games. It is considerably higher if you play numerous games.

b. The probability of winning ten games in a row is $0.48^{10} = 0.00065$, assuming you play only ten games. It is considerably higher if you play numerous games.

c. Once again, assuming all 2000 people play only five games, one would expect about 2.5% of them would win five games in a row (because the probability of five-in-a-row is 0.025, as shown in part **a**). This is $0.025 \times 2000 = 50$ people.

d. Assuming all 2000 people play only ten games, one would expect about $0.00065 \times 2000 = 1.3$ people to win all ten games.

56. a. The probability of not getting a hit on a single at-bat is 0.6, so the probability of getting at least one hit in four at-bats is $1 - 0.6^4 = 0.8704$.

b. Over the course of a particular 56 game sequence, the probability of getting a hit in all of those games is $0.8704^{56} = 0.00042$.

c. The probability that a player hitting .300 will get at least one hit in a game is $1 - 0.7^4 = 0.7599$, and thus the probability of a 56-game hitting streak (over a particular 56-game sequence) is $0.7599^{56} = 2.1 \times 10^{-7}$.

d. It's not too surprising that someone has hit for 56 games in a row as there have been many, many 56-game sequences where players had the chance to get a hit in all of them. This illustrates the idea that the probability of a particular coincidence may be small, but the probability that some coincidence occurs is large.

UNIT 8A

TIME OUT TO THINK

Pg. 477. As with the bacteria, colonization of other worlds cannot keep up with continued exponential growth. There may be good reasons why we should put colonies on other planets, but solving the population problem is not one of them.

QUICK QUIZ

1. **b.** The absolute change in the population was 10,000 people, and if population grows linearly, the absolute change remains constant. Thus the population at the end of the second year will be 110,000 + 10,000 = 120,000.

2. **c.** Because the population increases exponentially, it undergoes constant percent change. Its population increases by 10% in the first year, and thus at the end of the second year, the population will be 110,000 × 10% + 110,000 = 121,000.

3. **a.** Because your money is growing exponentially, if it doubles in the first 6 months, it will double every 6 months.

4. **b.** The absolute change in the number of songs is 200, and this occurred over the span of 3 months. Because the number of songs is increasing linearly, it will grow by 200 every 3 months, and it will take 6 months to grow to 800 songs.

5. **c.** Exponential decay occurs whenever a quantity decreases by a constant percentage (over the same time interval).

6. **c.** Based on the results of Parable 1 in the text, the total number of pennies needed is $2^{64} - 1 = 1.8 \times 10^{19}$, which is equivalent to $\$1.8 \times 10^{17}$. The federal debt is about $9 trillion ($9 \times 10^{12}$), which differs from the amount of money necessary by about a factor of 10,000.

7. **b.** Note that at 11:01, there are $2 = 2^1$ bacteria; at 11:02 there are $4 = 2^2$ bacteria; at 11:03 there are $8 = 2^3$, and so on. The exponent on the base of 2 matches the minute, and this pattern continues through 11:30, which means there are 2^{30} bacteria at that time.

8. **c.** At 11:31, there are 2^{31} bacteria, and as shown in exercise 7, there were 2^{30} bacteria at 11:30. The difference $2^{31} - 2^{30}$ is the number of bacteria added over that minute.

9. **a.** As with the population, the volume of the colony doubles every minute, so it only takes one minute for the volume to double from 1 to 2 m^3.

10. **b.** The growth of a population undergoing exponential change is comparatively slow in the initial stages, and then outrageously fast in the latter stages. This makes it difficult for members of the population to see that the growth they are currently experiencing is about to explode in short order.

DOES IT MAKE SENSE?

5. Makes sense. Any quantity that undergoes constant, positive percent change grows exponentially.

6. Makes sense. After only 20 days, the balance would be $\$2^{20} = \$1,048,576$.

7. Makes sense. Any quantity that grows exponentially will eventually become very large, so as long as the small town's rate of growth is large enough, it can become a large city within a few decades.

8. Does not make sense. Exponential growth cannot be sustained for any long period of time because the population will sooner or later outstrip its resources.

BASIC SKILLS & CONCEPTS

9. The population is growing linearly because its absolute change remains constant at 325 people per year. The population in four years will be 2500 + 4 × 325 = 4992.

10. The population is growing exponentially because its percent change remains constant at 3% per year. Each year, the population increases by a factor of 1.03, and thus in three years, the population will be $75,000(1.03)^3 = 81.955$ people.

11. This is exponential growth because the cost of food in increasing at a constant 30% per month. Each month, the cost increases by a factor of 1.30, so your food bill was R$100(1.30)^3 = R$220$.

12. The price is growing linearly because its absolute change remains constant at 3¢ per week. In ten weeks, the price will be $3.10 + 10 × 3¢ = $3.40.

13. The price is decreasing exponentially because the percent change remains at a constant –14% per year. Each year, the price decreases by a factor of 0.86, so its price in three years will be $50(0.86)^3 = $31.80.

14. The car's value is decreasing exponentially because its percent change remains constant at –10% per year. Each year, the value decreases by

a factor of 0.90, so the value in two years will be $12,000(0.90)^2 = 9720.

15. The house's value is increasing linearly because the price increases by the same amount each year. In five years, it will be worth $100,000 + 5 \times $2,000 = $110,000$.

16. The house's value is increasing exponentially because the percent change remains at a constant −7% per year. Its value decreases by a factor of 0.93 each year, so in three years, it will be worth $250,000(0.93)^3 = $201,089$.

17. There should be $2^{15} = 32,768$ grains placed on the 16th square. The total number of grains would be $2^{16} - 1 = 65,535$, and it would weigh $65,535 \times (1/7000) = 9.36$ pounds.

18. There should be $2^{31} = 2,147,483,648$ grains placed on the 32nd square. The total number of grains would be $2^{32} - 1 = 4,294,967,295$, and it would weigh $4,294,967,295 \times (1/7000) = 613,567$ pounds.

19. When the chessboard is full, there are $2^{64} - 1$ grains, with total weight of $(2^{64} - 1) \times (1/7000) = 2.64 \times 10^{15}$ pounds, or about 1.3×10^{12} tons.

20. Divide the total weight of the wheat on the chessboard by the weight of the harvest ($1.3 \times 10^{12} \div 2 \times 10^9 = 650$) to find that the chessboard wheat weighs about 650 times more than the harvest.

21. After 22 days, you would have $2^{22} = 4,194,304$ pennies, or $41,943.04.

22. Assuming 1.5 mm per penny, the stack would reach $4,194,304¢ \times \dfrac{1.5\ \text{mm}}{1¢} \times \dfrac{1\ \text{m}}{1000\ \text{mm}} \times \dfrac{1\ \text{km}}{1000\ \text{m}}$ $= 6.3\ \text{km}$.

23. After experimenting with various values of n in 2^n, you'll find that the balance has grown to about $1.4 billion after 37 days.

24. Experiment with various values of n in the conversion $2^n¢ \times \dfrac{1.5\ \text{mm}}{1¢} \times \dfrac{1\ \text{m}}{1000\ \text{mm}} \times \dfrac{1\ \text{km}}{1000\ \text{m}}$. When you get to $n = 65$, the height of the stack would be about 5.5×10^{13} km, enough to reach the star.

25. At 11:50, there are $2^{50} = 1.1 \times 10^{15}$ bacteria in the bottle. The bottle is full at 12:00 noon, so it was half-full at 11:59, 1/4-full at 11:58, 1/8-full at 11:57, and so on. Continuing in this manner, we find the bottle was 1/1024-full at 11:50. This could also be expressed as $1/2^{10}$-full at 11:50.

26. At 11:15, there are $2^{15} = 32,768$ bacteria in the bottle, and it is $1/2^{45}$-full at that time (refer to exercise 25).

27. As discussed in the text, the volume of the colony of 2^{120} bacteria would occupy a volume of 1.3×10^{15} m^3. Divide this by the surface area of the earth to get an approximate depth:
$$1.3 \times 10^{15}\ \text{m}^3 \div 5.1 \times 10^{14}\ \text{m}^2 = 2.5\ \text{m}.$$
This is quite a bit more than knee-deep (it's more than 8 feet).

28. Experiment with various values of n in the conversion $2^n \times 10^{-21}$ m^3. When you get to $n = 333$ days, the volume of the colony would be about 1.75×10^{79} m^3. Note that many calculators will have difficulty computing 2^{333}. One way around this is to first compute 2^{300}, and then multiply by 10^{-21}. This will buy you some "room" in your calculator's computing capacity, after which you can continue to multiply by factors of 2 until reaching 1.75×10^{79} m^3.

29. a. (Only 100-year intervals are shown here).

Year	Population
2000	6.0×10^9
2100	2.4×10^{10}
2200	9.6×10^{10}
2300	3.8×10^{11}
2400	1.5×10^{12}
2500	6.1×10^{12}
2600	2.5×10^{13}
2700	9.8×10^{13}
2800	3.9×10^{14}
2900	1.6×10^{15}
3000	6.3×10^{15}

b. In the year 2800, there would be 3.9×10^{14} people, each occupying slightly more than one square meter, and in 2850, there would be 7.9×10^{14} people (each occupying slightly less than one square meter). Since 5.1×10^{14} m^2 is in between these two values, it would happen between 2800 and 2850.

c. We would reach the limit when the earth's population reached $5.1 \times 10^{14} \div 10^4 = 5.1 \times 10^{10}$ people. This would happen shortly after the year 2150.

d. If by 2150 we've already reached the limit of 10^4 m^2 per person on earth, it will take only three more doubling periods to increase our need for space eight-fold. Since the doubling period is 50 years, this would take only 150 years, at which point we would have already exceeded the additional space available in the solar system (there is only five times more area out there).

30. a. You should take the penny. After only 5 days, the penny would have grown to $2^5 = 32$¢, whereas the dime has grown to only 20¢.

   b. The penny will grow to 2^n¢ in n days. Since $1000 is 100,000¢, and since it doubles only every 2 days, it will grow to $100,000 \times 2^{n/2}$¢ after n days. After experimenting with various values of n, you will find that the penny has grown to a balance larger than the $1000 in just 34 days.

   c. Based on parts **a** and **b**, it should be apparent that doubling time is more important in the long run than initial amount.

UNIT 8B

TIME OUT TO THINK

Pg. 481(1st). The formula tells us that the population after t = 30 years is:

New value =

$10,000 \times 2^{\frac{30 \text{ yr}}{10 \text{ yr}}} = 10,000 \times 2^3 = 80,000$,

agreeing with our earlier result.

After t = 50 years, the population is: New value =

$10,000 \times 2^{\frac{50 \text{ yr}}{10 \text{ yr}}} = 10,000 \times 2^5 = 320,000$.

Pg. 481(2nd). This is a subjective question, but it is difficult to imagine how we could feed, clothe, and house so many people. Fortunately, the population growth rate is already declining.

Pg. 484. Because of its 24,000-year half-life, substantial amounts of Pu–239 will remain radioactive even after 100,000 years. Thus, safe disposal requires putting the plutonium somewhere we can be sure that no one will touch it for hundreds of thousands of years — no easy task.

QUICK QUIZ

1. **a**. The factor by which an exponentially growing quantity grows is $2^{t/T_{double}}$.

2. **b**. The approximate doubling time formula says that a quantity's doubling time is about $70/r$, where r is the growth rate.

3. **a**. The approximate doubling time formula does not do a good job when the growth rate r goes higher than 15%.

4. **b**. The approximate doubling time formula, $T_{double} = 70/r$, can be rearranged to say $r = 70/T_{double}$.

5. **c**. During the first 12 years, half of the tritium decays, and during the second 12 years, half of that, or 1/4 decays.

6. **b**. Note that 2.8 billion years/4 = 700 million years. This implies the uranium-235 decayed by a factor of 2 four times, which means $1/2^4 = 1/16$ of the uranium-235 remains.

7. **b**. The half-life can be approximated by $T_{half} = 70/r$.

8. **c**. A property of logarithms states $\log_{10}(10^x) = x$.

9. **c**. The decimal equivalent of 20% is 0.2, though you should set $r = -0.2$ because the population is decreasing.

10. **a**. The doubling time formula states $T_{double} = \dfrac{\log_{10} 2}{\log_{10}(1+r)}$.

DOES IT MAKE SENSE?

9. Does not make sense. In 50 years, the population will increase by a factor of 4.

10. Makes sense. The approximate doubling time formula reads $T_{double} = 70/r$, so in this case, $T_{double} = 70/7 = 10$ years.

11. Does not make sense. While it's true that half will be gone in ten years, over the next ten years, only half of what remains will decay, which means there will still be 1/4 of the original amount.

12. Makes sense. After 100,000 years, the plutonium will have decayed by a factor of 2 about four times, which means there will still be about 1/16 of the original quantity left.

BASIC SKILLS & CONCEPTS

13. True. $10^0 = 1$, and $10^1 = 10$, so $10^{0.928}$ should be between 1 and 10 (because 0.928 is between 0 and 1).

14. False. $10^3 = 1000$, so $10^{3.334}$ must be larger than 1000 (because 3.334 is larger than 3).

15. False. $10^{-5.2} = \dfrac{1}{10^{5.2}}$, which is positive.

16. True. $10^{-2} = 0.01$, and $10^{-3} = 0.001$, so $10^{-2.67}$ is between 0.01 and 0.001 (because –2.67 is between –2 and –3).

17. False. While it is true that π is between 3 and 4, $\log_{10} \pi$ is not (it's between 0 and 1).

18. False. $\log_{10} 10 = 1$, and $\log_{10} 100 = 2$, so $\log_{10} 96$ is between 1 and 2.

19. False. $\log_{10}(10^6) = 6$, and $\log_{10}(10^7) = 7$. Because $1,600,000$ is between 10^6 and 10^7, $\log_{10} 1,600,000$ is between 6 and 7.

20. True. $\log_{10}(10^9) = 9$, and $\log_{10}(10^{10}) = 10$, so $\log_{10}(8 \times 10^9)$ is between 9 and 10, because 8×10^9 is between 10^9 and 10^{10}.

21. True. Since $\log_{10}\left(\dfrac{1}{4}\right) = \log_{10}\left(4^{-1}\right) = -\log_{10} 4$, we know $\log_{10}\left(\dfrac{1}{4}\right)$ is between –1 and 0 because $\log_{10} 4$ is between 0 and 1.

22. False. Note that $0.00045 = 4.5 \times 10^{-4}$, which is between 10^{-4} and 10^{-5}. This implies that $\log_{10}(0.00045)$ is between –5 and –4.

23. a. $\log_{10} 8 = \log_{10}(2^3) = 3\log_{10} 2 = 3 \times 0.301 = 0.903$.

   b. $\log_{10} 2000 = \log_{10} 2 + \log_{10} 10^3 = 0.301 + 3 = 3.301$.

   c. $\log_{10} 0.5 = \log_{10} 1 - \log_{10} 2 = 0 - 0.301 = -0.301$.

   d. $\log_{10} 64 = \log_{10} 2^6 = 6\log_{10} 2 = 6 \times 0.301 = 1.806$.

   e. $\log_{10}\left(\dfrac{1}{8}\right) = \log_{10} 2^{-3} = -3\log_{10} 2$
   $= -3 \times 0.301 = -0.903$.

   f. $\log_{10} 0.2 = \log_{10}\left(\dfrac{2}{10}\right) = \log_{10} 2 - \log_{10} 10$
   $= 0.301 - 1 = -0.699$.

24. a. $\log_{10} 50 = \log_{10} 5 + \log_{10} 10 = 0.699 + 1 = 1.699$.
   b. $\log_{10} 5000 = \log_{10} 5 + \log_{10} 1000 = 0.699 + 3 = 3.699$.

   c. $\log_{10} 0.05 = \log_{10}\left(\dfrac{5}{100}\right) = \log_{10} 5 - \log_{10} 100$
   $= 0.699 - 2 = -1.301$.

   d. $\log_{10} 25 = \log_{10} 5^2 = 2\log_{10} 5 = 2 \times 0.699 = 1.398$.

   e. $\log_{10} 0.2 = \log_{10}\left(\dfrac{1}{5}\right) = \log_{10} 1 - \log_{10} 5 = 0 - 0.699$
   $= -0.699$.

   f. $\log_{10} 0.04 = \log_{10}(5^{-2}) = -2\log_{10} 5 = -2 \times 0.699 = -1.398$.

25. In 24 hours, the fly population will increase by a factor of $2^{24/8} = 2^3 = 8$. Since one week is 168 hours, the population will increase by a factor of $2^{168/8} = 2^{21} = 2,097,152$ in one week.

26. The balance of the account grows by a factor of $2^{40/20} = 2^2 = 4$ in 40 years. In 100 years, it grows by a factor of $2^{100/20} = 2^5 = 32$.

27. The population will increase by a factor of four (quadruple) in 30 years because $2^{34/17} = 2^2 = 4$.

28. One year is 12 months, so prices will rise by a factor of $2^{12/2} = 2^6 = 64$.

29. In 12 years, the population will be $10,000 \times 2^{12/10} = 22,974$. In 24 years, it will be $10,000 \times 2^{24/10} = 52,780$.

30. In 12 years, the population will be $10,000 \times 2^{12/8} = 28,284$. In 24 years, it will be $10,000 \times 2^{24/8} = 80,000$.

31. Note that 2 years is 24 months, and 4 years is 48 months. In 2 years, the number of cells will be $1 \times 2^{24/2.5} = 776$. In 4 years, the number will be $1 \times 2^{48/2.5} = 602,249$.

32. In 6 years (72 months), there will be $1 \times 2^{72/6} = 4096$ cells. Ten years is 120 months, so there will be $1 \times 2^{120/6} = 1,048,576$ cells in 10 years.

33. The year 2019 is 10 years later than 2009, so the population will be $6.8 \times 2^{10/45} = 7.9$ billion. In 2059 (50 years later), the population will be $6.8 \times 2^{50/45} = 14.7$ billion. In 2101 (100 years later), it will be $6.8 \times 2^{100/45} = 31.7$ billion.

34. The year 2019 is 10 years later than 2009, so the population will be $6.8 \times 2^{10/60} = 7.6$ billion. In 2059 (50 years later), the population will be $6.8 \times 2^{50/60} = 12.1$ billion. In 2101 (100 years later), it will be $6.8 \times 2^{100/60} = 21.6$ billion.

35.

Month	Population
0	100
1	$100 \times (1.07)^1 = 107$
2	$100 \times (1.07)^2 = 114$
3	$100 \times (1.07)^3 = 123$
4	$100 \times (1.07)^4 = 131$
5	$100 \times (1.07)^5 = 140$

6	$100 \times (1.07)^6 = 150$
7	$100 \times (1.07)^7 = 161$
8	$100 \times (1.07)^8 = 172$
9	$100 \times (1.07)^9 = 184$
10	$100 \times (1.07)^{10} = 197$
11	$100 \times (1.07)^{11} = 210$
12	$100 \times (1.07)^{12} = 225$
13	$100 \times (1.07)^{13} = 241$
14	$100 \times (1.07)^{14} = 258$
15	$100 \times (1.07)^{15} = 276$

Because the population after ten months is 197, which is almost twice the initial population of 100, the doubling time is just over 10 months. The approximate doubling time formula claims that $T_{double} = 70/7 = 10$ months, which is pretty close to what we can discern from the table. Neither answer is exact, though.

36.

Month	Population
0	1000
1	$1000 \times (1.20)^1 = 1200$
2	$1000 \times (1.20)^2 = 1440$
3	$1000 \times (1.20)^3 = 1728$
4	$1000 \times (1.20)^4 = 2074$
5	$1000 \times (1.20)^5 = 2488$
6	$1000 \times (1.20)^6 = 2986$
7	$1000 \times (1.20)^7 = 3583$
8	$1000 \times (1.20)^8 = 4300$
9	$1000 \times (1.20)^9 = 5160$
10	$1000 \times (1.20)^{10} = 6192$
11	$1000 \times (1.20)^{11} = 7430$
12	$1000 \times (1.20)^{12} = 8916$
13	$1000 \times (1.20)^{13} = 10,699$
14	$1000 \times (1.20)^{14} = 12,839$
15	$1000 \times (1.20)^{15} = 15,407$

Because the population after four months is 2074, which is a little more than twice the initial population of 1000, the doubling time is just under 4 months. The approximate doubling time formula

claims that $T_{double} = 70/20 = 3.5$ months, which in not in perfect agreement from what we could discern from the table – this is due to the fact that the approximate doubling time formula doesn't work as well once r is greater than 15%.

37. $T_{double} \sim 70/4 = 17.5$ years. Prices will increase by a factor of $(1.04)^3 = 1.12$ in three years. Using the doubling time formula, prices would increase by a factor of $2^{3/17.5} = 1.13$, so the approximate doubling time formula does a reasonable job.

38. $T_{double} \sim 70/3.5 = 20$ years. The population will increase by a factor of $(1.035)^{50} = 5.58$. Using the doubling time formula, the population would increase by a factor of $2^{50/20} = 5.66$, so the approximate doubling time formula does a reasonable job.

39. $T_{double} \sim 70/0.3 = 233$ months. Prices will increase by a factor of $(1.003)^{12} = 1.04$ in one year, and by a factor of $(1.003)^{96} = 1.33$ in eight years. Using the doubling time formula, prices would increase by a factor of $2^{12/233} = 1.036$ in one year, and by a factor of $2^{96/233} = 1.33$ in eight years, so the approximate doubling time formula does a reasonable job.

40. $T_{double} \sim 70/2.2 = 32$ years. Oil consumption will increase by a factor of $(1.022)^{10} = 1.24$ in ten years. Using the doubling time formula, consumption would increase by a factor of $2^{10/32} = 1.24$, so the approximate doubling time formula does a reasonable job.

41. After 100 years, the fraction of radioactive substance that remains is $\left(\dfrac{1}{2}\right)^{100/50} = \dfrac{1}{4} = 0.25$. After 200 years, the fraction remaining is $\left(\dfrac{1}{2}\right)^{200/50} = \dfrac{1}{16} = 0.0625$.

42. After 120 years, the fraction of radioactive substance that remains is $\left(\dfrac{1}{2}\right)^{120/400} = 0.81$. After 2500 years, the fraction remaining is $\left(\dfrac{1}{2}\right)^{2500/400} = 0.013$.

43. The concentration of the drug decreases by a factor of $\left(\dfrac{1}{2}\right)^{24/18} = 0.40$ after 24 hours, and by a factor of $\left(\dfrac{1}{2}\right)^{48/18} = 0.16$ after 48 hours.

44. The concentration of the drug decreases by a factor of $\left(\dfrac{1}{2}\right)^{24/4} = \dfrac{1}{64} = 0.016$ after 24 hours, and by a factor of $\left(\dfrac{1}{2}\right)^{48/4} = 2^{-12} = \dfrac{1}{4096} = 0.00024$ after 48 hours.

45. In 30 years, the population will be $1,000,000 \times \left(\dfrac{1}{2}\right)^{30/20}$ or about 354,000, and it will be $1,000,000 \times \left(\dfrac{1}{2}\right)^{40/20} = 250,000$ in 40 years.

46. In 20 years, the population will be $1,000,000 \times \left(\dfrac{1}{2}\right)^{20/25}$ or about 574,000, and it will be $1,000,000 \times \left(\dfrac{1}{2}\right)^{40/25}$ or about 330,000 in 40 years.

47. In 150 days, $1 \times \left(\dfrac{1}{2}\right)^{150/77} = 0.26$ kg of cobalt will remain, and $1 \times \left(\dfrac{1}{2}\right)^{300/77} = 0.067$ kg of cobalt will remain after 300 days.

48. In 1000 years, $1 \times \left(\dfrac{1}{2}\right)^{1000/1600} = 0.65$ kg of radium will remain, and $1 \times \left(\dfrac{1}{2}\right)^{10,000/1600} = 0.013$ kg of radium will remain after 10,000 years.

49. $T_{\text{half}} \sim 70/7 = 10$ years. The fraction of the forest that will remain after 30 years is $(1 - 0.07)^{30} = 0.113$. Using the half-life formula, the fraction that will remain is $\left(\dfrac{1}{2}\right)^{30/10} = 0.125$, so the approximate half-life formula is doing a reasonable job.

50. $T_{\text{half}} \sim 70/3.5 = 20$ weeks. The fraction of the pollutant that will remain after 52 weeks is $(1 - 0.035)^{52} = 0.16$. Using the half-life formula,

the fraction that will remain is $\left(\dfrac{1}{2}\right)^{52/20} = 0.16$, so the approximate half-life formula is doing a reasonable job.

51. $T_{\text{half}} \sim 70/8 = 8.75$ years. After 50 years, the population will be $10,000(1 - 0.08)^{50} = 155$ elephants. Using the half-life formula, the population will be $10,000 \times \left(\dfrac{1}{2}\right)^{50/8.75} = 195$ elephants, so the approximate half-life formula does not do a reasonable job.

52. The annual production will be $5000(1 - 0.06)^{15} = 1976$ kg in 15 years. If you use the approximate half-life formula to find that $T_{\text{half}} \sim 70/6 = 11.7$ years, the annual production would be $5000 \times \left(\dfrac{1}{2}\right)^{15/11.7} = 2056$ or about 2060 kg, which shows that the approximate half-life formula does a reasonable job in making the prediction.

53. The approximate doubling time is $T_{\text{double}} \sim 70/12 = 5.8$ years. (A rounded value for) the exact doubling time is $\dfrac{\log_{10} 2}{\log_{10}(1 + 0.12)} = 6.11$ years. The price of a $500 item in four years will be $\$500 \times 2^{4/6.11} = \$787.12$. (Note that this answer is using the rounded value for the "exact" doubling time – if you use all the digits your calculator stores, you should get a price of $786.76).

54. The approximate doubling time is $T_{\text{double}} \sim 70/80 = 0.875$ month. (A rounded value for) the exact doubling time is $\dfrac{\log_{10} 2}{\log_{10}(1 + 0.80)} = 1.18$ months. The price of a $1000 item in one year (12 months) will be $\$1000 \times 2^{12/1.18} = \$1,151,654$. (Note that this answer is using the rounded value of the "exact" doubling time – if you use all the digits your calculator stores, you should get a price of $1,156,831).

55. The approximate doubling time is $T_{\text{double}} \sim 70/4 = 17.5$ years. (A rounded value for) the exact doubling time is $\dfrac{\log_{10} 2}{\log_{10}(1 + 0.04)} = 17.67$ years. The nation's population in 30 years will be $1,000,000 \times 2^{30/17.67} = 324,404,283$. (Note that this answer is using the rounded value for the "exact" doubling time – if you use all the digits

your calculator stores, you should get a population of 324,339,751).

56. The approximate doubling time is $T_{double} \sim 70/20 = 3.5$ weeks. (A rounded value for) the exact doubling time is $\dfrac{\log_{10} 2}{\log_{10}(1+0.20)} = 3.8$ weeks. The termite population in 52 weeks will be $100 \times 2^{52/3.8} = 1,316,309$. (Note that this answer is using the rounded value for the "exact" doubling time – if you use all the digits your calculator stores, you should get a population of 1,310,463).

FURTHER APPLICATIONS

57. The amount of plutonium found today would be
$$10^{12} \times \left(\frac{1}{2}\right)^{4.6\times10^9 / 24,000} = 0 \text{ tons.}$$
The reason there is no plutonium left is that 4.6 billion ÷ 24,000 is nearly 200,000, which means whatever amount of plutonium was originally present has undergone about 200,000 halving periods, and that's enough to reduce any amount imaginable to 0 (even if the entire mass of the earth were radioactive plutonium at the outset, it would have all decayed to other elements in 4.6 billion years).

58. After 50 years, there will be $1 \times \left(\dfrac{1}{2}\right)^{50/12} = 0.056$ kg of tritium remaining. If the weapons aren't maintained, but just stored for 50 years, they won't have the potency for which they were designed, as most of the radioactive material would have decayed.

TECHNOLOGY EXERCISES

63. a. $\log_{10} 8 = 0.903090$

    b. $\log_{10} 2000 = 3.301030$

    c. $\log_{10} 0.5 = -0.301030$

    d. $\log_{10} 64 = 1.806180$

    e. $\log_{10} 1/8 = -0.903090$

    f. $\log_{10} 0.2 = -0.698970$

64. a. $\log_{10} 50 = 1.698970$

    b. $\log_{10} 5000 = 3.689970$

    c. $\log_{10} 0.05 = -1.301030$

    d. $\log_{10} 25 = 1.397940$

    e. $\log_{10} 0.20 = -0.698970$

    f. $\log_{10} 0.04 = -1.397940$

UNIT 8C

TIME OUT TO THINK

Pg. 492. Longer lifespans would mean a dramatic drop in the death rate. Unless the birth rate dropped equally dramatically, the growth rate would rise.

Pg. 495. Opinions will vary, but many historians believe that overshoot and collapse affected many past civilizations. For example the decline of the Anasazi may have occurred, at least in part, because they overstressed their local environment, causing their agricultural production to fall.

Pg. 496. Food production has managed to keep up with population growth so far, so the argument comes down to faith in future technology. If we can keep up and follow a logistic model, everything will be fine. If we cannot keep up with food production, then we face overshoot and collapse, in which case Malthus's nightmare may come true.

QUICK QUIZ

1. **c.** Convert 75 million people per year into people per minute:
$$\frac{75\times10^6 \text{ people}}{\text{yr}} \times \frac{1 \text{ yr}}{365 \text{ d}} \times \frac{1 \text{ d}}{24 \text{ h}} \times \frac{1 \text{ hr}}{60 \text{ min}} = 143$$
people per minute (or about 140 people/min).

2. **b.** The text states the population is 6.8 billion people in 2009, growing at 1.2% per year. This implies a 2009 population of $6.8\times10^9 (1.012)^3 = 7.0$ billion.

3. **b.** The birth rate peaked in 1960, and has seen a significant decline since then, but it is not the primary reason for the rapid growth – the decreasing death rate has played the most important role over the last three centuries.

4. **b.** This answer gives the correct definition of carrying capacity.

5. **c.** Answers **a** and **b** would tend to decrease the carrying capacity, while developing a cheap source of energy would allow us to solve some of the barriers to population growth, such as clean water for all.

6. **a.** The bacteria in a bottle exhaust their resources, at which point the population collapses.

7. **c.** The logistic model looks like exponential growth at the outset, but then the growth rate declines, and the population levels out to a level at (or below) the carrying capacity.

8. **a.** The birth rate in 1950 was quite high, and with no change in the death rate, this would lead to rapid exponential growth.

9. **a.** The approximate doubling time of a population growing at 1.2% per year is 70/1.2 = 58.3 years.
10. **c.** Answers **a** and **b** would be required in order for the population to level out (the birth rate must decline to equal the death rate if population is to remain steady, and a population of 9 billion is 50% larger than the current level of 6 billion, and thus we would need an increase of 50% in food production). This leaves answer **c**, which is not necessary to sustain a population of 9 billion.

DOES IT MAKE SENSE?

7. Makes sense. If the current growth rate of 1.2% remains steady for the next decade, we can expect a population of $6.8 \times 10^9 (1.012)^{10} = 7.7$ billion, which is an increase of 900 million people (i.e. more than twice the size of the current U.S. population of 304 million).
8. Makes sense. Growth rate is equal to birth rate – death rate, so if the birth rate declines by a greater margin than the death rate, the difference between them will decrease, which means the growth rate will decrease.
9. Does not make sense. The carrying capacity depends upon many factors, such as our ability to produce food for the current population.
10. Does not make sense. The carrying capacity is influenced by a very complex set of parameters, and the best we can do is estimate its value, despite advances in computer technology.
11. Does not make sense. Predator/prey models often include the idea of overshoot and collapse.
12. Does not make sense. While past history gives us some indication that the human population is on a path toward logistic growth, some measures (such as the high growth rate in the 1960s) do not fit in well with the logistic model.

BASIC SKILLS & CONCEPTS

13. $T_{double} \sim 70/0.9 = 78$ years. Under this assumption, the population in 2050 would be $6 \times 2^{50/78} = 9.4$ billion.
14. $T_{double} \sim 70/1.8 = 39$ years. Under this assumption, the population in 2050 would be $6 \times 2^{50/39} = 14.6$ billion.
15. $T_{double} \sim 70/1.6 = 44$ years. Under this assumption, the population in 2050 would be $6 \times 2^{50/44} = 13.2$ billion.
16. $T_{double} \sim 70/0.7 = 100$ years. Under this assumption, the population in 2050 would be $6 \times 2^{50/100} = 8.5$ billion.
17. a. The growth rate in 1985 was 14.5 – 11.8 = 2.7 per 1000 people. In 1995, it was 9.3 – 11.4 = –2.1

per 1000 people. In 2007, it was 9.0 – 10.6 = –1.6 per 1000 people.
b. The birth rate decreased while the death rate remained fairly constant, which results in a declining growth rate. In this case, the growth rate became negative, which implies a declining population. If these trends continue, we can expect a decreasing population in the Czech Republic, though because there are so many factors that influence the growth rate of a country, it would be unwise to put much faith in these predictions 20 years hence.
18. a. The growth rate in 1985 was 23.8 – 6.6 = 17.2 per 1000 people. In 1995, it was 21.0 – 6.3 = 14.7 per 1000 people. In 2007, it was 17.7 – 6.2 = 11.5 per 1000 people.
b. The birth rate decreased while the death rate remained fairly constant, which results in a declining growth rate. In this case, the growth rate is still positive, which implies a population that is growing more slowly. If these trends continue, we can expect an increasing population in Israel, though because there are so many factors that influence the growth rate of a country, it would be unwise to put much faith in these predictions 20 years hence.
19. a. The growth rate in 1985 was 11.8 – 11.3 = 0.5 per 1000 people. In 1995, it was 11.7 – 11.0 = 0.7 per 1000 people. In 2007, it was 10.2 – 10.3 = – 0.1 per 1000 people.
b. The growth rate increased then decreased to a slightly negative value, which results in a slowly decreasing population. If these trends continue, we can expect a slightly declining or stable population in Sweden, though because there are so many factors that influence the growth rate of a country, it would be unwise to put much faith in these predictions 20 years hence.
20. a. The growth rate in 1985 was 15.7 – 8.7 = 7.0 per 1000 people. In 1995, it was 15.1 – 8.8 = 6.3 per 1000 people. In 2007, it was 14.2 – 8.3 = 5.9 per 1000 people.
b. The birth rate decreased, as did the death rate, though the difference between the two was small (it was, however, positive). This implies a slowly growing population. If these trends continue, we can expect a slowly growing population in the United States, though because there are so many factors that influence the growth rate of a country, it would be unwise to put much faith in these predictions 20 years hence.
21. When the population is 10 million, the actual growth rate is $4\% \times \left(1 - \dfrac{10,000,000}{60,000,000}\right) = 3.3\%$.
When the population is 30 million, the actual

growth rate is $4\% \times \left(1 - \dfrac{30,000,000}{60,000,000}\right) = 2.0\%$.

When the population is 50 million, the actual growth rate is $4\% \times \left(1 - \dfrac{50,000,000}{60,000,000}\right) = 0.67\%$.

22. When the population is 10 million, the actual growth rate is $6\% \times \left(1 - \dfrac{10,000,000}{80,000,000}\right) = 5.25\%$.

When the population is 50 million, the actual growth rate is $6\% \times \left(1 - \dfrac{50,000,000}{80,000,000}\right) = 2.25\%$.

When the population is 70 million, the actual growth rate is $6\% \times \left(1 - \dfrac{70,000,000}{80,000,000}\right) = 0.75\%$.

FURTHER APPLICATIONS

23. $T_{\text{double}} \sim 70/0.7 = 100$ years. In 2059, the population will be $3.05 \times 10^8 \times 2^{50/100} = 431$ million. In 2109, the population will be $3.05 \times 10^8 \times 2^{100/100} = 610$ million.

24. $T_{\text{double}} \sim 70/0.5 = 140$ years. In 2059, the population will be $3.05 \times 10^8 \times 2^{50/140} = 391$ million. In 2109, the population will be $3.05 \times 10^8 \times 2^{100/140} = 500$ million.

25. $T_{\text{double}} \sim 70/1.0 = 70$ years. In 2056, the population will be $3.05 \times 10^8 \times 2^{50/70} = 500$ million. In 2109, the population will be $3.05 \times 10^8 \times 2^{100/70} = 821$ million.

26. $T_{\text{double}} \sim 70/0.4 = 175$ years. In 2056, the population will be $3.05 \times 10^8 \times 2^{50/175} = 372$ million. In 2109, the population will be $3.05 \times 10^8 \times 2^{100/175} = 453$ million.

27. Answers will vary depending on your age.
28. Answers will vary depending on your age.
29. We must first compute the base growth rate r in the logistic model, using the 1960s data:

$$r = \frac{2.1\%}{\left(1 - \dfrac{3 \text{ billion}}{8 \text{ billion}}\right)} = 3.36\%.$$

The current growth rate can now be predicted using a population of 6.8 billion:

$$\text{growth rate} = 3.36\% \times \left(1 - \frac{6.8 \text{ billion}}{8 \text{ billion}}\right) = 0.5\%.$$

This is lower than the actual current growth rate of 1.2%, which indicates the assumed carrying capacity of 8 billion is too low to fit well with the data from the 1960s to present.

30. We must first compute the base growth rate r in the logistic model, using the 1960s data:

$$r = \frac{2.1\%}{\left(1 - \dfrac{3 \text{ billion}}{10 \text{ billion}}\right)} = 3\%.$$

The current growth rate can now be predicted using a population of 6.8 billion:

$$\text{growth rate} = 3\% \times \left(1 - \frac{6.8 \text{ billion}}{10 \text{ billion}}\right) = 0.96\%.$$

This is slightly lower than the actual current growth rate of 1.2%, which indicates the assumed carrying capacity of 10 billion is too low to fit well with the data from the 1960s to present.

31. We must first compute the base growth rate r in the logistic model, using the 1960s data:

$$r = \frac{2.1\%}{\left(1 - \dfrac{3 \text{ billion}}{15 \text{ billion}}\right)} = 2.625\%.$$

The current growth rate can now be predicted using a population of 6.8 billion:

$$\text{growth rate} = 2.625\% \times \left(1 - \frac{6.8 \text{ billion}}{15 \text{ billion}}\right) = 1.4\%.$$

This is higher than the actual current growth rate of 1.2%, which indicates the assumed carrying capacity of 15 billion is too high to fit well with the data from the 1960s to present.

32. We must first compute the base growth rate r in the logistic model, using the 1960s data:

$$r = \frac{2.1\%}{\left(1 - \dfrac{3 \text{ billion}}{20 \text{ billion}}\right)} = 2.47\%.$$

The current growth rate can now be predicted using a population of 6.8 billion:

$$\text{growth rate} = 2.47\% \times \left(1 - \frac{6.8 \text{ billion}}{20 \text{ billion}}\right) = 1.6\%.$$

This is higher than the actual current growth rate of 1.2%, which indicates the assumed carrying capacity of 20 billion is too high to fit well with the data from the 1960s to present.

33. With an annual growth rate of 2%, the approximate doubling time would be $T_{\text{double}} \sim 70/2 = 35$ years. The population of the city in the year 2020 (ten years beyond 2010) would have been about $100,000(2)^{10/35} = 122,000$. The predicted population in 2030 and 2070 would be 149,000 and 328,000, respectively (the computation is similar to the 2000 prediction). With an annual growth rate of 5%, the approximate doubling time would be $T_{\text{double}} \sim 70/5 = 14$ years. The population of the city in the year 2020 would have been $100,000(2)^{10/14} = 164,000$. The predicted

population in 2030 and 2070 would be 269,000 and 1,950,000, respectively.

UNIT 8D

TIME OUT TO THINK

Pg. 501. The building should be designed so that it can roll with the ground, and also include flex joints within it. No one has yet figured out how to make a building that can withstand any earthquake. Even well-designed buildings sometimes fail due to construction flaws.

Pg. 504. Answers will vary. This question should get you to realize that pH shows up on many common products. Recall that acids have a pH lower than 7 and bases have a pH higher than 7.

QUICK QUIZ

1. **a.** Each unit on the magnitude scale represents about 32 times as much energy as the previous magnitude.

2. **b.** Most deaths in earthquakes are caused by the collapse of buildings, landslides, and tsunamis.

3. **a.** By definition, a sound of 0 dB is the softest sound audible by a human.

4. **b.** From the definition of the decibel scale, we have

$$\frac{\text{intensity of sound}}{\text{intensity of softest audible sound}} = 10^{(95/10)} = 10^{9.5}$$

. The ratio on the left tells us this sound has intensity $10^{9.5}$ times as large as the softest audible sound.

5. **a.** From the definition of the decibel scale, we have

$$\frac{\text{intensity of sound}}{\text{intensity of softest audible sound}} = 10^{(10/10)} = 10.$$

The ratio on the left tells us a 10-dB sound is ten times as large as the softest audible sound, which is 0 dB.

6. **c.** Gravity follows the inverse square law, so its strength is proportional to the square of the distance between the objects. Thus if this distance is tripled (multiplied by 3), the strength of the force of gravity is decreased by a factor of $3^2 = 9$.

7. **c.** On the pH scale, a lower number corresponds to higher acidity.

8. **b.** Because $[H^+] = 10^{-pH}$, we have $[H^+] = 10^{-0} = 1$, so the hydrogen ion concentration is 1 mole per liter.

9. **c.** Because $pH = -\log_{10}[H^+]$, we have pH = $-\log_{10} 10^{-5} = -(-5) = 5$.

10. **a.** A lake damaged by acid rain has a relatively low pH. To bring it back to health, you want to raise the pH.

DOES IT MAKE SENSE?

5. Does not make sense. Each unit on the magnitude scale represents an increase of nearly 32 fold in the amount of energy released, and thus an earthquake of magnitude 8 releases about 32^4 (close to 1 million) times as much energy as an earthquake of magnitude 4. This does not imply that a magnitude 8 earthquake will do 1 million times as much damage, but it's not likely it will do only twice the damage of a magnitude 4 quake.

6. Does not make sense. As shown in Table 8.5, a 120-dB sound is 10^{12} times as loud as the softest audible sound, and a 100-dB sound is 10^{10} times as loud. This implies a 120-dB sound is 100 times as loud as a 100-dB sound.

7. Does not make sense. The pH of water is related to its hydrogen ion concentration, which is not affected by its volume.

8. Does not make sense. Lakes that have been affected by acid rain often have clear water because nothing is able to grow in them.

BASIC SKILLS & CONCEPTS

9. $E = (2.5 \times 10^4) \cdot 10^{1.5 \times 4} = 2.5 \times 10^{10}$ joules.

10. Because each unit on the magnitude scale represents an increase of nearly 32 fold in the amount of energy released, we can expect that a magnitude 6 quake is about 32^2 (1024) times as large as a magnitude 4 quake. To find the exact factor, one can compute the energy released by each quake. $E = (2.5 \times 10^4) \cdot 10^{1.5 \times 6} = 2.5 \times 10^{13}$ joules for the magnitude 6 quake, and $E = (2.5 \times 10^4) \cdot 10^{1.5 \times 4} = 2.5 \times 10^{10}$ joules for the magnitude 6 quake. Note that the energy released by the magnitude 6 quake is $10^3 = 1000$ times as large as the magnitude 4 quake.

11. $E = (2.5 \times 10^4) \cdot 10^{1.5 \times 9} = 7.9 \times 10^{17}$ joules.

12. $E = (2.5 \times 10^4) \cdot 10^{1.5 \times 7.9} = 1.8 \times 10^{16}$ joules.

13. The energy released by a magnitude 6 quake is 2.5×10^{13} joules (see exercise 10), and since $5 \times 10^{15} \div 2.5 \times 10^{13} = 200$, the bomb releases 200 times as much energy.

14. Use the relationship $\log_{10} E = 4.4 + 1.5M$, where $E = 5 \times 10^{15}$ joules (the energy of the bomb) and M is the magnitude of the earthquake.

$$\log_{10}(5 \times 10^{15}) = 4.4 + 1.5M$$
$$15.7 = 4.4 + 1.5M$$
$$M = 7.53$$

Assuming the bomb was deployed for the use it was designed, it would cause more destruction. Nuclear bombs are detonated above ground, and their blast cones wipe out entire cities. A significant amount of the energy released by an earthquake is absorbed by the earth.

15. As shown in Table 8.5, ordinary conversation is around 60 dB, and is $10^6 = 1,000,000$ times as loud as the softest audible sound.

16. As shown in Table 8.5, a siren at 30 meters is around 100 dB, and is $10^{10} = 10$ billion times as loud as the softest audible sound.

17. The loudness is $10\log_{10}(10 \times 10^6) = 70$ dB.

18. The loudness is $10\log_{10}(10 \times 10^{12}) = 130$ dB.

19. As with Example 4 in the text, we can compare the intensities of two sounds using the following:
$$\frac{\text{intensity of sound 1}}{\text{intensity of sound 2}} = 10^{(55-10)/10} = 31,623.$$
Thus a 55-dB sound is 31,623 times as loud as a 10-dB sound.

20. According to Table 8.5, a whisper is 20 dB, and is 10^2 times as loud as the softest audible sound. A 40 dB sound is 10^4 times as loud as the softest audible sound, and thus is 100 times as loud as a 20-dB sound.

21. The distance has decreased by a factor of 3, which means the intensity of sound will increase by a factor of $3^2 = 9$.

22. The distance has decreased by a factor of 200, which means the intensity of sound will increase by a factor of $200^2 = 40,000$.

23. The distance has decreased by a factor of 5, which means the intensity of sound will increase by a factor of $5^2 = 25$.

24. The distance has decreased by a factor of 10, which means the intensity of sound will increase by a factor of $10^2 = 100$.

25. Each unit of increase on the pH scale corresponds to a decrease by a factor of 10 in the hydrogen ion concentration. Thus an increase of 4 on the pH scale corresponds to a decrease in the hydrogen ion concentration by a factor of $10^4 = 10,000$. This makes the solution more basic.

26. Each unit of decrease on the pH scale corresponds to an increase by a factor of 10 in the hydrogen ion concentration. Thus a decrease of 3.5 on the pH scale corresponds to an increase in the hydrogen

ion concentration by a factor of $10^{3.5} = 3162$. This makes the solution more acidic.

27. $[\text{H}^+] = 10^{-8.5} = 3.16 \times 10^{-9}$ mole per liter.

28. $[\text{H}^+] = 10^{-3.5} = 3.16 \times 10^{-4}$ mole per liter.

29. $\text{pH} = -\log_{10}(0.001) = 3$. This is an acid, as is any solution with pH less than 7.

30. $\text{pH} = -\log_{10}(10^{-12}) = 12$. This is a base, as is any solution with pH greater than 7.

31. Acid rain (pH = 2) is $10^4 = 10,000$ times more acidic than ordinary water (pH = 6). See exercise 25.

32. Acid rain (pH = 2.5) is $10^{3.5} = 3162$ times more acidic than ordinary water (pH = 6). See exercise 25.

FURTHER APPLICATIONS

33. According to Table 8.4, earthquakes with magnitudes between 2 and 3 are labeled "very minor," and they occur about 1000 times per year worldwide. The glasses in the cupboards of the Los Angeles residents near the epicenter may rattle around a bit, but nothing serious would be expected to happen.

34. A 160-dB sound is 10,000 times as intense as a 120-dB sound, and 120 dB is the level at which there is a strong risk of damage to the human ear, according to Table 8.5. This would be decidedly bad: a burst eardrum, bleeding from the ear, and a permanent loss of hearing could ensue.

35. A solution with a pH of 12 is very basic: 100,000 times more basic than pure water. When children ingest such liquids, the mouth, throat, and digestive tracts are often burned. One would hope that a secondary effect of the incident would be that an adult would call the poison center immediately.

36. According to Table 8.4, an earthquake of magnitude 8.5 is in the "great" category; only 1 per year (on average) occurs worldwide. Such a quake could conceivably cause much death and destruction in Tokyo (though it is a modern city, with buildings designed to diminish the effects of an earthquake).

37. You probably would not be able to hear your friend (the noise of the sirens is louder). If your friend is shouting: "Watch out for that falling piano above you!" you might die.

38. The forest will suffer the serious effects of acid rain (which, with a pH of 4, is 100 times more acidic than normal rain of pH 6).

39. a. The distance has increased by a factor of 100, so the intensity of the sound will decrease by a factor

of 100^2 = 10,000 times (this is due to the inverse square law). According to Table 8.5, busy street traffic is 80 dB, and is 10^8 times as loud as the softest audible sound. Note that a 40-dB sound is 10^4 times as loud as the softest sound, and thus is 10,000 times less intense than an 80-dB sound.

b. As with Example 4 in the text, we can compare the intensities of two sounds using the following:

$$\frac{\text{intensity of sound 1}}{\text{intensity of sound 2}} = 10^{(135-120)/10} = 31.6.$$

Thus a 135-dB sound is 31.6 times as loud as a 120-dB sound. In order to reduce the intensity of the sound by a factor of 31.6, you need to increase the distance from the speaker by a factor of $\sqrt{31.6}$ = 5.6, so you should sit 5.6×10 m = 56 meters away.

c. The distance from you to the booth (8 meters) is 8 times as much as the distance between the people talking (1 meter), so the intensity of the sound will have decreased by a factor of 64 by the time it reaches you. A 20-dB sound is 100 times louder than the softest audible sound, and when decreased by a factor of 64, it becomes (100/64) times as loud as the softest sound. Therefore its loudness in decibels is $10\log_{10}\left(\dfrac{100}{64}\right)$ = 1.94 dB.

Note that a 60-dB sound is 10,000 times as loud as a 20-dB sound (Table 8.5). If you wanted to amplify the sound that reaches you to 60 dB, you would need to increase it by a factor of 64 to overcome the loss of intensity due to distance (this would bring it back to 20 dB), and increase it again by a factor of 10,000 to raise it to the 60-dB level. This is equivalent to amplifying the sound by a factor of 640,000. Pray that the waiter doesn't come to your table and say a loud "hello" while your earpiece is in.

40. a. The distance has decreased by a factor of 300, so the intensity of the sound will increase by a factor of 300^2 = 90,000.

b. A siren at 30 meters is 10^{10} times as loud as the softest audible sound. If the intensity is increased by a factor of 90,000, it will be $90,000 \times 10^{10}$ = 9×10^{14} times as loud as the softest sound. This means its loudness in decibels is $10\log_{10}(9 \times 10^{14})$ = 149.5 dB.

c. Note that a 150-dB sound is 10^3 = 1000 times as loud as a 120-dB sound, the level at which there is a strong risk of damage to the human ear. It is very likely your eardrum will be damaged.

41. a. $[H^+] = 10^{-4}$ mole per liter.

b. The lake water with pH = 7 has a hydrogen ion concentration of 10^{-7} mole per liter. There are 3.785 liters in a gallon, so a 100 million gallon lake has 378,500,000 = 3.785×10^8 liters in it. Multiplying the hydrogen ion concentration by the volume of the lake gives us 37.85 moles of hydrogen ions before the acid was added. In a similar fashion, we find that 100,000 gallons (378,500 liters) of acid with pH = 2 ($[H^+] = 10^{-2}$) has 3785 moles of hydrogen ions. Combining both the volumes of the liquids and the moles of hydrogen ions gives us a hydrogen ion concentration of $\dfrac{37.85 + 3785 \text{ mole}}{3.785 \times 10^8 + 378,500 \text{ L}} = 10^{-5}$ mole per liter. This implies the polluted lake has pH = $-\log_{10}(10^{-5})$ = 5.

c. Proceeding as in part **b**, the acid-rain lake (without added acid) has 37,850 moles of hydrogen ions. When the acid is added (increasing the number of moles by 3785), the hydrogen ion concentration becomes $\dfrac{37,850 + 3785 \text{ mole}}{3.785 \times 10^8 + 378,500 \text{ L}} =$ 1.1×10^{-4} mole per liter. This implies the polluted lake has pH = $-\log_{10}(1.1 \times 10^{-4})$ = 3.96.

d. The pollution could be detected if the acid was dumped into a lake with pH = 7 (part **b**), but it could not be detected if it was dumped into a lake with pH = 4 (part **c**).

UNIT 9A

TIME OUT TO THINK

Pg. 514. Many variable pairs that are plausibly related are possible. Examples could include: total amount spent on music per month with respect to number of songs downloaded or temperature with respect to time of day.

Pg. 515. Dependence does not necessarily imply causality. Time moving ahead does not cause the temperature to change. The sale of snow shovels does not cause the sale of snow tires, although both variables vary together.

Pg. 519. Answers will vary depending on when you cover this chapter. The fall equinox occurs near the beginning of most fall semesters and this is where the hours of daylight vary rapidly. Spring semesters typically begin within a few weeks after the winter solstice and this is where the hours of daylight vary slowly.

QUICK QUIZ

1. **a**. A function describes how a dependent variable changes with respect to one or more independent variables.
2. **a**. The variable s is the independent variable, upon which the variable r depends.
3. **c**. The DJIA changes with respect to the passage of time, and thus is a function of time.
4. **b**. It is customary to plot the values of the independent variable along the horizontal axis.
5. **b**. The dependent variable is normally plotted along the vertical axis, and in this case, the dependent variable is z (with an independent variable of w).
6. **b**. The range of a function consists of the values of the dependent variable.
7. **a**. The speed of the car is the independent variable (because gas mileage changes with respect to speed), and the domain of a function is the set of values of interest for the independent variable.
8. **c**. The range of a function is the set of values corresponding to the values in the domain, which in turn are the set of values that make sense in the function. If you used a function to predict values outside the range, you would be forced to use values outside the domain; these values don't make sense.
9. **c**. Traffic volume on an urban freeway peaks in the morning rush hour, peaks again in the evening rush hour, and typically repeats this pattern day after day. If weekend traffic were significantly different from the weekday pattern, we would still

see a weekly pattern repeating itself – this is a hallmark of a periodic function.

10. **b**. A model that does not agree well with past data probably won't do a good job of predicting the future.

DOES IT MAKE SENSE?

5. Makes sense. Climatologists use mathematical models to predict and understand the nature of the earth's climate.
6. Makes sense. The demand for concert tickets changes with respect to the price of the ticket: in general, if the price goes up, demand will fall, and vice versa.
7. Does not make sense. If your heart rate depends upon your running speed, heart rate is the dependent variable, and the range is used to describe the values of the dependent variable.
8. Does not make sense. A model may fit observed data very well, but if it is used to extrapolate beyond the data set, there's no telling what may happen.

BASIC SKILLS & CONCEPTS

9.

10.

11. As the volume of the tank increases, the cost of filling it also increases.
12. The price of the car increases with time.

13. The speed of the skydiver increases with time until reaching constant terminal velocity. This describes the relationship of a skydiver falling a sufficient distance before opening his chute. When the chute is opened, the speed decreases to a different terminal velocity until the skydiver reaches the ground.

14. As the price of DVDs increases, the number of DVDs sold decreases.

15. As the average speed of the car increases, the travel time decreases.

16. In a particular gear, the faster you pedal a bike, the faster the bike will go.

17. As the gas mileage increases, the cost of driving a fixed distance decreases (assuming that gas costs remain constant).

18. The balance after a fixed period of time increases with the APR.

19. a. The pressure at 6000 feet is about 24 inches of mercury; the pressure at 18,000 feet is about 17 inches; and the pressure at 29,000 feet is about 11 inches.

    b. The altitude is about 8000 feet when the pressure is 23 inches of mercury; the altitude is about 14,000 feet when the pressure is 19 inches; and the altitude is about 25,000 feet when the pressure is 13 inches.

    c. It appears that the pressure reaches 5 inches of mercury at an altitude of about 50,000. The pressure approaches zero as one moves out of earth's atmosphere and into outer space.

20. a. On April 1, there's about 12.4 hours of daylight, and on October 31, about 10.7 hours. For all of these questions, your answers may vary somewhat from those given here, as it is difficult to read a graph of this sort with any level of precision.

    b. There are 13 hours of daylight around April 19 and August 20.

    c. There are 10.5 hours of daylight around January 31 and November 8.

    d. At 20°N latitude (closer to the equator), the graph would be flatter (the variation in the length of a day is not as pronounced). At 60°N latitude (closer to the North Pole), the graph would be steeper and taller (the variation in the length of the day is larger). At 40°S latitude, the graph would have a similar shape, except that the location of the peaks and valleys would be exchanged (the shortest day of the year in the southern hemisphere is around June 21).

21. a. The independent variable is time (in years), and the dependent variable is world population. The domain is the set of years from 1950 to 2000, and the range is the set of population values between roughly 2.5 billion and 6 billion people.

b. The function shows a steadily increasing world population between 1950 and 2000.

22. a. The independent variable is age (measured in years), and the dependent variable is weight (measured in pounds). The domain is the set of ages between 0 and 40 years, and the range is all weights between about 8 pounds and 130 pounds.

23. a. The variables are (*time*, *temperature*), or (*date*, *temperature*). The domain is all days over the course of a year, and the range is the set of temperatures between 38°F and 85°F.

    b.

    c. The temperature increases during the first half of the year, and then decreases during the second half of the year.

24. a. The independent variable is altitude (in feet), and the dependent variable is boiling temperature (in °F). The domain is the set of altitudes between 0 and 9000 feet. The range is the set of temperatures between 193.6°F and 212°F.

    b.

    c. The boiling point of water decreases with altitude.

25. a. The variables are (*year*, *tobacco production*). The domain is the set of years between 1975 and 1990, and the range is the set of weights between 1.2 and 2.2 billion pounds.

    b.

    c. In this case, because the data consist of yearly figures for production, it would not be appropriate to fill in the graph between the data points. The function, then, is simply the production numbers associated with each year.

26. a. The variables are (*time, projected population*). The domain is the set of years between 2010 and 2040. The range is the set of population values between 309 and 393 million people.

    b.

    c. The projected population increases steadily with time.

27. a. The domain of the function (*altitude, temperature*) is the set of altitudes of interest – say, 0 ft to 15,000 ft (or 0 m to 4000 m). The range is the set of temperatures associated with the altitudes in the domain; the interval 30°F to 90°F (or about 0°C to 30°C) would cover all temperatures of interest (this assumes a summer ascent of a mountain in the temperate zone of the earth).

    b.

28. a. The domain of the function (*day of year, high temperature*) is the set of days over a two-year period. The days could be labeled (1, 2, 3, … , 730). The range consists of the high temperatures on those days. In a temperate location, temperatures between 10°C and 30°C (about 50°F and 90°F) might work.

    b.

29. a. The domain of the function (*blood alcohol content, reflex time*) consists of all reasonable BACs (in gm/100 mL). For example, numbers between 0 and 0.25 would be appropriate. The range would consist of the reflex times associated with those BACs.

    b.

30. a. The domain of the function (*number of pages in a book, time to read the book*) consists of the lengths of most books – say, 30 pages to 1000 pages. The range consists of the reading times for these books for a specific individual; for example, it may consist of times between 1 hour and 20 hours (assuming the person reads at a rate of 50 pages per hour). The reading time should increase steadily with the length of the book (assuming the material being read is at a similar level), as shown in the figure.

    b.

31. a. The domain of the function (*time of day, traffic flow*) consists of all times over a full day. The range consists of all traffic flows (in units of cars per minute) at the various times of the day. We would expect light traffic flow at night, medium traffic flow during the midday hours, and heavy traffic flow during the two rush hours.

b.

32. a. The domain of the function (*price of gasoline, number of tourists in Yellowstone*) would consist of all realistic gasoline prices, say, between $2 and $4 per gallon. The range includes all reasonable number of tourists in Yellowstone (the graph provides a qualitative model and general trend).

b.

33. a. The domain of the function (*time, world record in the 100-meter dash*) consists of all years from 1970 to 2004. The range consists of the world records for the race at all times between 1970 and 2004. Some research would be needed to find the exact records and the days on which they were lowered. The graph shows a slow decrease (from about 10.2 seconds to 9.8 seconds for men, and from about 11.0 seconds to 10.4 seconds for women) over this period of time.

b.

34. a. The domain of the function (*minutes after lighting, length of candle*) consists of all times between 0 minutes and the time at which the candle would be expected to disappear – say, 0 minutes to 100 minutes. The range is the set of numbers between zero and the initial length of the candle, say 0 to 5 inches.

b.

35. a. The domain of the function (*time, population of China*) is all years from 1900 to, say, 2010. The range consists of the population values of China during those years (roughly 400 million to 1.3 billion).

b.

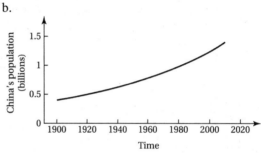

36. a. The domain of the function (*time of day, elevation of tide*) consists of all times over a two-day period. The range consists of the heights of the tides over that two-day period. Some research would be needed to find the exact tide heights at a given location, but the graph would be periodic, rising and falling twice per day.

b.

37. a. The domain of the function (*angle of cannon, horizontal distance traveled by cannonball*) is all cannon angles between 0° and 90°. The range would consist of all horizontal distances traveled by the cannonball for the various angles in the domain. It is well known that a projectile has maximum range when the angle is about 45°, so the graph shows a peak at 45°.

b.

Angle of cannon

38. a. The domain of the function (*weight of car, average gas mileage*) consists of the typical weights of cars – say, from 1000 pounds to 8000 pounds. The range consists of the average gas mileage for cars of various weights. This function should be roughly decreasing, because we expect gas mileage to decrease as the weight of the car increases. However, the function would probably not be a good model because of the many exceptions (heavy cars with good gas mileage, and vice versa).

b.

Weight of car (pounds)

UNIT 9B

TIME OUT TO THINK

Pg. 527. With t = 4, we see that N = 41, which is the value from the graph.

QUICK QUIZ

1. **c.** Constant absolute change over the same time interval (or other variable) gives rise to linear models, and this amounts to constant slope.

2. **b.** The slope of a linear function is the rate of change in the dependent variable with respect to the independent variable.

3. **c.** When a line slopes downward, the ratio of its change in *y* to change in *x* is negative, and this amounts to a negative slope or negative rate of change.

4. **c.** With only information about the first three miles of the trail, there's no knowing what will happen at mile 5.

5. **c.** Larger rates of change correspond with larger and steeper slopes.

6. **a.** The initial value corresponds with *time* = 0, and this results in an initial *price* = $100.

7. **c.** The coefficient on the independent variable is the slope, which also represents the rate of change. Since this coefficient is negative, we can expect a graph that slopes downward.

8. **a.** The y-intercept b = 7, and the slope m = –2, and thus the line, in the form y = mx + b, has equation y = –2x +7.

9. **b.** A line in the form y = mx + b has slope = m and y-intercept = b, so the slope of both y = 12x – 3 and y = 12x + 3 is m = 12, and they have different y-intercepts (–3 and 3).

10. **c.** Charlie picks 550 – 150 = 400 apples over the span of two hours, so the slope of the function is 400/2 = 200.

DOES IT MAKE SENSE?

7. Does not make sense. The graph of a linear function is always a line.

8. Makes sense. The rate of change is the slope.

9. Makes sense. The familiar relationship *distance = speed × time* can be solved for *speed* to produce *speed = distance ÷ time*, which is the rate of change in distance with respect to time.

10. Makes sense. To make a model connecting two data points, simply find the slope of the line segment that joins them, and compute the y-intercept.

BASIC SKILLS & CONCEPTS

11. a. Rain depth increases linearly with time.
    b. It appears that the change in depth over the first three hours is four inches, so the slope is 4/3 inches per hour.
    c. The model is realistic if the rainfall rate is a constant 4/3 inches per hour over four hours.

12. a. Population increases linearly with time.
    b. It appears that the population has increased by 20,000 over the span of two years, so the slope is 10,000 people per year.
    c. As long as the population growth is a constant 10,000 people per year for eight years, this is a good model.

13. a. On a long trip, the distance from home decreases linearly with time.
    b. The distance has decreased by 500 miles over the span of 7 hours, so the slope is –500 ÷ 7 = – 71.4 miles per hour.
    c. This is a good model if the speed of travel is a constant 71.4 miles per hour over 7 hours.

14. a. There is no profit from the first 1000 units sold, and then the profits increase linearly with sales.
    b. The profit changed by $10,000 when 1000 additional units were sold, so the slope is $10 per unit.

c. This is a good model assuming 1000 units must be sold to recover fixed costs, and assuming each unit sold thereafter produces a profit of $10.

15. a. Shoe size increases linearly with the height of the individual.
b. The change in shoe size was 11 while the change in height was 80 inches, and this produces a slope of $11 \div 80 = 0.1375$ size per inch.
c. This model is a rough approximation at best, and it would be difficult to find realistic conditions where the relationship held.

16. a. As the length of the race increases, the average speed of the record-setting runner decreases linearly.
b. The record pace decreases from about 38 km/hr to 20 km/hr as the length of the race increases from 0 km to 10 km, which results in a slope of $(38 - 20) \div (0 - 10) = -1.8$ km/hr.
c. The model is a rough approximation to the actual record times, and it would be difficult to find actual conditions under which the model would be realistic.

17. The *water depth* decreases with respect to *time* at a rate of 2 in./day, so the rate of change is –2 in./day. In 8 days, the water depth decreases by 2 in./day × 8 days = 16 inches. In 15 days, it decreases by 2 in./day × 15 days = 30 in.

18. Your *distance traveled* increases with respect to *time* at a rate of 65 miles per hour. In 3.5 hours, you travel 65 mi/hr × 3.5 hr = 227.5 miles. In 6.8 hours, you travel 65 mi/hr × 6.8 hr = 442 miles.

19. The *Fahrenheit temperature* increases with respect to the *Celsius temperature* at a rate of 9/5 degrees F per degree C. The rate of change is 9/5 degrees Fahrenheit/degrees C. An increase of 5 degrees C results in a change of 5 × 9/5 degrees Fahrenheit/degrees C = 9 degrees F. A decrease of 25 degrees C results in a change of 25 × 9/5 degrees Fahrenheit/degrees C = 45 degrees F.

20. At this gas station, *sales* (in gal/wk) decrease with respect to *price* (in ¢/gal), and the rate of change is $-120\left(\dfrac{\text{gal}}{\text{wk}}\right) \Big/ \left(\dfrac{¢}{\text{gal}}\right) = -120\dfrac{\text{gal}^2}{¢\cdot\text{wk}}$. If the price is increased by 10 cents per gallon, the sales change by $-120\dfrac{\text{gal}^2}{¢\cdot\text{wk}}\times 10\dfrac{¢}{\text{gal}} = -1200\dfrac{\text{gal}}{\text{wk}}$. If the price is decreased by 5 ¢/gal, the sales change by $-120\dfrac{\text{gal}^2}{¢\cdot\text{wk}}\times -5\dfrac{¢}{\text{gal}} = 600\dfrac{\text{gal}}{\text{wk}}$.

21. The *snow depth* increases with respect to *time* at a rate of 3.5 inches per hour. In 6.3 hours, the snow depth will have increased by 3.5 in./hr × 6.3 hr = 22.05 inches. In 9.8 hours, the snow depth will have increased by 3.5 in./hr × 9.8 hr = 34.3 in.

22. Your *maximum heart rate* decreases with respect to your *age*, and the rate of change is –1 beat per minute per year. If your age changes from 25 to 40 (a change of 15 years), then your maximum heart rate decreases by $1\dfrac{\text{beat}}{\text{min}\cdot\text{yr}}\times 15\text{yr} = 15\dfrac{\text{beats}}{\text{min}}$ (from 195 beats/min to 180 beats/min). Your maximum heart rate at age 70 is 220 – 70 = 150 beats/min.

23. The independent variable is time t, measured in years, where $t = 0$ represents today. The dependent variable is price p. The equation for the price function is $p = 15{,}000 + 800t$. A new car will cost $p = 15{,}000 + 800 \times 3.5 = \$17{,}800$. This function does not give a good model for car prices.

24. The independent variable is time t, measured in years, where $t = 0$ represents the year 2006. The dependent variable is record time R. The equation of the record time function is $R = 50.40 - 0.05t$. The world record time in 2020 ($t = 14$) would be $R = 50.40 - 0.05 \times 14 = 49.70$ seconds. This model may prove to be inaccurate.

25. The independent variable is snow depth d, measured in inches, and the dependent variable is maximum speed s, measured in miles per hour. The equation for the speed function is $s = 40 - 1.1d$. To find the depth at which the plow will not be able to move, set $s = 0$ and solve for d.
$$0 = 40 - 1.1d$$
$$1.1d = 40$$
$$d = 40/1.1 = 36 \text{ inches.}$$
The rate at which the speed decreases per inch of snow depth is probably not a constant, so this model is an approximation.

26. The independent variable is time (in months) t and the dependent variable is amount paid (in dollars) P. The equation for the function is $P = 800 + 240t$. You can find out how many months you can lease the car by setting $P = 3680$ and solving for t.
$$3680 = 800 + 240t$$
$$2880 = 240t$$
$$t = 2880/240 = 12 \text{ months.}$$
This function gives a very good model of the leasing costs.

27. The independent variable is time t, measured in minutes, and the dependent variable is rental cost r. As long as the copy business is willing to prorate rental charges per minute (rather than in 5-minute blocks), the change per minute is $1.50/5 = $0.30 per minute. This implies the rental cost function is $r = 8 + 0.30t$. To find out how many minutes can be rented for $25, set $r = 25$, and solve for t.
$$25 = 8 + 0.30t$$
$$17 = 0.30t$$

$t = 17/0.30 = 56.7$ minutes.
This function gives a very good model of rental costs.

28. The independent variable is time t, measured in years, where $t = 0$ represents 1980. The dependent variable is population p. The population function is $p = 2000 + 200t$. The population in 2010 ($t = 30$) is $p = 2000 + 200 \times 30 = 8000$ people. If the population grows at a constant absolute rate of change, at least in the average sense, then this model is reliable for as long as these conditions exist.

29. Let W represent the weight of the dog in pounds, and t the time in years. The slope of the model is $(15 - 2.5) \div (1 - 0) = 12.5$ pounds per year, so the linear function is $W = 12.5t + 2.5$. When the dog is 5 years old, its weight is $W = 12.5 \times 5 + 2.5 = 65$ pounds, and at age 10, it weighs $W = 12.5 \times 10 + 2.5 = 127.5$ pounds. The model is accurate only for small ages.

30. The cost of leasing the bike is $L = 150m + 200$, where L is the cost in dollars, and m is time, measured in months. Set $L = 6500$ and solve for m to find the length of the lease that costs as much as the purchase price of the bike.
$$6500 = 150m + 200$$
$$6300 = 150m$$
$$m = 6300/150 = 42 \text{ months.}$$
After 42 months, the cost of leasing the bike is more than the cost of buying it outright.

31. Let P represent the profit (or loss) realized when selling n raffle tickets. The initial cost of the raffle to the fundraisers is $350 (a negative profit), and the rate of change of the profit with respect to the number of tickets sold is $10 per ticket. Thus the profit function is $P = 10n - 350$. One can see by inspection that 35 tickets must be sold to break even.

32. Let P represent the profit (or loss) realized when selling n tickets. The initial cost to the fundraisers is $100 (a negative profit), and the rate of change of the profit with respect to the number of tickets sold is $4 per ticket. Thus the profit function is $P = 4n - 100$. One can see by inspection that 25 tickets must be sold to break even.

33. Let V represent the value of the washing machine, and let t represent time (in years). The value function is $V = -75t + 1200$. Set $V = 0$ and solve for t to find out how long it will take for the value to reach $0.
$$0 = -75t + 1200$$
$$75t = 1200$$
$$t = 1200/75 = 16 \text{ years.}$$

34. The daily cost of extracting 2000 tons of gold at $1000 per ton is $2,000,000. Each ton produces 3 ounces of gold, with revenue of $3p$, so the daily

revenue would be $2000 \times 3p = 6000p$. Thus the profit function is $P = 6000p - 2,000,000$. The profit will be $0 when the price of gold is $2,000,000/6000 = \$333.33$, so this is the minimum price that makes the mine profitable.

FURTHER APPLICATIONS

35. The slope is $m = 2$, and the y-intercept is $(0, 6)$.

36. The slope is $m = -3$, and the y-intercept is $(0, 3)$.

37. The slope is $m = -5$, and the y-intercept is $(0, -5)$.

38. The slope is $m = 4$, and the y-intercept is $(0, 1)$.

39. The slope is $m = 3$, and the y-intercept is $(0, -6)$.
40. The slope is $m = -2$, and the y-intercept is $(0, 5)$.
41. The slope is $m = -1$, and the y-intercept is $(0, 4)$.
42. The slope is $m = 2$, and the y-intercept is $(0, 4)$.
    Graphs for Exercises 39–42:

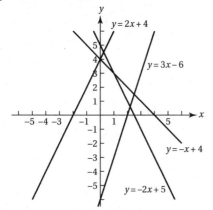

43. The independent and dependent variables are *time* and *elevation*, respectively.

After 3.5 hours, the elevation of the climbers is $6500 + 600 \times 3.5 = 8600$ feet. The model is reasonable provided the rate of ascent is nearly constant.

44. The independent and dependent variables are *time* and *diameter*, respectively.

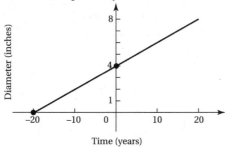

As shown in the graph, the tree needs 20 years to grow from 0 to 4 inches. This can be solved algebraically by creating an equation for the diameter of the tree: $d = 0.2t + 4$. Here it is understood that t is measured in years, beginning from the time you first measured the tree's diameter. Set $d = 0$ in the equation, and solve for t to find that $t = -20$, which means the tree began

growing 20 years ago. The assumption that the tree grows linearly with respect to time would need to be evaluated by a biologist.

45. The independent and dependent variables are *number of posters* and *cost*, respectively.

The cost of producing 2000 posters is $2000 + 2000 \times 3 = \$8000$. This function probably gives a fairly realistic estimate of printing costs.

46. The independent and dependent variables are *time* and *amount of sugar*, respectively.

Solve $0 = -0.1t + 5$ for t to find that the sugar is gone in 50 days (this is also evident from the graph). A biologist (or beer master at a brewery) would need to assess the assumption that the sugar consumption rate is constant.

47. The independent and dependent variables are *time* and *cost*, respectively.

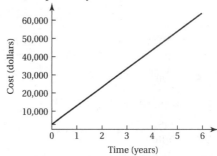

The cost of 6 years of school is $2000 + 10,000 \times 6 = \$62,000$. Provided costs do not change during the six-year period, this function is an accurate model of the cost.

48. The independent and dependent variables are *load* and *maximum speed*, respectively.

The maximum speed decreases by 10 mph for every additional 20 tons of cargo, so the slope of the graph is –0.5 mph/ton. To find the load at which the maximum speed is 0, solve $0 = -0.5w + 50$ for w (weight). This results in $w = 100$ tons. Maximum truck speeds most likely don't decrease linearly with load, but the model probably gives a rough approximation.

49. a. Half of the fish caught in the second outing are tagged, and this means the proportion of those tagged in the entire population is 1/2. Thus $200/N = 1/2$, which implies $N = 400$ fish.

b. One-fourth of the fish caught in the second outing are tagged, and this means the proportion of those tagged in the entire population is 1/4. Thus $200/N = 1/4$, which implies $N = 800$ fish.

c. If p represents the proportion of those caught in the second outing that are tagged, we have $200/N = p$, which implies $N = f(p) = 200/p$.

d. Graph not supplied, though it looks similar to $y = 1/x$, with domain of $0 < p \le 1$. When p is small, N is very large, and when p is close to 1, N is close to 200. Note that the above domain is the domain of the mathematical model, not the set of all possible values of p that could be observed in such a study. Consider a situation where only 200 fish are caught in the first outing from a very large lake with a large fish population. On the second outing, you may find that none of the 200 fish caught is tagged, in which case $p = 0$. This makes sense in the field, but it does not make sense in the mathematical model, because we cannot predict the fish population by using $N = 200/0$ (division by 0 is not allowed).

e. If $p = 15\% = 0.15$, $N = 200/0.15 = 1333$ fish.

UNIT 9C

TIME OUT TO THINK

Pg. 537. This guide was completed before the 2010 census results were available, but you should find them at the Census Bureau web site. Use

$Q = Q_0 \times (1+r)^{90}$, with the updated values of Q_0 and r to calculate the new projected population for 2100.

Pg. 539. This guide was completed before the 2010 census results were available, but you should find them at the Census Bureau web site. Use $Q = Q_0 \times (1.005)^{90}$ and $Q = Q_0 \times (1.009)^{90}$, with the updated value of Q_0 to calculate the new projected population for 2100.

QUICK QUIZ

1. **a.** Q_0 represents the initial value in the exponential model.

2. **b.** The variable r represents the growth rate, expressed as a decimal (and 3% = 0.03).

3. **a.** The population of India at any time t is given by $1,150,000,000 \times 1.016^t$.

4. **c.** Because the value of the dollar is decreasing, r is negative.

5. **c.** If you start out with a positive quantity, and remove half of it, half still remains (and it is a positive quantity, which can never equal 0).

6. **b.** If you know the initial amount and half-life of any exponentially decreasing quantity, you can use $Q = Q_0 \times \left(\dfrac{1}{2}\right)^{t/T_{\text{half}}}$ to predict the future amount after any time t.

7. **c.** You need to know both the initial amount Q_0 and the amount at some future time t in order to solve the exponential model $Q = Q_0 \times \left(\dfrac{1}{2}\right)^{t/T_{\text{half}}}$ for t (you must also know T_{half}, but we are given that).

8. **c.** Because 1/16 of the original uranium is present, we know it has undergone 4 halving periods, and since each of these is 700 million years, the rock is 4 × 700 million = 2.8 billion years old.

9. **a.** When you solve $\dfrac{1}{25}Q_0 = Q_0 \times \left(\dfrac{1}{2}\right)^{t/700,000,000}$ for t, you get the expression given in answer **a.**

10. **a.** We know $Q = Q_0 (1+r)^t$, and $Q = Q_0 \times 2^{t/T_{\text{double}}}$, and thus $Q_0 (1+r)^t = Q_0 \times 2^{t/T_{\text{double}}}$. Divide both sides by Q_0 to get the result shown in the answer.

DOES IT MAKE SENSE?

7. Does not make sense. After 100 years, the population growing at 2% per year will have increased by a factor of $1.02^{100} = 7.245$, whereas

the population growing at 1% per year will have increased by a factor of $1.01^{100} = 2.705$. Under only very special circumstances will the first population grow by twice as many people as the second population. (Let Q_0 represent the initial amount of the population growing by 2%, and R_0 the initial amount of the population growing by 1%. After 100 years, Q_0 will have grown to $7.245Q_0$, and thus will have grown by $7.245Q_0 - Q_0 = 6.245Q_0$. In a similar fashion, it can be shown that R_0 will have grown by $1.705R_0$. We need $6.245Q_0 = 2 \times 1.705R_0$ in order to satisfy the condition that the first population will grow by twice as many people as the second population. This implies that the ratio $R_0/Q_0 = 6.245/3.41 = 1.83$. In other words, whenever the initial amount of the second population is 1.83 times as large as the initial amount of the first population, the first population will grow by twice as many people in 100 years. (Try it with initial populations of 100 and 183.)

8. Makes sense. The growth rate for an exponentially decreasing quantity is always negative.

9. Makes sense. If we know the half-life of the radioactive material, we can create an exponential function that models the quantity remaining as time passes. In order to use this model to determine ages of bones, we only need to measure the amount of radioactive material present in the bone, and the amount it had originally (the latter is usually surmised by making assumptions about conditions present at the time of death).

10. Makes sense. Money invested in a bank grows at a constant rate of relative change as long as the APR is constant, and thus it is appropriate to use an exponential function.

BASIC CONCEPTS & SKILLS

11. $2^x = 128 \Rightarrow \log_{10} 2^x = \log_{10} 128 \Rightarrow x \log_{10} 2 = \log_{10} 128 \Rightarrow x = \dfrac{\log_{10} 128}{\log_{10} 2} = 7$.

12. $10^x = 23 \Rightarrow \log_{10} 10^x = \log_{10} 23 \Rightarrow x = 1.36$.

13. $3^x = 99 \Rightarrow \log_{10} 3^x = \log_{10} 99 \Rightarrow x \log_{10} 3 = \log_{10} 99 \Rightarrow x = \dfrac{\log_{10} 99}{\log_{10} 3} = 4.18$.

14. $5^{2x} = 240 \Rightarrow \log_{10} 5^{2x} = \log_{10} 240 \Rightarrow 2x \log_{10} 5 = \log_{10} 240 \Rightarrow x = \dfrac{\log_{10} 240}{2 \log_{10} 5} = 1.70$.

15. $7^{3x} = 623 \Rightarrow \log_{10} 7^{3x} = \log_{10} 623 \Rightarrow 3x \log_{10} 7 = \log_{10} 623 \Rightarrow x = \dfrac{\log_{10} 623}{3 \log_{10} 7} = 1.10$.

16. $3 \times 4^x = 180 \Rightarrow 4^x = 60 \Rightarrow \log_{10} 4^x = \log_{10} 60 \Rightarrow x \log_{10} 4 = \log_{10} 60 \Rightarrow x = \dfrac{\log_{10} 60}{\log_{10} 4} = 2.95$.

17. $9^x = 1748 \Rightarrow x = \dfrac{\log_{10} 1748}{\log_{10} 9} = 3.40$.

    (See exercise 13 for a similar process of solution.)

18. $3^{x/4} = 444 \Rightarrow x = \dfrac{4 \log_{10} 444}{\log_{10} 3} = 22.19$.

    (See exercise 14 for a similar process of solution).

19. $\log_{10} x = 4 \Rightarrow 10^{\log_{10} x} = 10^4 \Rightarrow x = 10,000$.

20. $\log_{10} x = -3 \Rightarrow 10^{\log_{10} x} = 10^{-3} \Rightarrow x = 0.001$.

21. $\log_{10} x = 3.5 \Rightarrow x = 10^{3.5} = 3162.28$.

    (See exercise 19 for a similar process of solution).

22. $\log_{10} x = -2.2 \Rightarrow x = 10^{-2.2} = 0.0063$.

    (See exercise 20 for a similar process of solution).

23. $3 \log_{10} x = 4.2 \Rightarrow \log_{10} x = 1.4 \Rightarrow x = 10^{1.4} = 25.12$.

24. $\log_{10} 3x = 5.1 \Rightarrow 3x = 10^{5.1} \Rightarrow x = 41,964.18$.

25. $\log_{10}(4 + x) = 1.1 \Rightarrow 4 + x = 10^{1.1} \Rightarrow x = 8.59$.

26. $4 \log_{10}(4x) = 4 \Rightarrow \log_{10}(4x) = 1 \Rightarrow 4x = 10^1 \Rightarrow x = 2.50$.

27. a. $Q = 60,000 \times (1.025)^t$, where Q is the population of the town, and t is time (measured in years).

    b.

Year	Population
0	60,000
1	61,500
2	63,038
3	64,613
4	66,229
5	67,884
6	69,582
7	71,321
8	73,104
9	74,932
10	76,805

c.

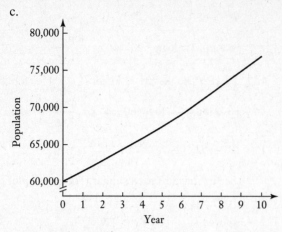

28. a. $Q = 800 \times (1.03)^t$, where Q is the number of restaurants, and t is time, measured in years, with $t = 0$ corresponding to 2001.

b.

Year	Restaurants
0	800
1	824
2	849
3	874
4	900
5	927
6	955
7	984
8	1013
9	1044
10	1075

c.

29. a. $Q = 1,000,000 \times (0.93)^t$, where Q is the number of acres of forest left after t years.

b.

Year	Acres ($\times 10^6$)
0	1.00
1	0.93
2	0.86
3	0.80
4	0.75
5	0.70
6	0.65
7	0.60
8	0.56
9	0.52
10	0.48

c.

30. a. $Q = 10,000 \times (0.997)^t$, where Q is the population of the town after t years.

b.

Month	Population
0	10,000
1	9970
2	9940
3	9910
4	9881
5	9851
6	9821
7	9792
8	9763
9	9733
10	9704

c.

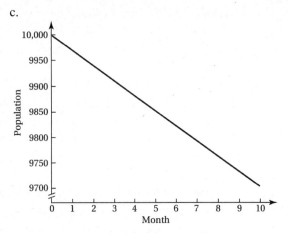

31. a. $Q = 175,000 \times (1.05)^t$, where Q is the average price of a home in dollars, and t is time, measured in years, with $t = 0$ corresponding to 2007.

   b.

Year	Average price
0	$175,000
1	$183,750
2	$192,938
3	$202,584
4	$212,714
5	$223,349
6	$234,517
7	$246,243
8	$258,555
9	$271,482
10	$285,057

   c.

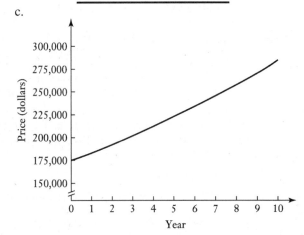

32. a. $Q = 8 \times (0.85)^t$, where Q is the amount of the drug remaining in the blood stream, measured in milligrams, and t is time, measured in hours.

b.

Hour	Drug (mg)
0	8.00
1	6.80
2	5.78
3	4.91
4	4.18
5	3.55
6	3.02
7	2.56
8	2.18
9	1.85
10	1.57

c.

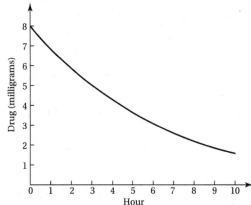

33. a. $Q = 2000 \times (1.05)^t$, where Q is your monthly salary in dollars, and t is time, measured in years.

   b.

Year	Monthly Salary
0	$2000.00
1	$2100.00
2	$2205.00
3	$2315.25
4	$2431.01
5	$2552.56
6	$2680.19
7	$2814.20
8	$2954.91
9	$3102.66
10	$3257.79

c.

34. a. $Q = 10,000 \times (0.5)^t$, where Q is the value of the 100,000 rubles, measured in dollars, and t is time in years, with $t = 0$ corresponding to 1991.

b.

Year	Value of rubles
0	$10,000
1	$5000
2	$2500
3	$1250
4	$625
5	$313
6	$156
7	$78
8	$39
9	$20
10	$10

c.

35. Over the span of a year, prices will increase by a factor of $(1.015)^{12} = 1.196$, which is a 19.6% increase.

36. Over the span of a year, the fraction by which the price of gold will change is $(0.99)^{12} = 0.886$, which implies a 11.4% decrease.

37. Over the course of a year, prices would have risen by a factor of $(1.8)^{12} = 1156.83$, or an annual increase of 115,683%. Assuming one day is 1/30 of a month, prices would rise by a factor of $(1.8)^{(1/30)} = 1.0198$ in one day, which is a 1.98% increase.

38. Over the course of a year, prices would have risen by a factor of $(1.9)^{12} = 2213.31$, or an annual increase of 221,231%. Assuming one day is 1/30 of a month, prices would rise by a factor of $(1.9)^{(1/30)} = 1.0216$ in one day, which is a 2.16% increase.

39. An exponential model for the animal population is $Q = 1500 \times (0.92)^t$. We need to find the time t that will produce a population $Q = 30$ animals, which amounts to solving $30 = 1500 \times (0.92)^t$ for t.

$$\frac{30}{1500} = 0.92^t \Rightarrow 0.02 = 0.92^t \Rightarrow \log_{10} 0.02 =$$

$$\log_{10} 0.92^t \Rightarrow \log_{10} 0.02 = t \log_{10} 0.92 \Rightarrow$$

$$t = \frac{\log_{10} 0.02}{\log_{10} 0.92} = 46.92 \text{ years.}$$

40. a. An exponential model for oil production, valid between 1950 and 1972, is $Q = 518 \times (1.07)^t$, where Q is measured in millions of tons, and $t = 0$ corresponds with 1950. In 1972, $t = 22$, so oil production was $Q = 518 \times (1.07)^{22} = 2295$ million tons, or about 2.3 billion tons.

b. In 2008, 36 years beyond 1972, oil production would have been $Q = 2.3(1.07)^{36} = 26.3$ billion tons, assuming a constant growth rate of 7%. This is considerably larger than the actual 2008 level of 3.9 billion tons.

c. In 2008, 36 years beyond 1972, oil production would have been $Q = 2.3 \times (1.03)^{36} = 6.7$ billion tons, assuming a constant growth rate of 3%. This is still larger than the actual 2008 level of 3.9 billion tons.

d. Based on the answer to part **c**, the average annual growth rate between 1972 and 2008 was less than 3%. Experiment with various values of r in $3.9 = 2.3 \times (1+r)^{36}$ to find that $r \sim 1.5\%$ per year. One can also solve the equation using algebra: $3.9 = 2.3 \times (1+r)^{36} \Rightarrow \frac{3.9}{2.3} = (1+r)^{36}$

Now raise both sides to the reciprocal power of 36, i.e. to the 1/36 power, and then subtract 1 to find $r = \left(\frac{3.9}{2.3}\right)^{1/36} - 1 = 0.014777 = 1.5\%$.

41. a. An exponential model for the amount of Valium in the bloodstream is $Q = 50 \times \left(\frac{1}{2}\right)^{t/36}$. After 12 hours, there will be $Q = 50 \times \left(\frac{1}{2}\right)^{12/36} = 39.7$ mg.

b. Ten percent of the initial amount is 5 mg, so solve $5 = 50 \times \left(\frac{1}{2}\right)^{t/36}$ for t:

$0.1 = (0.5)^{t/36} \Rightarrow \log_{10} 0.1 = \log_{10}(0.5)^{t/36} \Rightarrow$

$\log_{10} 0.1 = \frac{t}{36} \log_{10} 0.5 \Rightarrow t = \frac{36 \log_{10} 0.1}{\log_{10} 0.5} \Rightarrow$

$$t = 120 \text{ hours.}$$

42. a. At 6:00 p.m., there will be $Q = 300 \times \left(\frac{1}{2}\right)^{6/8} =$ 178.4 mg. At midnight, $Q = 300 \times \left(\frac{1}{2}\right)^{12/8} =$ 106.1 mg. At noon the next day, $Q = 300 \times \left(\frac{1}{2}\right)^{24/8} = 37.5$ mg.

b. Five percent of the original amount is 15 mg, so solve $15 = 300 \times \left(\frac{1}{2}\right)^{t/8}$ for t.

$0.05 = (0.5)^{t/8} \Rightarrow \log_{10} 0.05 = \log_{10}(0.5)^{t/8} \Rightarrow$

$\log_{10} 0.05 = \frac{t}{8} \log_{10} 0.5 \Rightarrow t = \frac{8 \log_{10} 0.05}{\log_{10} 0.5} \Rightarrow$

$$t = 35 \text{ hours.}$$

43. a. An exponential model for the amount of uranium left is $Q = Q_0 \times \left(\frac{1}{2}\right)^{t/4.5}$, where t is measured in billions of years. We want to determine t when the amount Q is equal to 65% of the original amount, i.e. when $Q = 0.65 Q_0$. Solve $0.65 Q_0 = Q_0 \times \left(\frac{1}{2}\right)^{t/4.5}$ for t – begin by dividing both sides by Q_0:

$0.65 = \left(\frac{1}{2}\right)^{t/4.5} \Rightarrow \log_{10} 0.65 = \log_{10}(0.5)^{t/4.5} \Rightarrow$

$\log_{10} 0.65 = \frac{t}{4.5} \log_{10} 0.5 \Rightarrow t = \frac{4.5 \log_{10} 0.65}{\log_{10} 0.5} \Rightarrow$

$$t = 2.8 \text{ billion years old.}$$

b. Following the same process shown in part **a**, we have $t = \frac{4.5 \log_{10} 0.45}{\log_{10} 0.5} = 5.2$ billion years old.

44. a. An exponential model for the amount of carbon-14 left is $Q = Q_0 \times \left(\frac{1}{2}\right)^{t/5700}$, where t is measured in years. We want to determine t when the amount Q is equal to 63% of the original amount, i.e. when $Q = 0.63 Q_0$. Solve $0.63 Q_0 = Q_0 \times \left(\frac{1}{2}\right)^{t/5700}$ for t – begin by dividing both sides by Q_0

$0.63 = \left(\frac{1}{2}\right)^{t/5700} \Rightarrow \log_{10} 0.63 = \log_{10}(0.5)^{t/5700}$

$\log_{10} 0.63 = \frac{t}{5700} \log_{10} 0.5 \Rightarrow t = \frac{5700 \log_{10} 0.63}{\log_{10} 0.5}$

$$t = 3799 \text{ years.}$$

The cloth was painted 3799 years ago.

b. Following the same process shown in part **a**, we have $t = \frac{5700 \log_{10} 0.123}{\log_{10} 0.5} = 17{,}233$ years ago.

c. The age of the earth is about 4.5 billion years old. The half-life of carbon-14 is only 5700 years, and thus carbon-14 present at the formation of the earth has long since decayed to immeasurably small amounts (it has undergone almost 800,000 halving periods, far more than necessary to decrease any imaginable amount of carbon-14 to an amount that is essentially zero).

FURTHER APPLICATIONS

45. An exponential model for the amount of radioactive substance is $Q = 3 \times \left(\frac{1}{2}\right)^{t/20}$, where Q is the density of the substance in mg/cm^2, and t is time in years, with $t = 0$ corresponding to the present. This model is valid for times in the past – we need only assign negative values for t. Thus 55 years ago corresponds with $t = -55$, so the density at that time was $Q = 3 \times \left(\frac{1}{2}\right)^{-55/20} = 20.2$ mg/cm^2. One can also solve $3 = Q_0 \times \left(\frac{1}{2}\right)^{55/20}$ for Q_0 to produce the same result.

46. In 2020 ($t = 10$ years beyond 2010), the population will be $Q = 110{,}000 \times (1.02)^{10}$ which is about 134,100.

To find the maximum growth rate cap, experiment with various values of r in $150{,}000 = 110{,}000 \times (1+r)^{15}$ to find that $r \approx 2.1\%$

per year. One can also solve the equation using algebra:

$$150,000 = 110,000 \times (1+r)^{15} \implies \frac{150,000}{110,000} = (1+r)^{15}.$$

Now raise both sides to the reciprocal power of 15, i.e. to the 1/15 power, and then subtract 1 to find $r = \left(\frac{150,000}{110,000}\right)^{1/15} - 1 = 0.021 = 2.1\%$.

47. The cart of groceries cost $Q = \$150 \times (1.032)^5 = \$175.59$.

48. a. An exponential model for the amount of antibiotic left in the bloodstream is $Q = Q_0 \times \left(\frac{1}{2}\right)^{t/8}$, where t is measured in hours.

The amount of antibiotic in the bloodstream *just prior* to the second dose (after 8 hours) is $100 \times \left(\frac{1}{2}\right)^{8/8} = 50$ milligrams. The amount of antibiotic in the bloodstream *just after* the second dose is 50 + 100 = 150 milligrams.

b. The amount of antibiotic in the bloodstream *just prior* to the third dose (after 16 hours) is $150 \times \left(\frac{1}{2}\right)^{8/8} = 75$ milligrams. The amount of antibiotic in the bloodstream *just after* the third dose is 75 + 100 = 175 milligrams.

The amount of antibiotic in the bloodstream *just prior* to the fourth dose (after 24 hours) is $175 \times \left(\frac{1}{2}\right)^{8/8} = 87.5$ milligrams. The amount of antibiotic in the bloodstream *just after* the fourth dose is 87.5 + 100 = 187.5 milligrams.

The amount of antibiotic in the bloodstream *just prior* to the fifth dose (after 32 hours) is $187.5 \times \left(\frac{1}{2}\right)^{8/8} = 93.75$ milligrams. The amount of antibiotic in the bloodstream *just after* the fourth dose is 93.75 + 100 = 193.75 milligrams.

If the doses every 8 hours continue to occur, the amount of antibiotic will approach 100 milligrams prior to each new dose.

c. Graph not provided.

d. Answers will vary

49. a. Experiment with various values of r in $380 = 290 \times (1+r)^{150}$ to find that $r \approx 0.0018$ or 0.18% per year. One can also solve the equation using algebra: $380 = 290 \times (1+r)^{150} \implies \frac{380}{290} = (1+r)^{150}$.

Now raise both sides to the reciprocal power of 150, i.e. to the 1/150 power, and then subtract 1 to find $r = \left(\frac{380}{290}\right)^{1/150} - 1 = 0.0018$ or 0.18%.

b. We want to determine t when the amount Q is double the original amount, i.e. when $Q = 2Q_0$. Since $Q_0 = 290$, $2Q_0 = 580$. Solve $580 = 290 \times (1.0018)^t$ for t. Begin by dividing both sides by 290: $2 = (1.0018)^t \implies$

$2 = (1.0018)^t \implies \log_{10} 2 = \log_{10}(1.0018)^t \implies$

$\log_{10} 2 = t \log_{10} 1.0018 \implies t = \frac{\log_{10} 2}{\log_{10} 1.0018} \implies$

t = 385 years. The CO_2 concentration will be double its 1860 level in 2245.

c. Answers will vary.

UNIT 10A

TIME OUT TO THINK

Pg. 553(1ˢᵗ). Answers will vary. This would be a good topic for a discussion either during or outside of class.

Pg. 553(2ⁿᵈ). Answers will vary. Possible answers include a golf ball in the air for a point, a straight handrail for a line segment, and the cover of a mathematics book for a plane segment.

Pg. 554. Acute means sharp in the context of both angles and illness. Obtuse means dull, or less sharp.

Pg. 556. Polytheism and polyester may come up. Polyester is a synthetic made from polymer resins which are made from two or more compounds. In most cases, the suffix poly-means "two or more."

QUICK QUIZ

1. **a**. As long as the points are distinct, two points are sufficient to determine a unique line.
2. **b**. The surface of a wall is similar to a plane, which is two-dimensional.
3. **a**. By definition, an acute angle has measure less than 90°.
4. **c**. By definition, a regular polygon is a many-sided figure where each side has the same length, and each internal angle is the same.
5. **b**. By definition, a right triangle has one 90° angle.
6. **a**. The formula for the circumference of a circle of radius r is $C = 2\pi r$.
7. **c**. The formula for the volume of a sphere of radius r is $V = \frac{4}{3}\pi r^3$.
8. **c**. Suppose the side length of a square is denoted by s. Its area is then s^2. If the lengths of the sides are doubled to $2s$, the area becomes $(2s)^2 = 4s^2$, and this is 4 times as large as the original area.
9. **c**. The volume of a sphere whose radius has tripled from r to $3r$ is $V = \frac{4}{3}\pi(3r)^3 = 3^3 \cdot \frac{4}{3}\pi r^3$.
10. **a**. The volume of a block does not increase when it is cut into pieces, though its surface area does, which implies is surface-area-to-volume ratio does as well.

DOES IT MAKE SENSE?

11. Does not make sense. If the highways are, in fact, straight lines, they will not intersect more than once.

12. Does not make sense. A triangle can have no more than one right angle, as the sum of its three angles is 180° (and thus two right angles would leave no room for a third).
13. Makes sense. A rectangular prism is just a box.
14. Makes sense. The distance across a circle (its diameter) is smaller than the distance half way around it.
15. Does not make sense. Basketballs are in the shape of a sphere (a can is shaped like a right circular cylinder).
16. Makes sense. Construct the fence along the diagonal of the yard, and you'll have two triangular yards.

BASIC SKILLS & CONCEPTS

17. One-half of a circle is 180°.
18. One-sixth of a circle is 60°.
19. One-tenth of a circle is 36°.
20. Two-thirds of a circle is 240°.
21. One-sixtieth of a circle is 6°.
22. Five-sixths of a circle is 300°.
23. A 45° angle subtends 45°/360° = 1/8 circle.
24. A 6° angle subtends 6°/360° = 1/60 circle.
25. A 120° angle subtends 120°/360° = 1/3 circle.
26. A 90° angle subtends 90°/360° = 1/4 circle.
27. A 270° angle subtends 270°/360° = 3/4 circle.
28. An 18° angle subtends 18°/360° = 1/20 circle.
29. A 300° angle subtends 300°/360° = 5/6 circle.
30. A 225° angle subtends 225°/360° = 5/8 circle.
31. $C = 2\pi \times 8 = 16\pi$ m = 50.3 m. $A = \pi \cdot 8^2 = 64\pi = 201.1$ m^2.
32. $C = 2\pi \times 3 = 6\pi$ km = 18.8 km. $A = \pi \cdot 3^2 = 9\pi = 28.3$ km^2.
33. $C = 2\pi \times 8 = 16\pi$ cm = 50.3 cm. $A = \pi \cdot 8^2 = 64\pi = 201.1$ cm^2.
34. $C = 2\pi \times 4.5 = 9\pi = 28.3$ m. $A = \pi \cdot 4.5^2 = 20.25\pi = 63.6$ m^2.
35. $C = 2\pi \times 15 = 30\pi$ mm = 94.2 mm. $A = \pi \cdot 15^2 = 225\pi = 706.9$ mm^2.
36. $C = 2\pi \times 0.75 = 1.5\pi$ km = 4.7 km. $A = \pi \cdot 0.75^2 = 0.5625\pi = 1.8$ km^2.
37. The perimeter is 4 × 9 = 36 mi. The area is 9 × 9 = 81 mi^2.
38. The perimeter is 2 × 8 + 2 × 14 = 44 in. The area is 8 × 14 = 112 in.^{2}.
39. The perimeter is 2 × 12 + 2 × 30 = 84 ft. The area is 30 × 6 = 180 ft^2.
40. The perimeter is 4 × 1.4 = 5.6 cm. The area is 1.4 × 1.4 = 1.96 cm^2.

41. The perimeter is $2 \times 2.2 + 2 \times 2.0 = 8.4$ cm. The area is $2.2 \times 2.0 = 4.4$ cm^2.

42. The perimeter is $2 \times 4.5 + 2 \times 12.2 = 33.4$ ft. The area is $12.2 \times 3.6 = 43.92$ ft^2.

43. The perimeter is $6 + 8 + 10 = 24$ units. The area is $\frac{1}{2} \times 8 \times 6 = 24$ units^2.

44. The perimeter is $3.125 + 1.875 + 2.5 = 7.5$ units. The area is $\frac{1}{2} \times 3.125 \times 1.5 = 2.34$ units^2.

45. The perimeter is $8 + 5 + 5 = 18$ units. The area is $\frac{1}{2} \times 8 \times 3 = 12$ units^2.

46. The perimeter is $13 + 13 + 24 = 50$ units. The area is $\frac{1}{2} \times 24 \times 5 = 60$ units^2.

47. The two semicircular caps together make a single circle, whose radius is 3 feet. The perimeter, then, is $2 \times 8 + 2\pi \times 3 = 34.85$ ft, and the area is $6 \times 8 + \pi \times 3^2 = 76.27$ ft^2.

48. The two semicircular ends of the track together make a single circle, whose radius is 30 yards. The perimeter, then, is $2 \times 100 + 2\pi \times 30 = 388.5$ yd, and the area is $60 \times 100 + \pi \times 30^2 = 8827.4$ yd^2.

49. The area is $\frac{1}{2} \times 12 \times 11 = 66$ ft^2.

50. The barn on the left has the greater area because the height of its triangular roof section is larger.

51. The area of the parallelogram is $180 \times 150 = 27,500$ yd^2.

52. The area of the park is $90 \times 60 = 5400$ m^2. The area of the playground is $20 \times 55 = 1100$ m^2. Thus the grassy area is 5400 m^2 – 1100 m^2 = 4300 m^2.

53. The pool holds $50 \times 30 \times 2.5 = 3750$ m^3.

54. The arena holds $30 \times 40 \times 8 = 9600$ m^3. One liter is 1000 cubic centimeters, and thus 0.001 cubic meters, which means each cubic meter holds 1000 liters. This implies the arena holds 9,600,000 liters.

55. The duct is in the shape of a cylinder, and so its volume is $\pi \times 1.5^2 \times 40 = 282.7$ ft^3 (note that 18 inches is 1.5 feet). The surface area of the duct is $2\pi \times 1.5 \times 40 = 377.0$ ft^2. We are assuming here that there are no circular end pieces on the duct that need to be painted. If there are end pieces, the area would increase by $2\pi \times 1.5^2 = 14.1$ ft^2.

56. The ball's circumference is 69 cm, so its radius is $r = 69 \div 2\pi = 10.98$ cm (rounded). Its volume is $\frac{4}{3} \times \pi \times r^3 = 5547.5$ cm^3 (using an un-rounded value for r), and its surface area is $4\pi \times r^2 = 1515.5$ cm^2.

57. The circumference is greater because it is π diameters (of a tennis ball) long, whereas the height is only 3 diameters tall.

58. When the canal is full, there are $3 \times 2 \times 30 = 180$ m^3 of water. If 60% of the water has evaporated, 40% of 180 cubic meters, or 72 cubic meters remain.

59. The volume of the reservoir is $250 \times 60 \times 12 = 180,000$ m^3. 30% of this volume, which is 54,000 m^3, must be added.

60. The first drum has greater volume ($\pi \times 2^2 \times 3 = 37.7$ ft^3), than the second drum (whose volume is $\pi \times 1.5^2 \times 4 = 28.3$ ft^3).

61. The first tree has greater volume ($\pi \times 2.1^2 \times 40 = 554.2$ ft^3) than the second tree (whose volume is $\pi \times 2.4^2 \times 30 = 542.9$ ft^3).

62. The height of the concert hall will be 30 times as large as the height of the model.

63. The surface area of the concert hall will be $30^2 = 900$ times as great as the surface area of the model (because areas always scale with the square of the scale factor).

64. The volume of the concert hall will be $30^3 = 27,000$ times as large as the volume of the model (because volumes always scale with the cube of the scale factor).

65. The height of the office complex will be 80 times as large as the height of the model.

66. The amount of paint needed is a function of the surface area, so you will need $80^2 = 6400$ times as much paint for the office complex than for the model (areas scale with the square of the scale factor).

67. You would need $80^3 = 512,000$ times as many marbles to fill the office complex (volumes always scale with the cube of the scale factor).

68. Your arm length has increased by a factor of 4.

69. Your waist size is a measurement of length, so it has increased by a factor of 4.

70. The material required for your clothes is a function of surface area, so the amount needed has increased by a factor of 16.

71. Your weight is a function of your volume, so it has increased by a factor of 64.

72. Answers will vary. Example: I'm 70 inches tall, and Sam is 1.2 × 70 = 84 inches tall.

73. Answers will vary. Example: My waist size is 32 inches, and Sam's is 1.2 × 32 = 38.4 inches.

74. Answers will vary. Example: My weight is 155 lb, and Sam weighs $1.2^3 \times 155 = 268$ lb.

75. Think of a soup can (a squirrel) and a trash can (a human), compute their surface areas and volumes, find their surface-area-to-volume ratios, and you will discover that the surface-area-to-volume ratio for squirrels is larger than that of humans. Another way to understand this fact: surface area scales with the square of the scale factor, whereas volume scales with the cube of the scale factor. Thus the surface-area-to-volume ratio decreases when objects are scaled up (and in fact, it scales with the reciprocal of the scale factor).

76. Squirrels lose more heat for their volume (or weight) than humans because of their larger surface-area-to-volume ratio, so squirrels must maintain a higher metabolism and eat more food for their weight.

77. The moon's surface-area-to-volume ratio is four (i.e. the scale factor) times as large as Earth's, (see discussion at the end of exercise 75).

78. Based only upon the result of exercise 77, the earth should have a hotter interior today because its surface-area-to-volume ratio is lower, and thus it radiates less heat per unit volume than the moon. A hot interior leads to more volcanic activity. Note that the earth also has the benefit of an atmosphere, which helps to retain heat.

79. If you understood the comment at the end of exercise 75, the surface-area-to-volume ratio of the bowling ball should be 1/3 the ratio of the softball, because the bowling ball is 3 times as large. Computing directly: The surface area of the softball is $4\pi \times 2^2 = 50.3$ in.^{2}, its volume is $\frac{4}{3}\pi \times 2^3 = 33.5$ in.^{3}, and its surface-area-to-volume ratio is 1.5. The surface area of the bowling ball is $4\pi \times 6^2 = 452.4$ in^2, its volume is $\frac{4}{3}\pi \times 6^3 = 904.8$ in^3, and its surface-area-to-volume ratio is 0.5. As expected, the ratio of the bowling ball is 1/3 the ratio of the softball.

80. The surface-area-to-volume ratio for any sphere is given by $\left(4\pi \times r^2\right) \div \left(\frac{4}{3}\pi \times r^3\right) = \frac{3}{r}$, so the ratio for the earth is 3 ÷ 6400 = 0.00047, and for Mars it is 3 ÷ 3400 = 0.00088 (Mars' ratio being larger). To compute these ratios from the surface areas and volumes of the planets, use the formulas shown above to find that the surface area for the Earth is 5.15×10^8 km^2, while its volume is 1.10×10^{12} km^3. The surface area of Mars is 1.45×10^8 km^2, while its volume is 1.65×10^{11} km^3.

FURTHER APPLICATIONS

81. a. The book occupies three-dimensional space, so three dimensions are needed to describe it.
    b. The cover of the book occupies a portion of a plane, so two dimensions are needed to describe it.
    c. An edge of the book lies along a line, so a single dimension is adequate for its description.
    d. A point is dimensionless, so anything on the book that corresponds to a point (such as a corner of a page) is of zero dimension.

82. Exactly one line can be drawn perpendicular to the first line through the given point. No other distinct parallel line can be drawn through the point.

83. The third line is necessarily perpendicular to both lines due to a theorem from geometry (when two parallel lines are cut by any other line, all three lying in the same plane, alternate interior angles are equal – this amounts to saying that if the angle between one of the parallel lines and the third line is 90°, the angle between the other parallel line and the third line is 90°).

84. The area of the backyard is $20 \times 10 = 200$ m^2, the area of the garden is $4 \times 4 = 16$ m^2, and the area of the patio is $\frac{1}{2}\pi \times 5^2 = 39.3$ m^2. Together these facts imply the area to be seeded is 200 – 16 – 39.3 = 144.7 square meters.

85. a. The surface area of an individual sac is $4\pi \times \left(\frac{1}{6}\right)^2 = 0.349$ mm^2, and the total surface area is 300 million times this value, which is 1.05×10^8 mm$^2 = 105$ m^2. The volume of a single sac is $\frac{4}{3}\pi \times \left(\frac{1}{6}\right)^3 = 0.0194$ mm^3, so the total volume is 5.82×10^6 mm^3 (multiply the individual volume by 300 million).
    b. We need to solve $5.82 \times 10^6 = \frac{4}{3}\pi \times r^3$ for r to find the radius of such a sphere. Multiply both sides of the equation by $\frac{3}{4\pi}$ and take the cube root to find $r = 112$ mm (rounded). This sphere has surface area of $4\pi \times (111.572)^2 = 1.56 \times 10^5$ mm^2.

The surface area of the air sacs is $1.05 \times 10^8 \div 1.56 \times 10^5 = 673$ times as large as the surface area of the hypothetical sphere.

c. We need to solve $1.05 \times 10^8 = 4\pi \times r^2$ for r to find the radius of such a sphere. Divide both sides by 4π and take the square root to find $r = 2891$ mm, or about 2.9 meters (i.e. more than 9 feet). The human lung has a remarkable design as it is able to take advantage of large surface area despite its relatively small volume.

86. a. The engine is $6 \times \pi \times 2.22^2 \times 3.25 = 302$ in.^{3}.

b. Convert 302 cubic inches into liters:

$$302 \text{ in.}^3 \times \left(\frac{2.54 \text{ cm}}{1 \text{ in.}}\right)^3 \times \frac{1 \text{ L}}{1000 \text{ cm}^3} = 4.95 \text{ L}.$$

The American engine is more than twice the size of the 2.2 L foreign engine.

87. The volume of one tunnel is $\frac{1}{2}\pi \times (4)^2 \times 50,000$

$= 1.26 \times 10^6$ m^3, so the volume of all three is 3.8×10^6 m$^3 = 0.0038$ km^3. Depending on whether the dimensions given are for a rough tunnel, or the structure that a motorist sees driving through it, the amount of earth removed may be considerably more than the answer provided.

UNIT 10B

TIME OUT TO THINK

Pg. 572. Any route from the library to the subway that moves only east and north will have the same length. If you have covered 7A, the correct answer of 3003 to the "how many" question can be found using the multiplication principle or with a tree. There are no shorter routes along the streets.

QUICK QUIZ

1. **c.** Each degree contains 60 minutes.
2. **b.** Each degree contains 60 minutes, and each minute contains 60 seconds.
3. **a.** Lines of latitude run east and west on the globe, parallel to the equator.
4. **b.** That you are at 30°S means you are in the southern hemisphere (and thus not in North America). A check of the globe will reveal these coordinates lie in the south Pacific.
5. **b.** Angular size is a function of the distance from the object: when the distance from an object increases, its angular size decreases.
6. **b.** Imagine a solar eclipse, when the Moon is positioned between the Earth and the Sun, and think of the triangle that stretches from a point on

Earth to the edges of the moon. Imagine another triangle that continues beyond the Moon to the edges of the Sun (a simple drawing will help you to visualize the situation). These two triangles are similar, and thus we can write the ratio $\frac{\text{diameter of Sun}}{\text{diameter of Moon}} = \frac{400x}{x}$, where x represents the distance from the Earth to the Moon. This ratio implies that the diameter of the Sun is 400 times the diameter of the Moon. One can also appeal to the angular size formula in the text to get the same result.

7. **a.** A 10% grade means the slope is 1/10, which implies a vertical change of 1 unit for every horizontal change of 10 units.

8. **a.** The Pythagorean theorem gives $x = \sqrt{6^2 + 9^2}$.

9. **a.** The statement in answer **a** is an application of the fact that the ratio of corresponding sides in a pair of similar triangles is equal to the ratio of a different set of corresponding sides.

10. **b.** As explained in Example 9 of the text, a circle is the solution to the problem of enclosing the largest possible area with a fixed perimeter.

DOES IT MAKE SENSE?

9. Does not make sense. Points south of the equator experience summer in December.
10. Does not make sense. We see the angular size of the Moon, not its physical size.
11. Makes sense. As long as the speaker can ride a bike, a 7% grade should pose no difficulty.
12. Does not make sense. The sum of the angles in all triangles is 180°, yet not all triangles are similar.
13. Makes sense. Triangle B is just a scaled up version of Triangle A, so they are similar.
14. Makes sense. As stated in Example 10 of the text, a cube-shaped box is the one with smallest surface area for a given volume.

BASIC SKILLS & CONCEPTS

15. $32.5° = 32° + 0.5° \times \frac{60'}{1°} = 32°30'$.

16. $280.1° = 280° + 0.1° \times \frac{60'}{1°} = 280°6'$.

17. $12.33° = 12° + 0.33° \times \frac{60'}{1°} = 12°19.8' =$

$12° + 19' + 0.8' \times \frac{60''}{1'} = 12°19'48''$.

18. $0.08° = 0.08° \times \frac{60'}{1°} = 0°4.8' = 0° + 4' + 0.8' \times \frac{60''}{1'} = 0°4'48''$.

19. $149.83° = 149° + 0.83° \times \dfrac{60'}{1°} = 149°49.8' =$

    $149° + 49' + 0.8' \times \dfrac{60''}{1'} = 149°49'48''$.

20. $47.6723° = 47° + 0.6723° \times \dfrac{60'}{1°} = 47°40.338' =$

    $47° + 40' + 0.338' \times \dfrac{60''}{1'} = 47°40'20''$.

21. $30°10' = 30° + 10' \times \dfrac{1°}{60'} = 30.17°$.

22. $60°30'30'' = 60° + 30' \times \dfrac{1°}{60'} + 30'' \times \dfrac{1°}{3600''} =$ $60.51°$.

23. $123°10'36'' = 123° + 10' \times \dfrac{1°}{60'} + 36'' \times \dfrac{1°}{3600''} =$ $123.18°$.

24. $2°2'2'' = 2° + 2' \times \dfrac{1°}{60'} + 2'' \times \dfrac{1°}{3600''} = 2.03°$.

25. $8°59'10'' = 8° + 59' \times \dfrac{1°}{60'} + 10'' \times \dfrac{1°}{3600''} = 8.99°$.

26. $150°14'28'' = 150° + 14' \times \dfrac{1°}{60'} + 28'' \times \dfrac{1°}{3600''} =$ $150.24°$.

27. A full circle is $360°$, and each degree is $60'$, so there are $360° \times \dfrac{60'}{1°} = 21,600'$ in a circle.

28. $360° \times \dfrac{60'}{1°} \times \dfrac{60''}{1'} = 1,296,000''$.

29. Copenhagen is at 56°N, 12°E (or 12.5°E).

30. La Paz is at 16°S, 68°W.

31. The latitude changes from 36°N to 36°S. To find the longitude, move 180° east from 115°W to arrive at 65°E. (Note that after moving 115°, you'll be at the prime meridian, or 0°, and you still have 65° to go). Thus the point opposite Las Vegas is 36°S, 65°E.

32. The latitude changes from 43°N to 43°S. To find the longitude, move 180° east from 88°W to arrive at 92°E. (Note that after moving 88°, you'll be at the prime meridian, or 0°, and you still have 92° to go). Thus the point opposite Milwaukee is 43°S, 92°E.

33. Buenos Aires is farther from the North Pole because its latitude (35°S) is further south than the latitude of Capetown (34°S).

34. Guatemala City is further from the South Pole because it is north of the equator while Lusaka is south of the equator.

35. Buffalo is 17° north of Miami, and each degree is 1/360 of the circumference of the Earth. Since the circumference is about 25,000 mi, Buffalo is

$\dfrac{17}{360} \times 25,000 = 1181$ mi, or about 1200 miles from Miami.

36. Washington is 50° north of Lima, and each degree is 1/360 of the circumference of the Earth. Since the circumference is about 25,000 mi, Washington is $\dfrac{50}{360} \times 25,000 = 3472$ mi, or about 3500 miles from Lima.

37. A quarter is about an inch in diameter, and 5 yards is 180 inches. Thus its angular size is

$1 \text{ in.} \times \dfrac{360°}{2\pi \times 180 \text{ in.}} = 0.32°$.

38. A quarter is about an inch in diameter, and 25 yards is 900 inches. Thus its angular size is

$1 \text{ in.} \times \dfrac{360°}{2\pi \times 900 \text{ in.}} = 0.064°$.

39. The Sun's true diameter (physical size) is

$0.5° \times \dfrac{2\pi \times 150,000,000 \text{ km}}{360°} = 1.31 \times 10^6 \text{ km}$.

40. The tree's height (physical size) is

$0.5° \times \dfrac{2\pi \times 2640 \text{ ft}}{360°} = 23.0 \text{ ft}$. Note that 0.5 mile is 2640 feet.

41. A roof with a pitch of 1 in 4 has a slope of 1/4, which is steeper than a roof with a slope of 2/10.

42. A road with a 12% grade has a slope of 12/100 = 0.12, and a road with a pitch of 1 in 8 has as slope of 1/8 = 0.125, so the road with a pitch of 1 in 8 is steeper.

43. A railroad with a 3% grade has a slope of 3/100 = 0.03, which is not as steep as a railroad with a slope of 1/25 = 0.04.

44. A sidewalk with a pitch of 1 in 6 has a slope of 1/6 = 0.17. This is steeper than a sidewalk with a 15% grade, which has a slope of 0.15.

45. The slope of a 7 in 12 roof is 7/12. The roof will rise $\dfrac{7}{12} \times 15 = 8.75$ feet in a horizontal run of 15 feet.

46. A road with a 5% grade has a slope of 5/100 = 1/20, which means it rises 1/20 foot for each horizontal foot. Imagine the road as a right triangle, where the ratio of the height to the base is 1/20. If you drive 6 miles along the road, you've gone 31,680 feet along the hypotenuse of this triangle. Let x represent the height of the triangle; the base is then $20x$ (because the slope is 1/20). Using the Pythagorean theorem, we have $x^2 + (20x)^2 = 31,680^2$, which yields $x = 1582$ ft. Note that if you take the 6 miles as the horizontal run (rather than the correct procedure of treating it

as the hypotenuse), you get an answer little different from above: 1584 feet.

47. Think of a right triangle with side lengths of 6 and 6 – this produces an isosceles triangle, which implies the non-right angles are both 45°. It is possible to have a 7 in 6 roof: it's just a steep roof that rises 7 feet for every 6 feet of horizontal run.

48. The slope of such a path is 1500/5280 = 0.284, which is an approximate grade of 28%.

49. The slope of such a road is 20/150 = 0.133, so its grade is 13.3%.

50. A trail with a 22% grade has a slope of 22/100, so it rises $\frac{22}{100} \times 200$ yd = 44 yards.

51. a. Walk 6 blocks east (6/8 mi) and 1 block north (1/5 mi) for a total distance of 19/20 = 0.95 mi.
    b. The Pythagorean theorem gives the straight-line distance as $\sqrt{(6/8)^2 + (1/5)^2} = 0.78$ mi.

52. a. Walk 3 blocks east (3/8 mi) and 4 blocks north (4/5 mi) for a total distance of 47/40 = 1.175 mi.
    b. The Pythagorean theorem gives the straight-line distance as $\sqrt{(3/8)^2 + (4/5)^2} = 0.88$ mi.

53. a. Walk 2 blocks west (2/8 mi) and 3 blocks north (3/5 mi) for a total distance of 17/20 = 0.85 mi.
    b. The Pythagorean theorem gives the straight-line distance as $\sqrt{(2/8)^2 + (3/5)^2} = 0.65$ mi.

54. a. Walk 8 blocks east (8/8 mi) and 2 blocks south (2/5 mi) for a total distance of 7/5 = 1.4 mi.
    b. The Pythagorean theorem gives the straight-line distance as $\sqrt{(8/8)^2 + (2/5)^2} = 1.08$ mi.

55. a. Walk 3 blocks east (3/8 mi) and 3 blocks south (3/5 mi) for a total distance of 39/40 = 0.975 mi.
    b. The Pythagorean theorem gives the straight-line distance as $\sqrt{(3/8)^2 + (3/5)^2} = 0.71$ mi.

56. a. Walk 5 blocks west (5/8 mi) and 1 block south (1/5 mi) for a total distance of 33/40 = 0.825 mi.
    b. The Pythagorean theorem gives the straight-line distance as $\sqrt{(5/8)^2 + (1/5)^2} = 0.66$ mi.

57. The height of the triangle in Figure 10.31 is $\sqrt{800^2 - 150^2} = 785.8$ ft, and thus the area of the lot is $\frac{1}{2} \times 150 \times 785.8 = 58{,}936$ ft^2, which is
$58{,}936$ ft$^2 \times \dfrac{1 \text{ acre}}{43{,}560 \text{ ft}^2} = 1.35$ acres.

58. The height of the triangle in Figure 10.31 is $\sqrt{1800^2 - 300^2} = 1774.8$ ft, and thus the area of

the lot is $\frac{1}{2} \times 300 \times 1774.8 = 266{,}224$ ft^2, which is
$266{,}224$ ft$^2 \times \dfrac{1 \text{ acre}}{43{,}560 \text{ ft}^2} = 6.11$ acres.

59. The height of the triangle in Figure 10.31 is $\sqrt{3800^2 - 600^2} = 3752.3$ ft, and thus the area of the lot is $\frac{1}{2} \times 600 \times 3752.3 = 1{,}125{,}700$ ft^2, which
is $1{,}125{,}700$ ft$^2 \times \dfrac{1 \text{ acre}}{43{,}560 \text{ ft}^2} = 25.84$ acres.

60. Note that 0.45 mi is 2376 ft, and 1.2 miles is 6336 ft. The height of the triangle in Figure 10.31 is $\sqrt{6336^2 - 2376^2} = 5873.6$ ft, and thus the area of the lot is $\frac{1}{2} \times 2376 \times 5873.6 = 6{,}977{,}871$ ft^2,
which is $6{,}977{,}871$ ft$^2 \times \dfrac{1 \text{ acre}}{43{,}560 \text{ ft}^2} = 160.19$
acres.

61. The larger triangle is just a scaled up version of the smaller triangle (or so it appears), and so they are similar.

62. The larger triangle is just a scaled up version of the smaller triangle (or so it appears), and so they are similar.

63. The triangle on the left appears to be an isosceles triangle, whereas the one on the right does not, which means the triangles don't have the same angle measure, and cannot be similar.

64. One triangle looks like a rotated version of the other, so they are similar.

65. 8/10 = x/5, which implies x = 4. Use the Pythagorean theorem to show that y = 3 (we know the triangles are right because the left triangle satisfies $6^2 + 8^2 = 10^2$).

66. x/9 = 2/3, which implies x = 6. Since the triangle on the left is isosceles, so is the one on the right, which means y = 2.

67. x/60 = 10/40, which implies x = 15. 50/60 = y/40, which implies y = 100/3 = 33.3.

68. a/3 = 12/9, which implies a = 4. 5/3 = c/9, which implies c = 15.

69. Refer to Figure 10.34, and note that a 12-ft fence that casts a 25-foot shadow is equivalent to a house of height h (set back 60 feet from the property line) that casts an 85-ft shadow. We can write the ratio 12/25 = h/85, which implies h = 40.8 ft.

70. As in exercise 69, we can write 12/20 = h/50, which implies h = 30 ft.

71. As in exercise 69, we can write 12/30 = h/80, which implies h = 32 ft.

72. As in exercise 69, we can write $12/10 = h/40$, which implies $h = 48$ ft.

73. The radius of a circle with circumference of 60 m is $60/2\pi = 9.55$ m, and so its area is $\pi \times (9.55)^2 = 286.5$ m^2. The side length of a square with perimeter of 60 m is $60/4 = 15$ m, and so its area is $15 \times 15 = 225$ m^2. The area of the circular region is larger.

74. The radius of a circle with circumference of 800 ft is $800/2\pi = 127.32$ ft, and so its area is $\pi \times (127.32)^2 = 50,930$ ft^2. The side length of a square with perimeter of 800 ft is $800/4 = 200$ ft, and so its area is $200 \times 200 = 40,000$ ft^2. The area of the circular region is larger.

75. The radius of a circle with circumference of 240 m is $240/2\pi = 38.2$ m, and so its area is $\pi \times (38.2)^2 = 4584$ m^2. The side length of a square with perimeter of 240 m is $240/4 = 60$ m, and so its area is $60 \times 60 = 3600$ m^2. The area of the circular region is larger.

76. The radius of a circle with circumference of 0.27 mi is $0.27/2\pi = 0.043$ mi, and so its area is $\pi \times (0.043)^2 = 0.0058$ mi^2. The side length of a square with perimeter of 0.27 mi is $0.27/4 = 0.0675$ mi, and so its area is $0.0675 \times 0.0675 = 0.00456$ mi^2. The area of the circular region is larger.

77. For the first can described, the area of the top and bottom is $2 \times \pi \times 4^2 = 100.53$ in.^{2}, and the area of the side is $2\pi \times 4 \times 5 = 125.66$ in.^{2}. The cost of the can is 100.53 in.$^2 \times \dfrac{\$1.00}{\text{in.}^2} + 125.66$ in.$^2 \times \dfrac{\$0.50}{\text{in.}^2} = \$163.36$. In a similar manner, it can be shown that the cost of the second can is 157.08 in.$^2 \times \dfrac{\$1.00}{\text{in.}^2} + 125.66$ in.$^2 \times \dfrac{\$0.50}{\text{in.}^2} = \$219.91$.

78. For the first bucket described, the area of the bottom is $\pi \times 6^2 = 113.1$ in.^{2}, and the area of the side is $2\pi \times 6 \times 18 = 678.58$ in.^{2}. The cost is $\left(2 \times 113.1 \text{ in.}^2 + 678.58 \text{ in.}^2\right) \times \left(\dfrac{1 \text{ ft}}{12 \text{ in.}}\right)^2 \times \dfrac{\$0.50}{\text{ft}^2} = \$3.14$. In a similar manner, it can be shown that the cost of the second can is $\left(2 \times 254.47 \text{ in.}^2 + 848.23 \text{ in.}^2\right) \times \left(\dfrac{1 \text{ ft}}{12 \text{ in.}}\right)^2 \times \dfrac{\$0.50}{\text{ft}^2} = \$4.71$.

79. Assuming a rectangular box, the most economical shape is a cube, with side length equal to 2 ft (see Example 10 in the text). Such a box has 6 faces, each with area of 4 ft^2, for a total area of 24 ft^2. At \$0.15 per square foot, the box would cost \$3.60.

80. The most economical shape of a rectangular prism is a cube (see Example 10 in the text). Since the volume of a cube with side length s is s^3, we must have $s^3 = 4$ ft^3, which implies $s = \sqrt[3]{4} = 1.587$ ft. The surface area of a cube is $6s^2$, so the surface area of the safe is $6 \times \left(\sqrt[3]{4}\right)^2 = 15.12$ ft^2. At a cost of \$6.50 per square foot, the material for the safe would cost 15.12 ft$^2 \times \dfrac{\$6.50}{\text{ft}^2} = \$98.27$.

FURTHER APPLICATIONS

81. a. The area of the storage region of the DVD, which is the area of the entire DVD minus the area of the inner circle (that is not part of the storage region), is $\pi \times 5.9^2 - \pi \times 2.5^2 = 89.7$ cm^2.

   b. The density is $\dfrac{4,700 \text{ million bytes}}{89.7 \text{ cm}^2} = 52$ million bytes/cm^2.

   c. The length of the groove is $\dfrac{\pi\left((5.9 \text{ cm})^2 - (2.5 \text{ cm})^2\right)}{1.5 \text{ micron}} \times \dfrac{10^6 \text{ micron}}{1 \text{ m}} \times \dfrac{1 \text{ m}}{100 \text{ cm}}$ $= 600,000$ cm, which is $600,000 \text{ cm} \times \dfrac{1 \text{ m}}{100 \text{ cm}}$ $\times \dfrac{1 \text{ km}}{1000 \text{ m}} \times \dfrac{1 \text{ mi}}{1.6093 \text{ km}} = 3.7$ mi.

82. The angular size of the star is $1.4 \times 10^6 \text{ km} \times \dfrac{360°}{2\pi \times 10^{14} \text{ km}} \times \dfrac{3600''}{1°} = 0.003''$, which is smaller than the resolution of a powerful telescope, so no surface details could be seen.

83. The throw goes along the hypotenuse of a right triangle, whose length is $\sqrt{90^2 + 90^2} = 127.3$ ft.

84. The cost of running the line along the edges of the field is $(1.5 \text{ mi} + 2.75 \text{ mi}) \times \dfrac{\$3500}{1 \text{ mi}} = \$14,875$. The cost of running the line along the hypotenuse is $\sqrt{(1.5 \text{ mi})^2 + (2.75 \text{ mi})^2} \times \dfrac{\$3500}{1 \text{ mi}} = \$10,964$, for a savings of $\$14,875 - \$10,964 = \$3911$.

85. For simplicity, assume you can row at a rate of 1.0 mph, and you can bike at a rate of 1.5 mph. Using

time $= \dfrac{\text{distance}}{\text{rate}}$, the time it takes to bike along the edges of the reservoir is $\dfrac{1.2 \text{ mi} + 0.9 \text{ mi}}{1.5 \text{ mph}} = 1.4$ hr. The time it takes to row along the hypotenuse is $\dfrac{\sqrt{(1.2 \text{ mi})^2 + (0.9 \text{ mi})^2}}{1.0 \text{ mph}} = 1.5$ hr, so biking is faster.

86. The sidewalk connecting the library to humanities is $\sqrt{15^2 + 15^2} = 21.2$ m, the sidewalk between humanities and chemistry is $\sqrt{10^2 + 30^2} = 31.6$ m, and the sidewalk between chemistry and the library is $\sqrt{15^2 + 25^2} = 29.2$ m. Together, the total length of the sidewalks is 82.0 m.

87. a. The volume of the water in the bed is $8 \times 7 \times 0.75 = 42$ ft^3. Divide this volume by the area of the lower room (80 ft^2) to find that the depth of the water is 0.525 ft.
   b. The weight of the water in the bed is $42 \text{ ft}^3 \times \dfrac{62.4 \text{ lb}}{1 \text{ ft}^3} = 2620.8$ lb.

88. The volume of the tank is $\dfrac{4}{3}\pi \times (25 \text{ ft})^3 \times \left(\dfrac{0.3048 \text{ m}}{1 \text{ ft}}\right)^3 = 1853$ m^3. The volume of the pool is $50 \text{ m} \times 25 \text{ m} \times 2 \text{ m} = 2500$ m^3, so the tank is not large enough to fill the pool.

89. The perimeter of a corral with dimensions of 10 m by 40 m is 100 m. One could use a square-shaped corral with side length of 20 m to achieve the desired area of 400 square meters; this corral would have a perimeter of 80 m, and would require less fencing.

90. The combined area of the right and left flaps of the box is $2 \times 0.75 \text{ m} \times 0.25 \text{ m} = 0.375$ m^2. The combined area for the top and bottoms flaps is $2 \times 1.25 \text{ m} \times 0.25 \text{ m} = 0.625$ m^2. The area of the base is $0.75 \text{ m} \times 1.25 \text{ m} = 0.9375$ m^2. The total surface area is 1.9375 square meters. The volume is $1.25 \text{ m} \times 0.75 \text{ m} \times 0.25 \text{ m} = 0.2344$ m^3. If the corner cuts were 0.3 m on a side, the volume would be $1.15 \text{ m} \times 0.65 \text{ m} \times 0.3 \text{ m} = 0.2243$ m^3 (smaller). The box of largest volume occurs when the corner cut length is about 0.24 m.

91. Your project will cost $3 \text{ mi} \times \dfrac{\$500}{1 \text{ mi}} + \sqrt{(2 \text{ mi})^2 + (1 \text{ mi})^2} \times \dfrac{\$1000}{1 \text{ mi}} =$ $3736. Using the plan suggested by your boss will cost $4 \text{ mi} \times \dfrac{\$500}{1 \text{ mi}} + \sqrt{(1 \text{ mi})^2 + (1 \text{ mi})^2} \times \dfrac{\$1000}{1 \text{ mi}} =$ $3414.

92. Following the hint in the exercise, if you draw a good diagram, you should see a pair of similar triangles that can be used to set up the ratio $\dfrac{10}{15} = \dfrac{h}{50}$, where h is the height of the building measured from the top of your head. Solving for h yields $h = 33.3$ ft. Add your height to find the height of the building.

93. a. With a lot of work and patience, you might be able to come up with the dimensions of the can that has the lowest surface area (and thus lowest cost): $r = 3.8$ cm and $h = 7.7$ cm. One way to save time is to observe that $355 = \pi r^2 h$, which implies that $h = \dfrac{355}{\pi r^2}$. Insert this expression for h into the surface area formula $2\pi r h + 2\pi r^2$ to find that the surface area can be expressed as a function of r: $A = \dfrac{710}{r} + 2\pi r^2$. Since the cost is directly proportional to the surface area, the object is to find the value of r that yields the smallest surface area A. If you graph A on a calculator, and use the trace function, you'll see that $r = 3.8$ at the low point of the graph.
   b. The dimensions of the optimal can found above imply the can is as wide (diameter) as it is high. Soda cans aren't built that way, probably for a variety of reasons. (Among them: the can needs to fit into the hand of an average human, and the top and bottom of the can cost more because the aluminum is thicker).

94. The volume of the glacier is $100 \text{ m} \times 20 \text{ m} \times 3 \text{ m} = 6000$ m^3. The surface area of the lake is $\pi \times (1000 \text{ m})^2 = 3.14 \times 10^6$ m^2. Divide the volume by the surface area to find the amount by which the water level would rise: $6000 \text{ m}^3 \div 3.14 \times 10^6 \text{ m}^2 = 0.002$ meters, or about 2 millimeters. This solution assumes a cubic meter of ice melts into a cubic meter of water.

95. a. Note that the radius of the cone will be 6 ft (because the height is 1/3 the radius). The volume is $\dfrac{1}{3}\pi \times 6^2 \times 2 = 75.4$ ft^3.
   b. Again, note that $r = 3h$, and solve $1000 \text{ ft}^3 = \dfrac{1}{3}\pi \times (3h)^2 \times h = 3\pi \times h^3$ for h to find $h = 4.7$ ft.

c. Assuming 10,000 grains per cubic inch, there are

$$75.4 \text{ ft}^3 \times \left(\frac{12 \text{ in.}}{1 \text{ ft}}\right)^3 \times \frac{10,000 \text{ grains}}{\text{in.}^3} = 1.3$$

billion grains. The figure of 10,000 grains per cubic inch is very much dependent upon the size of sand grain assumed, which varies.

96. The radius of the tank is 3.25 ft, so the water's weight is

$$\pi \times (3.25 \text{ ft})^2 \times 22 \text{ ft} \times \left(\frac{12 \text{ in.}}{1 \text{ ft}}\right)^3 \times \frac{0.03613 \text{ lb}}{1 \text{ in.}^3} = 46$$

,615 lb, which is 22.8 tons. The empty tank weighs $1750 \div 2000 = 0.875$ ton. The truck's gross weight is $16.3 + 22.8 + 0.875$ tons, which is just shy of 40 tons. You can be confident in crossing the bridge because load limit signs always have a built-in safety margin.

97. a. The pyramid's height is $481 \div 3 = 160.3$ yards, which is about 1.6 times the length of a football field (excluding the end zones).

b. The volume of the pyramid is

$$\frac{1}{3} \times (756 \text{ ft})^2 \times 481 \text{ ft} = 91,636,272 \text{ ft}^3, \text{ which is}$$

$$91,636,272 \text{ ft}^3 \times \left(\frac{1 \text{ yd}}{3 \text{ ft}}\right)^3 = 3,393,936 \text{ yd}^3.$$

c. Divide the result in part **b** by 1.5 to get around 2,263,000 blocks.

d.

$$2,263,000 \text{ blocks} \times \frac{2.5 \text{ min}}{\text{block}} \times \frac{1 \text{ hr}}{60 \text{ min}} \times \frac{1 \text{ d}}{12 \text{ hr}}$$

$$\times \frac{1 \text{ yr}}{365 \text{ d}} = 21.5 \text{ years}.$$ This is comparable to the amount of time suggested in historical records, which indicates that Lehner's estimate of 10,000 workers is in error. However, we don't have all the facts – perhaps Lehner began with the assumption that, with a work force of 10,000 laborers, one stone could be placed every 2.5 minutes, or maybe he assumed laborers worked on the project 24 hours per day.

e. The volume of the Eiffel tower is

$$\frac{1}{3} \times (120 \text{ ft})^2 \times 980 \text{ ft} = 4,704,000 \text{ ft}^3, \text{ which is}$$

about 5% of the pyramid's volume.

UNIT 10C

TIME OUT TO THINK

Pg. 585. The L2 segments are 1/9 the length of the L0 segments because we have twice divided by 3. The L3 segments are 1/27 the length of the L0 segments.

QUICK QUIZ

1. **b.** As noted in the text, fractals successfully replicate natural forms, especially when random iteration is used.

2. **a.** A coastline can be modeled with fractal curves which have dimension between 1 and 2, and by the very definition of fractal dimension, we see that shortening the length of the ruler increases the number of elements (which, in turn, represents the length of the coastline).

3. **b.** The edge of a leaf (think of a maple leaf) has many of the properties of a fractal, such as self similarity, and a length that increases as one decreases the size of the ruler used to measure it.

4. **c.** Fractals often have the property of self similarity, which means that under greater magnification, the underlying pattern repeats itself.

5. **c.** The definition of the fractal dimension of an object leads to fractional values for the dimension.

6. **c.** Data suggest that most coastlines have a fractal dimension of about 1.25.

7. **a.** The curve labeled L_6 in Figure 10.53 is simply the sixth step (or iteration) of the process required to generate the snowflake curve. The snowflake curve itself is denoted by L_∞ (the end product of performing infinite iterations).

8. **c.** An area bounded by a finite curve (it is understood that by this we mean a closed curve of finite length) cannot possibly be of infinite area. If it were possible, we'd have to throw all of our notions about the areas of bounded plane regions out the door. How could the area of a region contained within a region of a finite area be infinitely large?

9. **a.** The definition of a self-similar fractal is that its patterns repeat themselves under greater magnification.

10. **b.** From previous units, we know that if you take, say, an ice cube, and break it into smaller pieces, the aggregate surface area of the pieces is larger than the surface area of the original cube of ice. The same idea is illustrated by the process of creating the Sierpinski sponge. In the first step, when the four subcubes are removed, it can be shown that the surface area increases by a factor of 4/3. In fact, this happens in every step, and thus the surface area becomes infinitely large as the process continues.

DOES IT MAKE SENSE?

9. Makes sense. The boundary of a rectangle is made of straight lines whose lengths are well defined, and so can be measured with a standard ruler (to a reasonable degree of accuracy).

10. Does not make sense. A mountain skyline is similar to a coastline in that it reveals ever more detail at greater magnification, and thus it is very difficult to define its length, let alone measure it with any degree of accuracy.

11. Does not make sense. The boundary of the snowflake island is infinitely long, and though its area is finite, it is not computed with a simple "length times width" formula.

12. Does not make sense. The measured length of a fractal increases as the ruler length *decreases*.

13. Makes sense. Data have been collected that shows many boundaries in nature, such as coastlines and edges of leaves, have fractal dimensions greater than one.

14. Makes sense. A leaf riddled with holes, whose boundaries are fractals, has some of the properties of the Sierpinski triangle, and this object has a fractal dimension between 1 and 2, with an area of 0. In the same way it is difficult to define the length of a coastline, it is difficult to compute the surface area of a leaf riddled with holes – our standard notions of surface area don't work well with regions that are bounded by fractals.

BASIC SKILLS & CONCEPTS

15. According to the definition of fractal dimension, R = 2 and N = 2, so we have $2 = 2^D$, where D is the fractal dimension. It is evident that $D = 1$ in this case, and thus the object is not a fractal (it behaves like an ordinary geometric object with regard to length measurements).

16. According to the definition of fractal dimension, R = 2 and N = 4, so we have $4 = 2^D$, where D is the fractal dimension. It is evident that $D = 2$ in this case, and thus the object is not a fractal (it behaves like an ordinary geometric object with regard to area measurements).

17. According to the definition of fractal dimension, R = 2 and N = 8, so we have $8 = 2^D$, where D is the fractal dimension. It is evident that $D = 3$ in this case, and thus the object is not a fractal (it behaves like an ordinary geometric object with regard to volume measurements).

18. According to the definition of fractal dimension, R = 2 and N = 3, so we have $3 = 2^D$, where D is the fractal dimension. Solving for D using logarithms produces a value of $D = \dfrac{\log_{10} 3}{\log_{10} 2} = 1.585$, and thus the object is a fractal (it does not behave like an ordinary geometric object with regard to length measurements).

19. According to the definition of fractal dimension, R = 2 and N = 6, so we have $6 = 2^D$, where D is the fractal dimension. Solving for D using logarithms produces a value of $D = \dfrac{\log_{10} 6}{\log_{10} 2} = 2.585$, and thus the object is a fractal (it does not behave like an ordinary geometric object with regard to area measurements).

20. According to the definition of fractal dimension, R = 2 and N = 12, so we have $12 = 2^D$, where D is the fractal dimension. Solving for D using logarithms produces a value of $D = \dfrac{\log_{10} 12}{\log_{10} 2} = 3.585$, and thus the object is a fractal (it does not behave like an ordinary geometric object with regard to volume measurements).

21. According to the definition of fractal dimension, R = 5 and N = 5, so we have $5 = 5^D$, where D is the fractal dimension. It is evident that $D = 1$ in this case, and thus the object is not a fractal (it behaves like an ordinary geometric object with regard to length measurements).

22. According to the definition of fractal dimension, R = 5 and N = 25, so we have $25 = 5^D$, where D is the fractal dimension. It is evident that $D = 2$ in this case, and thus the object is not a fractal (it behaves like an ordinary geometric object with regard to area measurements).

23. According to the definition of fractal dimension, R = 5 and N = 125, so we have $125 = 5^D$, where D is the fractal dimension. It is evident that $D = 3$ in this case, and thus the object is not a fractal (it behaves like an ordinary geometric object with regard to volume measurements).

24. According to the definition of fractal dimension, R = 5 and N = 7, so we have $7 = 5^D$, where D is the fractal dimension. Solving for D using logarithms produces a value of $D = \dfrac{\log_{10} 7}{\log_{10} 5} = 1.209$, and thus the object is a fractal (it does not behave like an ordinary geometric object with regard to length measurements).

25. According to the definition of fractal dimension, R = 5 and N = 30, so we have $30 = 5^D$, where D is the fractal dimension. Solving for D using logarithms produces a value of $D = \dfrac{\log_{10} 30}{\log_{10} 5} = 2.113$, and thus the object is a fractal (it does not behave like an ordinary

geometric object with regard to area measurements).

26. According to the definition of fractal dimension, $R = 5$ and $N = 150$, so we have $150 = 5^D$, where D is the fractal dimension. Solving for D using logarithms produces a value of $D = \dfrac{\log_{10} 150}{\log_{10} 5} = 3.113$, and thus the object is a fractal (it does not behave like an ordinary geometric object with regard to volume measurements).

27. a. Suppose that the original line segment has length of 1 unit. When we measure the length of the first iteration of the quadratic Koch curve with a ruler of length 1 unit (or one element), we find the length is 1 unit, the distance from one endpoint to the other. When we shorten the ruler by a factor of $R = 4$ so that its length is 1/4 unit, the length of the first iteration is $N = 8$ elements (i.e., the length is 8/4 = 2 units). This is true at every stage of the process.

b. According to the definition of fractal dimension, we have $8 = 4^D$. Solving for D yields $D = \dfrac{\log_{10} 8}{\log_{10} 4} = 1.5$. The length of the quadratic Koch curve is infinite, because at each iteration, the length increases by a factor of 2, and thus its length grows without bound as the process continues.

c. Consider what happens to the area of the quadratic Koch island as we go from the first stage (a square) to the second stage. Along the upper boundary, the area is increased by a small square drawn above the boundary, but it is decreased by a small square drawn below the boundary. This is true along every edge of the original square, and the net effect is no change in the area. The same is true for every step of the process, so the area of the final island is equal to the area of the original square. The coastline of the island is infinite, as noted above in part **b**.

28. a.

$\log_{10} r$	2	1	0	−1	−2	−3
$\log_{10} L$	2.5	3.1	3.7	4.3	4.9	5.5

b. Graph not shown.

c. The graph is a straight line if you use the rounded values shown in the above table, which indicates the coastline is a self-similar fractal.

d. The slope s is −0.6, so the fractional dimension is $D = 1 - (-0.6) = 1.6$.

FURTHER APPLICATIONS

29. When the ruler is reduced by a factor of $R = 9$, there will be $N = 4$ elements found (each of length 1/9). This gives $4 = 9^D$, which when solved leads to $D = \dfrac{\log_{10} 4}{\log_{10} 9} = 0.631$. (Note that this is the answer you get no matter what stage of the process you choose to analyze). The dimension is less than 1 due to the fact that the end result of the process of constructing the Cantor set is a set of isolated points. Though there are infinitely many points, there aren't "enough" of them to constitute a line segment of measurable length (that is, this fractal object does not behave like an ordinary geometric object with regard to length).

30. a. Start with a meter stick and measure the length of the sidewalk, counting the number of times you lay the stick down on the sidewalk. Now reduce the length of the stick to 0.1 meter – a reduction by a factor of $R = 10$. Repeat the measurement of the sidewalk, counting the number of times you lay the stick down on the sidewalk. You should find that the number of elements for this second measurement is about $N = 10$ times the number of elements of the first sidewalk. If this pattern continues (every time the ruler is decreased in length by a factor of 10, the number of elements increases by an approximate factor of $N = 10$), then the sidewalk is a one-dimensional object. To illustrate the process, imagine a sidewalk that is about 5.724 meters in length. In the first measurement, you'll find 5 full elements because the last placement of the 1-meter stick would extend beyond the end of the walk. On the second measurement, you'll find 57 full elements, again because the last element will extend beyond the end of the walk. On a third measurement, you'll find 572 elements, and on the fourth measurement, you'll find about 5724 elements, depending upon the exact length of the walk. In each step, N is approximately 10, and in fact, N gets closer and closer to 10 as you repeat the process. If you compute N for each step of the process just described, you'll find the following values: $N = 57/5 = 11.4$; $N = 572/57 = 10.035$; and $N = 5724/572 = 10.007$. In then end, we can conclude that N is very close to R, and so we have $10 = 10^D$, which implies $D = 1$.

b. Start with a meter stick and measure the length and width of the room, counting the number of square elements with an area of 1 m^2 that you create in the process (exclude the rectangles of less than 1 m^2 that will likely occur at the edges of the room, as described in part **a**). Now reduce the length of the stick to 0.1 meter – a reduction by a factor of $R = 10$. Repeat the measurement of the room, counting the number of elements with an area of 0.01 m^2 that you create. You should find that the number of elements for this second measuring is approximately $N = 100$ times the number of elements in the first measurement. If this pattern continues (every time the ruler is decreased in length by a factor of $R = 10$, the number of elements increases by an approximate factor of $N = R^2 = 100$), then the room is a two-dimensional object.

c. The process used to determine that $N = R^3$ is very similar to that described in parts **a** and **b**, except that you will measure the length, width, and depth of the pool at each stage, and find with each reduction of length in the ruler by a factor of $R = 10$, the number of cubical elements will increase by an approximate factor of $N = 1000$.

31. a. Note that every time the ruler is decreased in length by a factor of $R = 10$, the number of elements increases by a factor of $N = 20$, which leads to $20 = 10^D$. This implies the fractal dimension is $D = \dfrac{\log_{10} 20}{\log_{10} 10} = 1.301$.

b. Note that every time the ruler is decreased in length by a factor of $R = 2$, the number of area elements increases by a factor of $N = 3$, which leads to $3 = 2^D$. This implies the fractal dimension is $D = \dfrac{\log_{10} 3}{\log_{10} 2} = 1.585$. The fractal dimension is less than two because the standard notion of surface area for ordinary objects does not carry over to the surface area of fractal objects.

c. Note that every time the ruler is decreased in length by a factor of $R = 2$, the number of volume elements increases by a factor of $N = 6$, which leads to $6 = 2^D$. This implies the fractal dimension is $D = \dfrac{\log_{10} 6}{\log_{10} 2} = 2.585$. A fractal dimension between 2 and 3 is reasonable because such a rock exhibits the same properties as the Sierpinski sponge – it is somewhat "less" than a solid three-dimensional cube because material has been removed in a fractal pattern.

32. Answers will vary, but patterns seen in leaves, the branches of trees, lungs, capillaries, coastlines, rock formations, and clouds are good examples.

33. The branching in many natural objects has the same pattern repeated on many different scales. This is the process by which self-similar fractals are generated. Euclidean geometry is not equipped to describe the repetitions of patterns on many scales.

UNIT 11A

TIME OUT TO THINK

Pg. 596. The frequency an octave higher is 880, and an octave lower is 220.

QUICK QUIZ

1. **b.** Instruments with strings (guitar, violin, piano), woodwinds with reeds (clarinet, bassoon), and instruments with a column of air in a tube (organ pipe, horn, flute) – all produce their sound with an object that vibrates.

2. **a.** In the case of a string vibrating, a single cycle of vibration corresponds to the string moving to its high point and to its low point, so 100 cps means the string is at its high point (and low point) 100 times each second.

3. **a.** Higher pitches go hand in hand with higher frequencies.

4. **c.** The fundamental frequency of a string occurs when the string vibrates up and down along its entire length, and this produces the lowest possible pitch from that string. (Though the text does not discuss it, you may know that a longer wavelength produces a lower frequency – the wavelength can't get any longer for a particular string than the wave associated with the fundamental frequency).

5. **a.** Every time you raise the pitch of a sound by an octave, the pitch doubles.

6. **c.** The 12-tone scale uses twelve equally spaced (in the sense described below) notes for every octave. The factor f by which the frequency changes in moving from one note to the next is constant, which means that in multiplying an initial frequency by f 12 times in a row, you've moved an octave up the scale, and doubled the frequency. This gives us the relationship $f^{12} = 2$, which in turn implies that $f = \sqrt[12]{2}$.

7. **c.** Table 11.1 shows the frequencies of each of the notes in a particular octave; the names of the notes repeat every octave. As you can see in the table, increasing the frequency of middle C by a factor of 1.5 moves you to a G, so if you increase the frequency of the next higher C by a factor of 1.5, you'll end up at the next higher G.

8. **b.** The frequency of each note in the 12-tone scale is related to the note one half-step below it by a multiplicative factor of $f = \sqrt[12]{2} = 1.05946$. This means the frequencies increase by about 5.9% every half-step, which is exponential growth.

9. **b.** The mathematician Fourier discovered that musical sounds are the sum of several constant-frequency waves.

10. **a.** The process of digitizing analog sound changes wave forms that represent sound waves into lists of numbers that can be stored on CDs, and reinterpreted by a CD player to produce a musical sound.

DOES IT MAKE SENSE?

7. Does not make sense. The pitch of a string is a function of the length of the string, not the number of times the string is plucked.

8. Makes sense. When the length of a string is halved, its frequency doubles, and a doubling in frequency corresponds to an increase in pitch of one octave. Decrease the length of the string by a factor of 4, and its pitch will increase by a factor of 4, which corresponds to two octaves.

9. Makes sense. The frequency of each note in the 12-tone scale increases by a factor of $f = \sqrt[12]{2} = 1.05946$, and this is exponential growth.

10. Makes sense. Each key on a piano corresponds to a note one half-step above the preceding key, and as there are 12 half-steps in an octave, there are 88/12, or about 7 octaves on a standard piano (some pianos have even more than 88 keys).

11. Does not make sense. The scratch on the record would be difficult to repair. However, if it is a minor scratch, one might be able to digitize the sound the record produces, and at that point a digital filter could be used to reduce or remove the effects of the scratch.

BASIC SKILLS & CONCEPTS

12. The next higher octave corresponds to a doubling in frequency, so the requested frequencies are 440 cps, 880 cps, 1760 cps, and 3520 cps.

13. The next lower octave corresponds to a halving in frequency, so the requested frequencies are 880 cps, 440 cps, 220 cps, and 110 cps.

14.

Note	Frequency (cps)
F	347
F#	368
G	389
G#	413
A	437
A#	463
B	491
C	520

C#	551
D	584
D#	618
E	655

The table can be generated beginning with the initial frequency of 347 cps, and multiplying by $f = \sqrt[12]{2}$ to produce each successive note. Realize that you will get slightly different values for some of the entries in the table if you generate it from middle C, whose frequency is 260 cps. This is due to rounding errors, and it explains the different values shown in this table and in Table 11.1 at the middle G entry. We began with an initial value of 347 cps to generate this table, but that's a rounded value for the true frequency of middle F.

15.

Note	Frequency (cps)
G	390
G#	413
A	438
A#	464
B	491
C	521
C#	552
D	584
D#	619
E	656
F	695
F#	736

The table can be generated beginning with the initial frequency of 390 cps, and multiplying by $f = \sqrt[12]{2}$ to produce each successive note. Realize that you will get slightly different values for some of the entries in the table if you generate it from middle C, whose frequency is 260 cps. This is due to rounding errors, and it explains the different values shown in this table and in Table 11.1 at the A, A#, and C entries. We began with an initial value of 390 cps to generate this table, but that's a rounded value for the true frequency of middle G. If we had used an exact value for middle G, we should find that the frequency of the C in this table, which is one octave higher than middle C, is 520 (because frequencies double every octave).

16. Raise A by a fifth to produce a frequency of $437 \text{ cps} \times \frac{3}{2} = 655.5 \text{ cps}$. Raise this by a fifth to

produce $655.5 \text{ cps} \times \frac{3}{2} = 983.25 \text{ cps}$. Lower this by a sixth to produce $983.25 \text{ cps} \times \frac{3}{5} = 589.95 \text{ cps}$. Finally, lower this by a fourth to produce $589.95 \text{ cps} \times \frac{3}{4} = 442.4625 \text{ cps}$, or about 442 cps.

We have not returned to the same frequency, because the ratios used to increase or decrease by the various intervals are approximations to the actual ratio between the given intervals. In essence, we began with 437 and multiplied it by $\frac{3}{2} \times \frac{3}{2} \times \frac{3}{5} \times \frac{3}{4} = \frac{81}{80}$, which is just over 1.

17. a. $260 \times \left(\sqrt[12]{2}\right)^7 = 390$ cps.

b. $260 \times \left(\sqrt[12]{2}\right)^9 = 437$ cps.

c. An octave is 12 half-steps, so use a total of 19 half-steps. $260 \times \left(\sqrt[12]{2}\right)^{19} = 779$ cps.

d. $260 \times \left(\sqrt[12]{2}\right)^{25} = 1102$ cps.

e. An octave is 12 half-steps, so use a total of 39 half-steps. $260 \times \left(\sqrt[12]{2}\right)^{39} = 2474$ cps.

18. a. $390 \times \left(\sqrt[12]{2}\right)^6 = 552$ cps.

b. $390 \times \left(\sqrt[12]{2}\right)^4 = 491$ cps.

c. An octave is 12 half-steps, so use a total of 17 half-steps. $390 \times \left(\sqrt[12]{2}\right)^{17} = 1041$ cps.

d. $390 \times \left(\sqrt[12]{2}\right)^{25} = 1653$ cps.

e. An octave is 12 half-steps, so use a total of 26 half-steps. $390 \times \left(\sqrt[12]{2}\right)^{26} = 1751$ cps.

19. To compute the frequency for a note one half-step below a particular frequency, we simply divide by $f = \sqrt[12]{2}$, which is equivalent to multiplying by the factor f raised to the power of –1. Thus to find the note 7 half steps below middle A, use $437 \times \left(\sqrt[12]{2}\right)^{-7} = 292$ cps. Ten half-steps below middle A is $437 \times \left(\sqrt[12]{2}\right)^{-10} = 245$ cps.

20. a. $\left(\sqrt[12]{2}\right)^7 = 2^{7/12}$.

b. From part **a**, it raises by a factor of $\left(2^{7/12}\right)^2 = 2^{14/12} = 2.245$.

c.

Note	Frequency (cps)
C	260
G	390
D	584
A	875
E	1310
B	1963
F#	2942
C#	4407
G#	6604
D#	9894
A#	14,825
F	22,212
C	33,280

The table can be generated beginning with the initial frequency of 260 cps, and multiplying by a factor of $2^{7/12}$ to produce successive notes.

d. As shown in the table in part **c**, you need 12 fifths to return to a C, which is 7 octaves. You can also understand this by analyzing the factor $2^{7/12}$.

e. The ratio is $33,280/260 = 118$. This, too, can be understood in the context of the multiplicative factor $2^{7/12}$ used to raise a note by a fifth. If you use this factor 12 times, you will have increased the frequency of the initial note by a factor of $\left(2^{7/12}\right)^{12} = 2^7 = 128$. Another way to look at it: move one octave up, and you double the frequency. Here we have moved up 7 octaves, so the frequency has increased by a factor of 2^7.

21. The factor by which the tone has increased is $\left(\sqrt[12]{2}\right)^5 = 2^{5/12} = 1.335$. Because $\left(2^{5/12}\right)^{12} = 2^5$, you need 12 fourths. This is the first time the factor of $2^{5/12}$ turns into a factor of 2, and that is what is necessary to return to the same-named note (raising an octave is a doubling in frequency). There are 5 octaves in the circle of fourths, as evidenced by the factor by which the initial frequency has changed: 2^5.

22. There are 2 half notes in a 4/4-time measure, 8 eighth notes, and 16 sixteenth notes.

UNIT 11B

TIME OUT TO THINK

Pg. 604. The vanishing point goes at the place where the parallel lines appear to converge.

Pg. 605. The vanishing points are located where the dotted lines converge. One such point is inside the arch in the upper right of the picture. This would be a good topic for a discussion either during or outside of class.

Pg. 609. Close inspection will verify that all the tilings use only regular pentagons. This would be a good topic for a discussion either during or outside of class.

QUICK QUIZ

1. **b**. The principal vanishing point in a painting is the point of intersection of those lines in the painting that are parallel in the real scene, and perpendicular to the canvas. We are assuming here that the tracks are, in fact, perpendicular to the canvas, and that they are straight.

2. **b**. The *horizon line* is the line (horizontal, of course) though the principal vanishing point. According to the principals of perspective, all sets of parallel lines in the real scene intersect at some point along the horizon line in the painting.

3. **a**. Not only does the painting show this fact, but the parallel beams in the ceiling are perpendicular to the canvas, so they should intersect at the principal vanishing point.

4. **c**. There is a vertical line of symmetry in the center of da Vinci's sketch, as both sides of the drawing are nearly identical on either side of this line.

5. **c**. If the letter **W** were reflected across this line, it would appear unchanged from the original.

6. **b**. Rotate the letter **Z** through 180°, and it remains unchanged in appearance.

7. **a**. Because a circle can be rotated through any angle and remain unchanged, it has rotation symmetry. It also has reflection symmetry over any line through its center, for the same reason.

8. **c**. The only regular polygons that admit complete tilings are equilateral triangles, squares, and regular hexagons.

9. **a**. Refer to Figure 11.23 in the text.

10. **c**. A periodic tiling is one where a pattern repeats itself throughout the tiling.

DOES IT MAKE SENSE?

9. Does not make sense. The principal vanishing point is often very apparent in paintings that are rendered in proper perspective (see Figures 11.6 and 11.8, for example).

10. Does not make sense. Real landscapes are never so perfectly flat that perspective needn't be considered. Bands of color and light that are nearer to the artist need to be painted wider than bands of equal width (in the real world) that are farther away, due to the laws of perspective. Good

artists paint even the dim shadows of a slowly rolling desert floor in perspective. One might argue that the statement makes sense if the desert really *is* a flat, monochrome surface, with nothing in it to indicate depth, and meeting the horizon in a straight line. But such a painting would be exceedingly dull (two fat strips of paint, with sand-colored paint at the bottom, and sky-blue paint on the top), and no one would recognize it as a realistic desert scene.

11. Makes sense. It is the science and art of perspective painting that allows talented artists to render realistic three-dimensional scenes on a two-dimensional canvas.

12. Does not make sense. Perhaps Kenny prefers the letter **R** over the letter **O**, but not out of any sense of symmetry. The letter **R** has none.

13. Does not make sense. Only equilateral triangles, squares, and regular hexagons allow for complete tilings. Susan should rent a tile saw.

14. Makes sense. The Washington Monument's shape has both rotation symmetry and reflection symmetry.

BASIC SKILLS & CONCEPTS

15. a. The only obvious vanishing point is depicted in the diagram below. It is not the principal vanishing point because the lines of the road do not meet the canvas at right angles. However, it does lie on the horizon line.

    b.

16. The box on the left is drawn in proper perspective because the edges of the box that recede into the distance converge at a vanishing point.

17.

18.

19. a. In order to draw the equally spaced poles, first draw a perspective line along the bases of the existing poles, and draw one along the tops. These two lines should intersect at a vanishing point (directly on, or very near to the horizon). Now measure 2.0 cm along the base line, and draw a vertical pole to meet the top perspective line. Repeat this procedure for the second pole.

b. The heights of the poles can be measured directly with a ruler. You should find the first pole you drew is about 1.0 cm, and the second about 0.5 cm. Notice that the lengths of the poles are decreasing in a linear fashion (2.0, 1.5, 1.0, and 0.5 cm). This is due to the fact that the poles are sandwiched between two lines of constant slope, and that the distances between them are equal. (Also note that the diagram in part **a** is not to scale).

c. If your drawing is an accurate depiction of the scene, the poles are not equally spaced in the actual scene. This is due to perspective: equal distances on the canvas do not correspond with equal distances in the real scene. Because the heights of the poles are assumed to be equal, the short pole you drew in the background is much farther away from you than the first pole you drew, despite the fact that they are equally spaced in the drawing.

20.

horizon line

21. a. The letters with right/left reflection symmetry are A, H, I, M, O, T, U, V, W, X, and Y.
b. The letters with top/bottom reflection symmetry are B, C, D, E, H, I, K, O, and X.
c. The letters with both of these symmetries are H, I, O, and X.
d. The letters with rotational symmetry are H, I, N, O, S, X, and Z.

22. a. There are four reflection symmetries and three rotational symmetries.
b. There are seven reflection symmetries and six rotational symmetries.

23. a. Rotating the triangle about its center 120° or 240° will produce an identical figure.
b. Rotating the square about its center 90°, 180°, or 270° will produce an identical figure.
c. Rotating the pentagon around its center 72°, 144°, 216°, or 288° will produce an identical figure.
d. Rotating an n-gon about its center 360°/n (and multiples of this angle less than 360°) will produce an identical figure. There are $n - 1$ different angles of rotational symmetry for an n-gon.

24. The figure has reflection symmetries (about vertical and horizontal lines drawn though its center, and either of its diagonals), and it has rotation symmetries (angles of 90°, 180°, and 270°).

25. The figure has reflection symmetries (about vertical and horizontal lines drawn through its center), and it has rotation symmetry (an angle of 180°).

26. The figure has reflection symmetry (about a horizontal line through its center, and about a vertical line through its center if we could locate its left-to-right center), and it has translation symmetry.

27. The figure has reflection symmetries (about 6 diagonal lines drawn through its center; these lines go through the spaces between the petals), and it has rotation symmetries (angles of 60°, 120°, 180°, 240°, and 300°).

28.

29.

30.

31.

32.

33.

34. Answers will vary.

35. The angles around a point P are precisely the angles that appear inside of a single quadrilateral. Thus, the angles around P have a sum of 360°, and the quadrilaterals around P fit perfectly together.

36.

UNIT 11C

TIME OUT TO THINK

Pg. 616. There are numerous other golden ratios in the pentagram. The ratio of any side of the pentagon to an arm of the star will have a ratio that is the golden ration. Also, the ratio of one entire side of the star (from one point on the circle to another) to the sum of a side of the pentagon and an arm of the star will have a ratio that is the golden ration.

Pg. 618. Opinions will vary. This would be a good topic for a discussion either during or outside of class.

Pg. 620. It is a straightforward calculation to confirm F_3 through F_{10}. $F_{11} = 34 + 55 = 89$. This would be a good topic for a discussion either during or outside of class.

QUICK QUIZ

1. **c.** The value of the golden ratio can be derived by solving $\frac{L}{1} = \frac{L+1}{L}$ for L. This equation comes from the idea that the most aesthetically pleasing way to divide a line is one where the ratio of the length of the long piece (L) to the length of the short piece (1) is equal to the ratio of the length of the entire line ($L + 1$) to the length of the long piece L, and it is this idea that produces the golden ratio.

2. **c.** The fourth number in the Fibonacci series is 3, which is not the value for the golden ratio.

3. **c.** The value of ϕ is about 1.6, and the ratio of the long piece to the short piece should be around 1.6 before claiming the line is divided into the golden ratio. Since 0.6/0.4 = 1.5, these are roughly the correct lengths for a golden ratio.

4. **b.** A golden rectangle is defined to be a rectangle whose ratio of its long side to short side is ϕ.

5. **b.** A golden rectangle is defined to be a rectangle whose ratio of its long side to short side is ϕ. Note than $10 \div 6.25 = 1.6$.

6. **a.** The golden rectangle became a cornerstone of their philosophy of aesthetics.

7. **a.** Refer to Figure 11.46.

8. **b.** Because the ratio of successive Fibonacci numbers converges to $\phi \sim 1.62$, each Fibonacci number is about 62% larger than the preceding number.

9. **b.** The 21st number in the series is the sum of the preceding two numbers.

10. **b.** Refer to Table 11.3.

DOES IT MAKE SENSE?

7. Does not make sense. The ratio of lengths of Maria's two sticks is 2/2 = 1, which is not the golden ratio.

8. Makes sense. The dimensions of a standard domino are close to the dimensions of a golden rectangle.

9. Does not make sense. While circles have a lot of symmetry, they do not embody the golden ratio.

10. Does not make sense. Each year, Juliet's age increases by one, and the Fibonacci numbers do not increase like that.

BASIC SKILLS & CONCEPTS

11. The longer segment should have a length of 3.71 inches, and the shorter segment a length of 2.29 inches.

12. The ratio of the length of the longer piece (call it L) to the shorter piece should be ϕ, which implies $L \div 5 = \phi$. Thus $L = 5\phi$, and the length of the entire line is $5 + 5\phi = 13.1$ meters.

13. The middle and right rectangles are golden rectangles.

14. If 2.7 in. is the longer side, and S the shorter side, we have $2.7 \div S = \phi$, which means $S = 2.7 \div 1.62 = 1.67$ in. If 2.7 in. is the shorter side, and L the longer side, we have $L \div 2.7 = \phi$, which means $L = 2.7\phi = 4.37$ in.

15. If 5.8 m is the longer side, and S the shorter side, we have $5.8 \div S = \phi$, which means $S = 5.8 \div 1.62 = 3.58$ m. If 5.8 m is the shorter side, and L the longer side, we have $L \div 5.8 = \phi$, which means $L = 5.8\phi = 9.40$ m.

16. If 12.6 km is the longer side, and S the shorter side, we have $12.6 \div S = \phi$, which means $S = 12.6 \div 1.62 = 7.78$ km. If 12.6 km is the shorter side,

and L the longer side, we have $L \div 12.6 = \phi$, which means $L = 12.6\,\phi = 20.41$ km.

17. If 0.66 cm is the longer side, and S the shorter side, we have $0.66 \div S = \phi$, which means $S = 0.66 \div 1.62 = 0.41$ cm. If 0.66 cm is the shorter side, and L the longer side, we have $L \div 0.66 = \phi$, which means $L = 0.66\,\phi = 1.07$ cm.

18. Answers will vary.

FURTHER APPLICATIONS

19. a. Begin with $\dfrac{L}{1} = \dfrac{L+1}{L}$, and multiply both sides

by L to arrive at $L^2 = L+1$, which can be rearranged to produce $L^2 - L - 1 = 0$.

b. The two roots are

$$L = \frac{-(-1) + \sqrt{(-1)^2 - 4(1)(-1)}}{2(1)} = \frac{1+\sqrt{5}}{2} \text{ and}$$

$$L = \frac{-(-1) - \sqrt{(-1)^2 - 4(1)(-1)}}{2(1)} = \frac{1-\sqrt{5}}{2}.$$

The first is $\phi = 1.618034\ldots$.

20. a. $\dfrac{1}{\phi} = \dfrac{1}{1.618034} = 0.618034 = \phi - 1$.

b. $\phi^2 = 1.618034^2 = 2.618034 = \phi + 1$.

21. Answers will vary.

22. a. The second column in the table below shows the first ten Lucas numbers.

n	L_n	L_n/L_{n-1}
1	1	–
2	3	3
3	4	1.33
4	7	1.75
5	11	1.57
6	18	1.64
7	29	1.61
8	47	1.62
9	76	1.617
10	123	1.618

b. The ratios of successive Lucas numbers are shown in the right column of the table above. It appears that the ratio is approaching the golden ratio ϕ.

UNIT 12A

TIME OUT TO THINK

Pg. 628. Yes. Continuing the given example, if a vote for Sharon changes to a vote for Robert, then Robert wins by 10 to 9 instead of Sharon winning by 10 to 9.

Pg. 629. Opinions will vary. This would be a good topic for a discussion either during or outside of class.

Pg. 631. Opinions will vary. Students might consider whether your local elections (e.g., mayor) use runoff or plurality. This would be a good topic for a discussion either during or outside of class.

Pg. 634. There are many possible examples; college football polls are among the easiest and most interesting to study.

Pg. 636. Candidate A is the winner by plurality, with the most first-place votes. By a Borda count, Candidate A gets $3 \times 14 + 2 \times 12 + 1 \times 10 = 76$ points, which is the highest point total of the 3 candidates, so A is again the winner.

QUICK QUIZ

1. **b**. In a three-candidate race, it's possible that none of the candidates receives a majority of the votes.

2. **c**. Gore won 48.38% of the vote, which is not a majority, only a plurality.

3. **b**. A 60% vote is required to end a filibuster, which means 41% of the senators (a minority) can prevent a bill from coming to a vote by staging a filibuster.

4. **a**. In a runoff, the two candidates with the most votes go in a head-to-head competition, and Perot would be eliminated at this stage.

5. **b**. A preference schedule is a ballot where voters list, in order of their preference, the choices before them.

6. **c**. In an election where preference schedules are used, a voter is expected to fill in all choices.

7. **a**. Look at the second row of Figure 12.3.

8. **c**. Candidate D showed up in third place on $12 + 4 + 2 = 18$ ballots.

9. **b**. Candidate E received only 6 first-place votes.

10. **b**. As shown in the text, a different winner would be declared for each of the five methods discussed (plurality, runoff, sequential runoff, a Borda count, and the Condorcet method).

DOES IT MAKES SENSE?

9. Does not make sense. If both candidates received more than 50% of the vote, the total vote would exceed 100%.

10. Makes sense. In an election with more than two candidates, the candidate that wins the most votes has won a plurality of the votes (in some cases this might also be a majority of votes).

11. Makes sense. Imagine a race with three candidates. Herman could win a plurality of the votes in the first election, with Hanna coming in second, in which case a runoff election would ensue. Hanna would win the election if she beat Herman in the runoff.

12. Makes sense. As shown in the analysis of the preference schedule outcomes of Table 12.3, there are scenarios where one candidate beats the other using a particular method of election, but the situation is reversed when using a different method of election.

13. Makes sense. This is the way most U.S. presidential elections are decided – a candidate wins both the popular and electoral vote.

14. Does not make sense. In the situation described, a hung jury would be declared, and the defendant would not be found guilty. (To be found guilty of a criminal offense in most states, a unanimous vote is often required).

BASIC SKILLS & CONCEPTS

15. a. Hayes won $\dfrac{4,034,142}{8,418,659} = 47.9\%$ of the popular vote while Tilden won $\dfrac{4,286,808}{8,418,659} = 50.9\%$ of the popular vote. Neither candidate received a popular majority.

b. Hayes won $\dfrac{185}{185+184} = 50.1\%$ of the electoral vote while Tilden won $\dfrac{184}{185+184} = 49.9\%$ of the electoral vote. The percentage of popular and electoral votes were similar. Hayes won the electoral vote but did not win the popular vote.

16. a. Garfield won $\dfrac{4,453,337}{9,217,410} = 48.3\%$ of the popular vote while Hancock won $\dfrac{4,444,267}{9,217,410} = 48.2\%$ of the popular vote. Neither candidate received a popular majority.

b. Garfield won $\dfrac{214}{214+155} = 58.0\%$ of the electoral vote while Hancock won $\dfrac{155}{214+155} = 42.0\%$ of the electoral vote. The percentage of popular and electoral votes were not similar.

17. a. Harrison won $\dfrac{5,443,633}{11,388,846} = 47.8\%$ of the popular vote while Cleveland won $\dfrac{5,538,163}{11,388,846} = 48.6\%$ of the popular vote. Neither candidate received a popular majority.

b. Harrison won $\dfrac{233}{233+168} = 58.1\%$ of the electoral vote while Cleveland won $\dfrac{168}{233+168} = 41.9\%$ of the electoral vote. The percentage of popular and electoral votes were not similar. Harrison won the electoral vote but did not win the popular vote.

18. a. Harrison won $\dfrac{9,126,868}{18,536,585} = 49.2\%$ of the popular vote while Cleveland won $\dfrac{8,548,728}{18,536,585} = 46.1\%$ of the popular vote. Neither candidate received a popular majority.

b. Harrison won $\dfrac{277}{277+254} = 52.2\%$ of the electoral vote while Cleveland won $\dfrac{254}{277+254} = 47.8\%$ of the electoral vote. The percentage of popular and electoral votes were similar.

19 a. Clinton won $\dfrac{44,909,806}{104,423,923} = 43.0\%$ of the popular vote while Bush won $\dfrac{39,104,550}{104,423,923} = 37.4\%$ of the popular vote. Neither candidate received a popular majority.

b. Clinton won $\dfrac{370}{370+168} = 68.8\%$ of the electoral vote while Bush won $\dfrac{168}{370+168} = 31.2\%$ of the electoral vote. The percentage of popular and electoral votes were not similar.

20 a. Clinton won $\dfrac{47,400,125}{96,275,401} = 49.2\%$ of the popular vote while Dole won $\dfrac{39,198,755}{96,275,401} = 40.7\%$ of the popular vote. Neither candidate received a popular majority.

b. Clinton won $\dfrac{379}{379+159} = 70.4\%$ of the electoral vote while Dole won $\dfrac{159}{379+159} = 29.6\%$ of the electoral vote. The percentage of popular and electoral votes were not similar.

21. a. Bush won $\dfrac{62,040,610}{122,293,548} = 50.7\%$ of the popular vote while Kerry won $\dfrac{59,028,439}{122,293,548} = 48.3\%$ of the popular vote. Bush received a popular majority.

b. Bush won $\dfrac{286}{286+251} = 53.3\%$ of the electoral vote while Kerry won $\dfrac{251}{286+251} = 46.7\%$ of the electoral vote. The percentage of popular and electoral votes were similar.

22. a. Obama won $\dfrac{69,498,216}{131,442,598} = 52.9\%$ of the popular vote while McCain won $\dfrac{59,948,240}{131,442,598} = 45.6\%$ of the popular vote. Obama received a popular majority.

b. Obama won $\dfrac{365}{365+173} = 67.8\%$ of the electoral vote while McCain won $\dfrac{173}{365+173} = 32.2\%$ of the electoral vote. The percentage of popular and electoral votes were not similar.

23. a. 62/100 = 62% of the senators would vote to end the filibuster, so the filibuster will likely end, and the bill could come to a vote where it would pass.

b. A 2/3 vote of an 11-member jury requires at least 8 votes (because 7/11 = 63.6% < 2/3), so there will be no conviction in this trial. (A hung jury is likely).

c. Only 72% of the states support the amendment (75% is required), so it will fail to pass.

d. It is not likely to become law because 68/100 = 68% of the Senate will support it, and 270/435 = 62% of the House will support it, and this isn't enough for the veto to be overturned.

24. a. The percentage of shareholders favoring the merger is 6650/10,100 = 65.84%, which is just shy of the required 2/3 = 66.67% vote needed.

b. A 3/4 vote of a 12-member jury requires at least 9 votes; thus, there will be no conviction.

c. Only 70% of the states support the amendment (75% is required), so it will fail to pass.

d. It is likely to become law because 68/100 = 68% of the Senate will support it, and 292/435 = 67.1% of the House will support it, so the veto can be overturned.

25. a. Wilson earned 6,286,214/13,896,156 = 45.24% of the popular vote, Roosevelt won 29.69%, and

Taft won 25.07%. Wilson won the popular vote by a plurality, but no one won a majority.

b. Wilson won 435/531 = 81.92% of the electoral vote, Roosevelt won 16.57%, and Taft won 1.51%. Wilson won both a plurality and a majority of the electoral vote.

c. If Taft had dropped out of the election, and Roosevelt had won most of Taft's popular votes, then Roosevelt could have won the popular vote. For Roosevelt to win the presidency, his additional popular votes would need to have been distributed among the states in a way that put him ahead of Wilson in many of the states that Wilson had won – Roosevelt would have needed Taft's 8 electoral votes, plus 170 of Wilson's electoral votes to win.

d. If Roosevelt had dropped out of the election and Taft had won most of Roosevelt's popular votes, then Taft could have won the popular vote. However, his additional popular votes would need to have been distributed among states in a way that allowed him to win the electoral vote.

26. a. Bush won $\dfrac{2,912,790}{5,963,049} = 48.85\%$ of the popular

vote while Gore won $\dfrac{2,912,253}{5,963,049} = 48.84\%$ of the

popular vote. Bush's margin of victory was 2912790 – 2912253 = 537 votes.

b. Bush would have won 2,912,790 + 60% × 17,484 + 40% × 97,421 = 2,962,249 votes while Gore would have won 2,912,253 + 40% × 17,484 + 60% × 97,421 = 2,977,699 votes. Gore would have won the election.

c. Bush would have won 2,912,790 + 51% × 17,484 + 49% × 97,421 = 2,969,443 votes while Gore would have won 2,912,253 + 49% × 17,484 + 51% × 97,421 = 2,970,505 votes. Gore would have won the election.

d. Buchanan won $\dfrac{17484}{5963049} = 0.29\%$ of the

statewide vote, which is lower than the percentage in Palm Beach County.

e. Gore needed 537 votes to win so he would have

needed $\dfrac{537}{3407} = 15.8\%$ of Buchanan's votes, so he

would have needed 15.8% × 0.8% = 0.13% of the overall Palm Beach County vote. With the Reform Party estimate that Buchanan would have won 0.3% of the vote, Gore would have won 0.8% – 0.3% = 0.5% of the overall vote, which would have been enough for him to win the election.

27. a. A total of 66 votes were cast.

b. Candidate D is the plurality winner (22 first-place votes), but not by a majority.

c. In a runoff, candidate D would win, because 40 voters prefer D to B (who finished in second place in part **b**), while only 26 prefer B to D.

d. In a sequential runoff, the candidate with the fewest votes is eliminated at each stage. Candidate A received the fewest first-place votes in the original results (only 8), so A is eliminated, and those votes are redistributed among the other candidates. Recounting the votes after A has been eliminated, we find that B has 20 first-place votes, C has 16, and D has 30. Thus C is now eliminated, and the votes counted again. In this final stage, we find that B has 26 first-place votes, and D has 40 votes (as in part **b**), so D wins the sequential runoff.

e. In a Borda count, first-place votes receive a value of 4, second-place votes receive a value of 3, and so on. Working through each column of the table, and noting the number of voters who cast such ballots, the count for candidate A is computed as follows:

$20 \times 1 + 15 \times 3 + 10 \times 2 + 8 \times 4 + 7 \times 3 + 6 \times 3 = 156$.

The count for candidate B is

$20 \times 4 + 15 \times 1 + 10 \times 1 + 8 \times 1 + 7 \times 2 + 6 \times 2 = 139$.

The count for candidate C is

$20 \times 2 + 15 \times 2 + 10 \times 4 + 8 \times 2 + 7 \times 1 + 6 \times 4 = 157$.

The count for candidate D is

$20 \times 3 + 15 \times 4 + 10 \times 3 + 8 \times 3 + 7 \times 4 + 6 \times 1 = 208$.

Candidate D wins in this case.

f. Since there are 4 candidates, there are 6 pairings to consider. The results for each pairing are shown below.

A beats B, 46 to 20.   C beats A, 36 to 30.
D beats A, 52 to 14.   C beats B, 39 to 27.
D beats B, 40 to 26.   D beats C, 50 to 16.

Since D wins more pairwise comparisons than any other candidate, D is the winner.

g. As the winner by all five methods, candidate D is clearly the winner of the election.

28. a. A total of 29 votes were cast.

b. Candidate D is the plurality winner (13 first-place votes), but not by a majority.

c. In a runoff, candidate D would win, because 16 voters prefer D to B (who finished in second place in part **b**), while only 13 prefer B to D.

d. Using the process illustrated in exercise 27d, it can be shown that D wins a sequential runoff.

e. Using the process illustrated in exercise 27e, the counts of the five candidates are A = 91, B = 115, C = 76, D = 100, and E = 53. Candidate B has the highest count, so B wins in this case.

f. Checking all 10 possible pairwise comparisons (AB, AC, AD, AE, BC, BD, BE, CD, CE, and DE), you should find that each of candidates A, B, and D wins 3 of the match-ups, so no winner can be declared by this method.

g. Candidates B and D both win by at least one method, so the outcome is in contention. However, D won three of the five methods, so one could argue the election should go to D.

29. a. A total of 100 votes were cast.
    b. Candidate C is the plurality winner (40 first-place votes), but not by a majority.
    c. In a runoff, candidate A would win, because 55 voters prefer A to C.
    d. With only three candidates, the sequential runoff method is the same as the standard runoff between the top two candidates, and thus A would win.
    e. Using the process illustrated in exercise 27e, the counts of the three candidates are A = 200, B = 210, and C = 190. Candidate B has the highest count, so B wins a Borda count.
    f. Since there are 3 candidates, there are 3 pairings to consider. The results of each pairing are:
    B beats A, 55 to 45.   A beats C, 55 to 45.
    B beats C, 55 to 45.
    Since B wins two of the pairwise comparisons, B is the winner.
    g. Candidate A wins by runoff, B wins by a Borda count and pairwise comparisons, and C is the plurality winner. Thus there is no clear winner.

30. a. A total of 30 votes were cast.
    b. Candidates A, B, and D tie by the plurality method, all with 10 first-place votes.
    c. The runoff method does not produce a winner, because only one candidate can be eliminated based on fewest first-place votes. The remaining three candidates (A, B, and D) tie.
    d. Like the runoff method, the sequential runoff method fails to produce a winner: candidates A, B, and D tie.
    e. Using the process illustrated in exercise 27e, the counts of the candidates are A = 80, B = 90, C = 60, and D = 70. Candidate B wins in this case.
    f. Checking all 6 possible pairwise comparisons (AB, AC, AD, BC, BD, and CD), you should find that candidate B wins more head-to-head match-ups (3) than any other candidate, so B is the winner.
    g. As the winner by the only two conclusive methods, candidate B is the winner of the election.

31. a. A total of 90 votes were cast.
    b. Candidate E is the plurality winner (40 first-place votes), but not by a majority.
    c. Candidate B wins a runoff, because 50 voters prefer B over E, who would receive 40 votes (D is eliminated at the beginning).
    d. With only three candidates earning first-place votes, the sequential runoff method is the same as the standard runoff between the top two candidates, and thus B would win.

e. Using the process illustrated in exercise 27e, the counts of the candidates are A = 260, B = 290, C = 200, D = 290, and E = 310. Candidate E has the highest count, so E wins a Borda cont.
f. Since there are 5 candidates, there are 10 pairings to consider. The results for each pairing are shown below.

A beats B, 60 to 30.   A beats C, 60 to 30.
D beats A, 60 to 30.   E beats A, 70 to 20.
B beats C, 90 to 0.   D beats B, 60 to 30.
B beats E, 50 to 40.   D beats C, 60 to 30.
C beats E, 50 to 40.   E beats D, 70 to 20.

Since D wins more pairwise comparisons than any other candidate (3), D is the winner.
g. Candidates B and E each win two of the five methods, and D wins one method, so all have some claim on the prize. The outcome is debatable.

32. Since there are 4 candidates, there are 6 pairings to consider. The results for each pairing are shown below.

B beats A, 60 to 50.   A beats C, 110 to 0.
A beats D, 110 to 0.   B beats C, 60 to 50.
B beats D, 60 to 50.

At this point, we don't even need to check the last pairing because we have already found the solution: candidate B wins all three of his head-to-head races, and thus is the Condorcet winner. (If you are curious, C beats D, 60 votes to 50 votes).

33. The results of the three head-to-head races are shown below.

A beats B, 18 to 9.   B beats C, 19 to 8.
C beats A, 17 to 10.

No winner can be determined, and the curious situation where voters prefer A to B, B to C, and C to A is called the *Condorcet paradox*, or *voting paradox*.

FURTHER APPLICATIONS

34. a. Best won a plurality, because he won more votes than the other candidates, but no one won a majority, as more than 50% of the vote is required before a majority winner can be claimed.
    b. Able needs just over 15 percentage points to gain a majority and win a runoff. Since 15%/23% = 0.652, Able needs just over 65.2% of Crown's votes.

35. a. Fillipo won a plurality, because he won more votes than the other candidates, but no one won a majority, as more than 50% of the vote is required before a majority win can be claimed.
    b. Earnest needs just over 23 percentage points to gain a majority and win a runoff. Since 23%/26% = 0.8846, Earnest needs just over 88.46% of Davis's votes.

36. a. Irving won a plurality because he won more votes than the other candidates, but no one won a majority (Irving won 205/485 = 42.3% of the vote, which isn't enough).

b. To overtake Irving, Heyduke needs 83 additional votes (this would give Heyduke a total of 243 votes, with Irving winning only 242 votes).

37. a. King won a plurality because he won more votes than the other candidates, but no one won a majority (King won 382/943 = 40.5% of the vote, which isn't enough).

b. To overtake King, Lord needs 166 additional votes (this would give Lord a total of 472 votes, with King winning only 471 votes).

38.

First	A	A	C	C
Second	B	C	A	B
Third	C	B	B	A
	4	2	3	1

39.

First	A	A	C	C	D
Second	B	C	A	B	A
Third	C	D	D	A	B
Fourth	D	B	B	D	C
	5	1	2	2	2

40. a. Label the four candidates as A, B, C, and D. It is easy enough to list all possible pairings: AB, AC, AD, BC, BD, and CD, for a total of 6 pairings. Note that this list is a list of combinations of four objects taken two at a time, so there should be $_4C_2 = 6$ pairings.

b. With 5 candidates, there are $_5C_2 = 10$ pairings.

c. With 6 candidates, there are $_6C_2 = 15$ pairings.

41. Each voter will record a first, second, third, fourth, fifth and sixth place vote. The points for these places total $6 + 5 + 4 + 3 + 2 + 1 = 21$ points. With 30 voters, there are $30 \times 21 = 630$ total points.

42. Each voter will record a first, second, third, and fourth place vote. The points for these places total $4 + 3 + 2 + 1 = 10$ points. With 30 voters, there are $30 \times 10 = 300$ total points. Candidate D has $300 - 125 - 80 - 75 = 20$ points, and thus candidate A wins the election.

UNIT 12B

TIME OUT TO THINK

Pg. 643. In general, an election in which one candidate receives a majority will meet the fairness criteria.

Pg. 644(1st). Opinions will vary. This would be a good topic for a discussion either during or outside of class.

Pg. 644(2nd). Opinions will vary. You might try to identify a situation in which it would be appropriate or acceptable to use an approval system. This would be a good topic for a discussion either during or outside of class.

Pg. 645. Opinions will vary . Many people consider this to be a serious drawback to approval voting, but others do not. This would be a good topic for a discussion either during or outside of class.

QUICK QUIZ

1. **c.** An election isn't declared fair until all four fairness criteria are satisfied.

2. **a.** Berman wins a plurality because he has the most votes.

3. **b.** Goldsmith won the least number of first-place votes, and so is eliminated in a runoff. Freedman wins Goldsmith's 18 votes, and so beats Berman.

4. **c.** Criterion 1 is only applicable when a candidate wins a majority of votes.

5. **b.** Freedman wins both head-to-head races, and thus by Criterion 2, Freedman should win if this is a fair election.

6. **a.** See exercise 5.

7. **a.** Candidate X (Freedman) needs to be declared the winner of the first election before Criterion 4 comes into play.

8. **b.** There are plenty of elections where all four fairness criteria are satisfied. Arrow's theorem says only that no election system can be satisfied in *all* circumstances.

9. **b.** The text gives examples of approval voting scenarios that are not fair (and Arrow's theorem guarantees there are such cases).

10. **c.** In a small state, the number of voters per senator is much smaller than in a large state, and thus each voter has more voting power.

DOES IT MAKE SENSE?

5. Makes sense. Karen feels that because she won all head-to-head races, she should win the election so that Criterion 2 is satisfied – otherwise, it's not a fair election.

6. Makes sense. Kai feels the election is not fair, because under Criterion 1, he should win.

7. Does not make sense. Assuming the plurality method is used to decide the second election, Table 12.12 claims Criterion 3 is always satisfied (and thus Wendy could not have managed to win).

8. Does not make sense. Arrow's impossibility theorem states that no voting system can satisfy all four fairness criteria all of the time (see Example 4 in the text).

BASIC SKILLS & CONCEPTS

9. A candidate who wins a majority is the only person to receive a plurality. Thus the candidate will win the election, and Criterion 1 is satisfied.

10. Candidate A is the plurality winner, but candidate B wins in head-to-head races against both A and C. This implies the plurality method violates Criterion 2.

11. The following preference schedule is just one possible example.

First	B	A	C	C
Second	A	B	A	B
Third	C	C	B	A
	2	4	2	3

C is the plurality winner, but A beats both C and B, which means Criterion 2 is violated.

12. Suppose a candidate wins by the plurality method, and in a second election, moves up in at least one ranking (while the other candidates keep their relative rankings). That candidate's first-place votes must either remain the same or increase, so that candidate will win the second election.

13. Candidate A would win by the plurality method. However if candidate C were to drop out of the election, then B would win by the plurality method, and Criterion 4 would be violated.

14. The following preference schedule is just one possible example.

First	A	B	C
Second	B	A	B
Third	C	C	A
	3	2	4

Candidate C would win by plurality. However, if candidate A drops out, candidate B wins by plurality.

15. Assume a candidate receives a majority. In either runoff method, votes are redistributed as candidates are eliminated. But it is impossible for another candidate to accumulate enough votes to overtake a candidate who already has a majority.

16. By the sequential runoff method (which is the same as the top two runoff method with three candidates), candidate C is eliminated, and A wins the runoff. Candidate A also wins head-to-head races against B and C, so Criterion 2 is satisfied.

17. By the sequential runoff method (which is the same as the top two runoff method with three candidates), candidate B is eliminated, and C wins the runoff. However, candidate B wins head-to-head races against A and C, so Criterion 2 is violated.

18. The following preference schedule is just one possible example.

First	B	A	C
Second	A	C	A
Third	C	B	B
	3	2	4

Candidate C wins in a sequential runoff. But A beats B and C in head-to-head races, violating Criterion 2.

19. In the sequential runoff method, candidate B is eliminated first, then candidate A, making C the winner. Now suppose that the 4 voters on the third ballot (ACB) move C up and vote for the ranking CAB. Now A is eliminated first, and B wins the election. Thus criterion 3 is violated.

20. After candidate C is eliminated, candidate B wins the runoff. However, if A were to drop out, C would win the election. So Criterion 4 is violated.

21. The following preference schedule is just one possible example.

First	A	B	C
Second	B	A	B
Third	C	C	A
	4	3	5

After candidate B is eliminated, A wins the runoff. However, if C were to drop out, B would win the election. So Criterion 4 is violated.

22. We see that candidate A has a majority of votes (3/5 = 60%). By the point system (using 2, 1, and 0 points), A has 6 points, B has 7, and C has 2. So B wins by the point system, and Criterion 1 is violated, since the majority winner lost.

23. The following preference schedule is just one possible example.

First	A	B	C
Second	B	C	B
Third	C	A	A
	4	2	1

Candidate A has a majority of the votes, but loses in a Borda count (A gets 8 points, B gets 9, and C gets 4, using 2, 1, and 0 points).

24. Using the point system (with 2, 1, and 0 points), candidate A receives 10 points, B receives 11 points, and C receives 6 points. However, A beats B and C in head-to-head races, violating Criterion 2.

25. The following preference schedule is just one possible example.

First	A	D	C
Second	B	B	B
Third	C	A	D
Fourth	D	C	A
	4	8	3

Using the Borda count (with 3, 2, 1, and 0 points), A gets 20 points, B gets 30, C gets 13, and D gets 27 points, making B the winner. However, D wins head-to-head races against all other candidates, and thus Criterion 2 is violated.

26. Suppose a candidate wins by the point system, and in a second election, that candidate moves up in at least one ranking. That candidate's point total must increase at the expense of other candidates, and so will he win the second election.

27. Using the point system (with 2, 1, and 0 points), candidate A gets 11 points, B gets 11 points, and C gets 14 points, which makes C the winner. However, if Candidate A were to drop from the race, then B would receive 7 points and C would receive 5 points (notice that the point values become 1 and 0 with only two candidates). Thus Criterion 4 is violated.

28. The following preference schedule is just one possible example.

First	A	B
Second	C	A
Third	B	C
	2	3

Using the point system (with 2, 1, and 0 points), Candidate A gets 7 points, B gets 6, and C gets 2 points, which makes A the winner. However, if C were to drop from the race, then B would receive 3 points, and B would receive 2 (notice that the point values become 1 and 0 with only two candidates). Thus criterion 4 is violated.

29. Assume candidate A wins a majority of first-place votes. Then in every head-to-head race with another candidate, A must win (by a majority). Thus, A wins every head-to-head race and is the winner by pairwise comparisons, so Criterion 1 is satisfied.

30. If a candidate wins every head-to-head contest against other candidates then that candidate wins by the method of pairwise comparisons, so Criterion 2 is satisfied.

31. Suppose candidate A wins by the method of pairwise comparisons, and in a second election, moves up above candidate B in at least one ballot. A's position relative to B remains the same or improves, and A's position and B's position

relative to the other candidates remains the same, so A must win the second election.

32. With the pairwise comparison method, A beats C, D, and E; B beats A; C beats B and D; D beats B and E; and E beats B and C. Thus A wins with three points. If C, D, and E drop out, then B beats A on three of the five ballots and wins the election. The outcome of the election is changed when C, D, and E drop out, which violates Criterion 4.

33. The following preference schedule is just one possible example.

First	B	C	D
Second	A	A	C
Third	D	D	B
Fourth	C	B	A
	2	2	2

By the pairwise comparison method, A would beat D, B would beat A, C would beat A and B, and D would beat B and C. This would lead to a tie between C and D. However, if A were to drop out of the election, then D would have two pairwise wins, and C would have one pairwise win. Criterion 4 is violated because the outcome of the election is changed when A drops out.

34. a. Voting only for their first choices, candidate C wins by plurality with 40% of the vote.
    b. By an approval vote, 30% + 29% = 59% of the voters approve of candidate B, 30% + 29% + 1% = 60% approve of candidate A, and 40% of the voters approve of candidate C. The winner is A.

35. a. Voting only for their first choices, candidate C wins by plurality with 42% of the vote.
    b. By an approval vote, 28% + 29% = 57% of the voters approve of A, 28% + 29% + 1% = 58% approve of B, and 42% of the voters approve of C. The winner is B.

36. Imagine that there is a vote of the four shareholders. Regardless of how the three largest shareholders (26%, 26%, 25%) vote, their votes will give a majority to one side or the other (try all combinations). The vote of the third shareholder (23%) cannot change the outcome.

37. The electoral votes per person for each of the states can be computed by dividing the number of electoral votes by the population. The results are as follows:

New York 1.61×10^{-6} Illinois 1.65×10^{-6}

Rhode Island 3.70×10^{-6} Alaska 4.58×10^{-6}

It is evident that voters in Alaska have more voting power than those in Illinois.

38. The voters in Alaska have more voting power than those in New York (see exercise 37).

39. The voters in Rhode Island have more voting power than those in Illinois (see exercise 37).

40. The voters in Illinois have more voting power than those in New York (see exercise 37).

41. From the least to greatest voting power, the ranking is: New York, Illinois, Rhode Island, Alaska.

FURTHER APPLICATIONS

42. The winner by plurality, but not majority, is A. So Criterion 1 does not apply. Candidate A beats all other candidates one-on-one and is also declared winner by the plurality method, so Criterion 2 is satisfied. The plurality method always satisfies Criterion 3. If C were to drop out of the election, then B would win by plurality, violating Criterion 4.

43. A single runoff would eliminate C and D. Candidate A would win the runoff, 23 to 18. There is no majority winner, so Criterion 1 does not apply. Candidate A beats all other candidates one-on-one, and is also declared winner in a single runoff, so Criterion 2 is satisfied. If A is moved up in any of the rankings, it doesn't affect the outcome of the election, so Criterion 3 is satisfied. If any combination of {B, C, D} drops out of the race, the outcome is not changed. So in this case (though not in general), Criterion 4 is satisfied.

44. A sequential runoff eliminates candidate D, followed by B and C, leaving A as the winner. There is no majority winner, so Criterion 1 does not apply. Candidate A beats all other candidates one-to-one, and is also declared winner by the sequential runoff method, so Criterion 2 is satisfied. If A is moved up in any of the rankings, it doesn't affect the outcome of the election, so Criterion 3 is satisfied. If any combination of {B, C, D} drops out of the race, the outcome is not changed. So in this case (though not in general), Criterion 4 is satisfied.

45. Candidate A wins the point system (using 3, 2, 1, and 0 points) with 83 points. There is no majority winner, so Criterion 1 does not apply. Candidate A beats all other candidates one-on-one, and is also declared winner by the point system, so Criterion 2 is satisfied. The point system always satisfies Criterion 3. If any combination of {B, C, D} drops out of the race, the outcome is not changed. So in this case (though not in general), Criterion 4 is satisfied.

46. Candidate A wins by the pairwise comparison method because A beats all other candidates in head-to-head races. There is no majority winner, so Criterion 1 does not apply. Candidate A beats all other candidates one-on-one and is automatically declared winner by the pairwise comparison method, so Criterion 2 is satisfied. The pairwise comparison method always satisfies Criterion 3. Since A beats all other candidates, the removal of any other candidate cannot affect the outcome of the election, and thus Criterion 4 is satisfied.

47. Candidate A wins by a plurality, but not by a majority. There is no majority winner, so Criterion 1 does not apply. Candidate E beats all other candidates one-on-one, but loses by the plurality method, so Criterion 2 is violated. The plurality method always satisfies Criterion 3. If any of B, C, or D were to drop out of the election, the outcome of A winning would change, so Criterion 4 is violated.

48. After candidates C, D, and E are eliminated, B wins the runoff. There is no majority winner, so Criterion 1 does not apply. Candidate E beats all other candidates one-to-one, but loses by the runoff method, so Criterion 2 is violated. If B were to move up in any of the rankings, it would not affect the outcome of the election (in this case), so Criterion 3 is satisfied. If candidate A were to drop out of the race, then D would win, so Criterion 4 is violated.

49. The candidates E, D, and B are eliminated sequentially, leaving a final runoff between A and C, which C wins. There is no majority winner, so Criterion 1 does not apply. Candidate E beats all other candidates one-on-one, but loses in the sequential runoff method, so Criterion 2 is violated. If candidate C moved up in any of the rankings, the outcome is not affected, so Criterion 3 is satisfied. If A were to drop out of the election, D would win instead of C, so Criterion 4 is violated.

50. Candidate D wins the election by the Borda count (using 4, 3, 2, 1, and 0 points) with 136 points. There is no majority winner, so Criterion 1 does not apply. Candidate E beats all other candidates one-on-one, but loses by the point system, so Criterion 2 is violated. The point system always satisfies Criterion 3. If C drops out of the race, then the winner is no longer D, but E – this is a violation of Criterion 4.

51. We have seen that E beats all other candidates in pairwise races (see exercise 47) and is the winner by the pairwise comparison method. There is no majority winner, so Criterion 1 does not apply. The pairwise comparison method always satisfies Criteria 2 and 3. It can be shown that if any combination of {A, B, C, D} drops out of the race, the winner is still E, so Criterion 4 is satisfied.

52. If the two major parties deadlock at 49 votes apiece, then the deciding votes are held by the

Independents. If both Independents vote with one party, that party wins the vote.

UNIT 12C

TIME OUT TO THINK

Pg. 651. Answers will vary. This would be a good topic for a discussion either during or outside of class.

Pg. 653. Answers will vary. The main point is that the sum of the standard quotas must sum to 14. To find the average class size for a school, divide the number of students at the school by the standard quota for that school.

Pg. 655. The Constitution does not clearly specify whether the 1 per 30,000 limit applies only to the total population and total number of representatives, or to the populations and numbers of representatives within each individual state. Washington's second point was basing his veto on the fact that 8 states had allotments of more than 1 per 30,000, but the allotment was less than this for the United States as a whole. Therefore his veto on this ground made sense only if he assumed the Constitution meant for this limit to apply to individual states. His wording about context was his way of justifying this assumption.

Pg. 660. Yes: The number of seats assigned to each state is its standard quota rounded either up or down to the nearest integer

Pg. 662. State C gets an extra seat by the Hill-Huntington method and therefore prefers this method. State D prefers Webster's method.

QUICK QUIZ

1. **c.** The Constitution does not specify the number of representatives, and the House has, in fact, had 435 members only since 1912. The number briefly rose by two when Hawaii and Alaska were granted statehood (1959), but dropped back to 435 in the next apportionment (and will likely remain at that level, unless a 1941 law is changed).

2. **b.** Apportionment is a process used to divide the available seats among the states.

3. **a.** The standard divisor is defined to be the total U.S. population divided by the number of seats in the House.

4. **b.** The standard quota is defined to be the population of a state divided by the standard divisor. In this case, the standard divisor is 1 million.

5. **b.** In this scenario, the standard divisor would be defined as the population of students divided by the number of teachers, or $25,000 \div 1000 = 25$.

6. **b.** In this scenario, the standard quota would be defined as the population of the school divided by the standard divisor computed in exercise 5. Thus it would be $220 \div 25 = 8.8$.

7. **c.** Parks Elementary would get the eight teachers because the Hamilton method assigns the extra teacher to the school with the highest standard quota.

8. **c.** The Hamilton, Jefferson, Webster, and Hill-Huntington methods are the only four methods of apportionment that have been used (to date) to assign the seats in the House to various states.

9. **c.** At present, the law states that the Hill-Huntington method is to be used to reapportion seats at every census.

10. **a.** M. L. Balinsky and H. P. Young proved that it is impossible to devise a method of apportionment that satisfies the fairness criteria in all cases.

DOES IT MAKE SENSE?

9. Makes sense. If the number of staff support persons needed in a division depends on the number of employees in that division, an apportionment method would be a good idea.

10. Does not make sense. The points allocated to the skaters should be determined by the merits of their performances. Apportionment methods are used in situations in which the population or size of various groups determines how much representation each group should receive.

11. Does not make sense. All apportionment methods have deficiencies, and no single method (of those discussed in the text) is better than the others due to the level of math required to carry it out.

12. Makes sense. This is an example of the Alabama paradox. Ideally, a fair apportionment method should not be prone to the paradox.

BASIC SKILLS & CONCEPTS

13. The number of people per representative would be $350,000,000 \div 435 = 804,598$. If the constitutional limit were observed, the number of representatives would be $350,000,000 \div 30,000 = 11,667$.

14. The number of people per representative would be $400,000,000 \div 500 = 800,000$. If the constitutional limit were observed, the number of representatives would be $400,000,000 \div 30,000 = 13,333$.

15. In order to compute the standard quota, the standard divisor must first be computed. The standard divisor is $\frac{304 \text{ million}}{435} = 698,851$. For Connecticut, the standard quota is $\frac{3,501,252}{698,851} = 5.01$, which is the same as the 5 seats

the state actually has, so Connecticut is fairly represented.

16. The standard divisor is 698,851 (see exercise 15). For Georgia, the standard quota is $\frac{9,685,744}{698,851} = 13.86$, which is larger than the 13 seats the state actually has, so Georgia is underrepresented.

17. The standard divisor is 698,851 (see exercise 15). For Florida, the standard quota is $\frac{18,328,340}{698,851} = 26.23$, which is larger than the 25 seats the state actually has, so Florida is underrepresented.

18. The standard divisor is 698,851 (see exercise 15). For Ohio, the standard quota is $\frac{11,485,910}{698,851} = 16.44$, which is smaller than the 18 seats the state actually has, so Ohio is overrepresented.

19. The total number of employees is $250 + 320 + 380 + 400 = 1350$. The standard divisor is then $\frac{1350}{35} = 38.57$. For the first division, the standard quota is $\frac{250}{38.57} = 6.48$. The standard quotas for the other divisions are 8.30, 9.85, and 10.37, respectively (computed in a similar fashion).

20. The total student population is $560 + 1230 + 1490 + 1760 + 2340 = 7380$. The standard divisor is then $\frac{7380}{18} = 410$. For the first college, the standard quota is $\frac{560}{410} = 1.37$. The standard quotas for the other divisions are 3.00, 3.63, 4.29, and 5.71, respectively (computed in a similar fashion).

21. Refer to exercise 19. Using Hamilton's method for the assignments, round each standard quota down to get $6 + 8 + 9 + 10 = 33$ technicians. Since the first and third divisions have the highest remainders, the extra two technicians will be assigned to them, giving a final apportionment of 7, 8, 10, and 10 technicians to each of the four divisions.

22. Refer to exercise 20. Using Hamilton's method for the assignments, round each standard quota down to get $1 + 3 + 3 + 4 + 5 = 16$ advisors. Since the third and fifth colleges have the highest remainders, the extra two advisors will be assigned to them, giving a final apportionment of 1, 3, 4, 4, and 6 advisors to each of the five colleges.

23. The total population is $950 + 670 + 246 = 1866$, so with 100 seats to be apportioned, the standard divisor is $1866 \div 100 = 18.66$. This is used to compute the standard quota and the minimum quotas in the table below. Hamilton's method applied to these three states yields:

State	A	B	C	Total
Pop.	950	670	246	1866
Std. Q.	50.91	35.91	13.18	100
Min. Q.	50	35	13	98
Frac. R.	0.91	0.91	0.18	2
Final A.	51	36	13	100

Assuming 101 delegates, Hamilton's method yields:

State	A	B	C	Total
Pop.	950	670	246	1866
Std. Q.	50.42	35.26	13.32	101
Min. Q.	51	36	13	100
Frac. R.	0.42	0.26	0.32	1
Final A.	52	36	13	101

No state lost seats as a result of the additional available seat, so the Alabama paradox does not occur here.

24. The total population is $2540 + 1140 + 6330 = 10{,}010$, so with 100 seats to be apportioned, the standard divisor is $10{,}010 \div 100 = 100.10$. This is used to compute the standard quota and the minimum quotas in the table below. Hamilton's method applied to these three states yields:

State	A	B	C	Total
Pop.	2540	1140	6330	10,010
Std. Q.	25.37	11.39	63.24	100
Min. Q.	25	11	63	99
Frac. R.	0.37	0.39	0.24	1
Final A.	25	12	63	100

Assuming 101 delegates, Hamilton's method yields:

State	A	B	C	Total
Pop.	2540	1140	6330	10,010
Std. Q.	25.63	11.50	63.87	101
Min. Q.	25	11	63	99
Frac. R.	0.63	0.50	0.87	2
Final A.	26	11	64	101

State B lost a seat as a result of the additional available seat, so the Alabama paradox does occur here.

25. The total population is 770 + 155 + 70 + 673 = 1668, so with 100 seats to be apportioned, the standard divisor is 1668 ÷ 100 = 16.68. This is used to compute the standard quota and the minimum quotas in the table below. Hamilton's method applied to these four states yields:

State	A	B	C	D	Total
Pop.	770	155	70	673	1668
Std. Q.	46.16	9.29	4.20	40.35	100
Min. Q.	46	9	4	40	99
Frac. R.	0.16	0.29	0.20	0.35	1
Final A.	46	9	4	41	100

Assuming 101 delegates, Hamilton's method yields:

State	A	B	C	D	Total
Pop.	770	155	70	673	1668
Std. Q.	46.62	9.39	4.24	40.75	101
Min. Q.	46	9	4	40	99
Frac. R.	0.62	0.39	0.24	0.75	2
Final A.	47	9	4	41	101

No state lost seats as a result of the additional available seat, so the Alabama paradox does not occur here.

26. The total population is 562 + 88 + 108 + 242 = 1000, so with 100 seats to be apportioned, the standard divisor is 1000 ÷ 100 = 10. This is used to compute the standard quota and the minimum quotas in the table below. Hamilton's method applied to these four states yields:

State	A	B	C	D	Total
Pop.	562	88	108	242	1000
Std. Q.	56.20	8.80	10.80	24.20	100
Min. Q.	56	8	10	24	98
Frac. R.	0.20	0.80	0.80	0.20	2
Final A.	56	9	11	24	100

Assuming 101 delegates, Hamilton's method yields:

State	A	B	C	D	Total
Pop.	562	88	108	242	1000
Std. Q.	56.76	8.89	10.91	24.44	101
Min. Q.	56	8	10	24	98
Frac. R.	0.76	0.89	0.91	0.44	3
Final A.	57	9	11	24	101

No state lost seats as a result of the additional available seat, so the Alabama paradox does not occur here.

27. The total population is 98 + 689 + 212 = 999, so with 100 seats to be apportioned, the standard divisor is 999 ÷ 100 = 9.99. This is used to compute the standard quota and the minimum quotas in the table below. Using a modified divisor of 9.83 instead, we get the modified quotas listed, and the new minimum quotas. Jefferson's method then yields:

State	A	B	C	Total
Pop.	98	689	212	999
Std. Q.	9.81	68.97	21.22	100
Min. Q.	9	68	21	98
Mod. Q.	9.97	70.09	21.57	101.63
N. Min. Q.	9	70	21	100

Since the new minimum quota successfully apportions all 100 seats, we can stop. Note, however, that the quota criterion is violated, because state B's standard quota is 68.97, yet it was given 70 seats.

28. The total population is 1280 + 631 + 2320 = 4231, so with 100 seats to be apportioned, the standard divisor is 4231 ÷ 100 = 42.31. This is used to compute the standard quota and the minimum quotas in the table below. Using a modified divisor of 42.00 instead, we get the modified quotas listed, and the new minimum quotas. Jefferson's method then yields:

State	A	B	C	Total
Pop.	1280	631	2320	4231
Std. Q.	30.25	14.91	54.83	100
Min. Q.	30	14	54	98
Mod. Q.	30.48	15.02	55.24	100.74
N. Min. Q.	30	15	55	100

Since the new minimum quota successfully apportions all 100 seats, we can stop. The quota criterion is satisfied.

29. The total population is 979, so with 100 seats to be apportioned, the standard divisor is 979 ÷ 100 = 9.79. This is used to compute the standard quota and the minimum quotas in the table below. Using a modified divisor of 9.60 instead, we get the modified quotas listed, and the new minimum quotas. Jefferson's method then yields:

State	A	B	C	D	Total
Pop.	69	680	155	75	979
Std. Q.	7.05	69.46	15.83	7.66	100
Min. Q.	7	69	15	7	98
Mod. Q.	7.19	70.83	16.15	7.81	101.98
NMQ	7	70	16	7	100

Since the new minimum quota successfully apportions all 100 seats, we can stop. The quota criterion is satisfied.

30. The total population is 9400, so with 100 seats to be apportioned, the standard divisor is $9400 \div 100 = 94.00$. This is used to compute the standard quota and the minimum quotas in the table below. Using a modified divisor of 92.00 instead, we get the modified quotas listed, and the new minimum quotas. Jefferson's method then yields:

State	A	B	C	D	Total
Pop.	1220	5030	2460	690	9400
Std. Q.	12.98	53.51	26.17	7.34	100
Min. Q.	12	53	26	7	98
Mod. Q.	13.26	54.67	26.74	7.50	102.17
NMQ	13	54	26	7	100

Since the new minimum quota successfully apportions all 100 seats, we can stop. The quota criterion is satisfied.

31. After trial and error, a modified divisor of 38.4 was found to work. The results are summarized in the table below.

Division	I	II	III	IV
Number in division	250	320	380	400
Modified Quota	6.51	8.33	9.90	10.42
Number assigned	7	8	10	10

32. No modified divisor is necessary in this case. The standard quotas from exercise 30 are 1.37, 3.00, 3.63, 4.29, and 5.71, respectively, and Webster's method directs us to round quotas using standard rounding rules. This yields an apportionment of 1, 3, 4, 4, and 6 advisors to the respective colleges. Since this apportionment leaves no extra advisors, we have found a suitable apportionment.

33. An interesting situation arises in this problem: if the standard divisor, standard quotas, and geometric means are computed without rounding, it turns out a modified divisor is not necessary. That is, after computing said values, the Hill-Huntington method immediately produces an apportionment with no leftover technicians, and it is not necessary to seek a modified divisor. The results are summarized in the table below.

Division	I	II	III	IV
Number in division	250	320	380	400
Standard Quota	6.4815	8.30	9.85	10.37
Geometric Mean	$\sqrt{6 \times 7}$ 6.4807	$\sqrt{8 \times 9}$ 8.49	$\sqrt{9 \times 10}$ 9.49	$\sqrt{10 \times 11}$ 10.49
Number assigned	7	8	10	10

Division I is the culprit – the standard quota and geometric mean are so close to one another that it is hard to determine whether one should round up or down (note that the values at the other entries in the table are not shown to the same precision, because the decision about whether to round up or down can be made with less precise values). If the rounded values from exercise 30 are used, you will need to use a modified divisor in order to find an apportionment that uses all 35 technicians. A divisor of 38.4 is suitable (and realize that modified divisors are not unique, in that divisors close to one another produce the same results).

34. No modified divisor is necessary in this case. The standard quotas from exercise 30 are 1.37, 3.00, 3.63, 4.29, and 5.71, respectively, and the Hill-Huntington method directs us to round quotas based on geometric means. The required geometric means are (respectively): $\sqrt{1 \times 2} = 1.414$; $\sqrt{3 \times 4} = 3.464$; $\sqrt{3 \times 4} = 3.464$; $\sqrt{4 \times 5} = 4.472$; and $\sqrt{5 \times 6} = 5.477$. This yields an apportionment of 1, 3, 4, 4, and 6 advisors to the respective colleges. Since this apportionment leaves no extra advisors, we have found a suitable apportionment.

FURTHER APPLICATIONS

35. The total population is 7710, so with 100 seats to be apportioned, the standard divisor is $7710 \div 100 = 77.10$. This is used to compute the standard quota and the minimum quotas in the table below. Hamilton's method applied to these three states yields:

State	A	B	C	Total
Pop.	1140	6320	250	7710
Std. Q.	14.79	81.97	3.24	100
Min. Q.	14	81	3	98
Frac. R.	0.79	0.97	0.24	2
Final A.	15	82	3	100

With the addition of a new state D of population 500, for whom 5 new delegates are added,

Hamilton's method (with a new standard divisor of 8210 ÷ 105 = 78.19) yields:

State	A	B	C	D	Total
Pop.	1140	6320	250	500	8210
Std. Q.	14.58	80.83	3.20	6.39	105
Min. Q.	14	80	3	6	103
Frac. R.	0.58	0.83	0.20	0.39	2
Final A.	15	81	3	6	105

Even though 5 new seats were added with state D representation in mind, Hamilton's method assigned 6 seats to this state, 1 of them at the expense of state B. Since B lost a seat as a result of the additional seats for the new state, the New State paradox occurs here.

36. The total population is 9948, so with 100 seats to be apportioned, the standard divisor is 9948 ÷ 100 = 99.48. This is used to compute the standard quota and the minimum quotas in the table below. Hamilton's method applied to these three states yields:

State	A	B	C	Total
Pop.	5310	1330	3308	9948
Std. Q.	53.38	13.37	33.25	100
Min. Q.	53	13	33	99
Frac. R.	0.38	0.37	0.25	1
Final A.	54	13	33	100

With the addition of a new state D of population 500, for whom 5 new delegates are added, Hamilton's method (with a new standard divisor of 10,448 ÷ 105 = 99.50) yields:

State	A	B	C	D	Total
Pop.	5310	1330	3308	500	10,448
Std. Q.	53.36	13.37	33.24	5.02	105
Min. Q.	53	13	33	5	104
Frac. R.	0.36	0.37	0.24	0.02	1
Final A.	53	14	33	5	105

While Hamilton's method assigned 5 seats to the new state, as intended, it also gave State B an additional state at the expense of state A. Since A lost a seat as a result of the additional seats for the new state, the New State paradox occurs here.

37. a. The total population is 999, so with 100 seats to be apportioned, the standard divisor is 999 ÷ 100 = 99.9. This is used to compute the standard quota and the minimum quotas in the table below. Hamilton's method yields:

State	A	B	C	Total
Pop.	535	334	120	999
Std. Q.	53.55	34.43	12.01	100
Min. Q.	53	34	12	99
Frac. R.	0.55	0.43	0.01	1
Final A.	54	34	12	100

b. Jefferson's method begins as with Hamilton's. As noted in part **a**, the standard divisor is 9.99, so we try lower modified divisors until the apportionment comes out just right. By trial and error, the modified divisor 9.90 is found to work, as documented in the last two rows of the table below. Note that this choice of the modified divisor is not unique, as other nearby values also work.

State	A	B	C	Total
Pop.	535	334	120	999
Std. Q.	53.55	34.43	12.01	100
Min. Q.	53	34	12	98
Mod. Q.	54.04	34.75	12.12	100.91
N. Min. Q.	54	34	12	100

c. Webster's method requires us to find a modified divisor such that the corresponding modified quotas round (not truncate) to numbers that sum to the desired 100 delegates. Inspecting the table in part **a**, we see that the standard divisor and standard quotas are already adequate – we don't need to seek a modified divisor in this case.

State	A	B	C	Total
Pop.	535	334	120	999
Std. Q.	53.55	34.43	12.01	100
Min. Q.	53	34	12	99
Rou. Q.	54	34	12	100

d. The Hill-Huntington method requires us to find a modified divisor such that the corresponding modified quotas, *rounded relative to the geometric mean*, yield numbers which sum to the required 100 delegates. As in part **c**, the standard divisor and standard quotas are already sufficient because they round (per the geometric means) to the desired apportionment. Thus there is no need to seek out a modified divisor in this case.

State	A	B	C	Total
Pop.	535	334	120	999
Std. Q.	53.55	34.43	12.01	100
Min. Q.	53	34	12	99
Geo. M.	53.50	34.50	12.49	-
Rou. Q.	54	34	12	100

The geometric means are for the whole numbers bracketing the standard quotas, namely: $\sqrt{53 \times 54}$ = 53.50, $\sqrt{34 \times 35}$ = 34.50, and $\sqrt{12 \times 13}$ = 12.49. The modified quotas (in this case the standard quotas) are compared to these, and hence 34.43 and 12.01 are rounded down to 34 and 12, respectively, whereas 53.55 is rounded up to 54.

e. All four methods gave the same results.

38. Refer to exercise 37 for a detailed explanation of the method of solution that yields the following apportionments.

a. Standard divisor = 9.76.

State	A	B	C	Total
Pop.	144	443	389	976
Std. Q.	14.75	45.39	39.86	100
Min. Q.	14	45	39	98
Frac. R.	0.75	0.39	0.86	2
Final A.	15	45	40	100

b. Modified divisor = 9.63.

State	A	B	C	Total
Pop.	144	443	389	976
Std. Q.	14.75	45.39	39.86	100
Min. Q.	14	45	39	98
Mod. Q.	14.95	46.00	40.39	101.35
N. Min. Q.	14	46	40	100

c. Modified divisor not necessary.

State	A	B	C	Total
Pop.	144	443	389	976
Std. Q.	14.75	45.39	39.86	100
Min. Q.	14	45	39	98
Rou. Q.	15	45	40	100

d. Modified divisor not necessary.

State	A	B	C	Total
Pop.	144	443	389	976
Std. Q.	14.75	45.39	39.86	100
Min. Q.	14	45	39	98
Geo. M.	14.49	45.50	39.50	-
Rou. Q.	15	45	40	100

e. The Hamilton, Webster, and Hill-Huntington methods all give the same result, so one could argue that these yield the best apportionment.

39. Refer to exercise 37 for a detailed explanation of the method of solution that yields the following apportionments.

a. Standard divisor = 100.

State	A	B	C	D	Total
Pop.	836	2703	2626	3835	10,000
Std. Q.	8.36	27.03	26.26	38.35	100
Min. Q.	8	27	26	38	99
Frac. R.	0.36	0.03	0.26	0.35	1
Final A.	9	27	26	38	100

b. Modified divisor = 98.3.

State	A	B	C	D	Total
Pop.	836	2703	2626	3835	10,000
Std. Q.	8.36	27.03	26.26	38.35	100
Min. Q.	8	27	26	38	99
Mod. Q.	8.50	27.50	26.71	39.01	101.73
NMQ	8	27	26	39	100

c. Modified divisor = 99.5.

State	A	B	C	D	Total
Pop.	836	2703	2626	3835	10,000
Std. Q.	8.36	27.03	26.26	38.35	100
Min. Q.	8	27	26	38	99
Mod. Q.	8.40	27.17	26.39	38.54	100.50
Rou. Q.	8	27	26	39	100

d. Modified divisor = 99.5.

State	A	B	C	D	Total
Pop.	836	2703	2626	3835	10,000
Std. Q.	8.36	27.03	26.26	38.35	100
Min. Q.	8	27	26	38	99
Mod. Q.	8.40	27.17	26.39	38.54	100.49
Geo. M.	8.49	27.50	26.50	38.50	-
Rou. Q.	8	27	26	39	100

e. The Jefferson, Webster, and Hill-Huntington methods all gave the same result, so one could argue that these yield the best apportionment.

40. Refer to exercise 37 for a detailed explanation of the method of solution that yields the following apportionments.

a. Standard divisor = 125.57.

State	A	B	C	D	Total
Pop.	1234	3498	2267	5558	12,557
Std. Q.	9.83	27.86	18.05	44.26	100
Min. Q.	9	27	18	44	98
Frac. R.	0.83	0.86	0.05	0.26	2
Final A.	10	28	18	44	100

b. Modified divisor = 123.5.

State	A	B	C	D	Total
Pop.	1234	3498	2267	5558	12,557
Std. Q.	9.83	27.86	18.05	44.26	100
Min. Q.	9	27	18	44	98
Mod. Q.	9.99	28.32	18.36	45.00	101.68
NMQ	9	28	18	45	100

c. Modified divisor not necessary.

State	A	B	C	D	Total
Pop.	1234	3498	2267	5558	12,557
Std. Q.	9.83	27.86	18.05	44.26	100
Min. Q.	9	27	18	44	98
Rou. Q.	10	28	18	44	100

d. Modified divisor not necessary.

State	A	B	C	D	Total
Pop.	1234	3498	2267	5558	12,557
Std. Q.	9.83	27.86	18.05	44.26	100
Min. Q.	9	27	18	44	98
Geo. M.	9.49	27.50	18.49	44.50	-
Rou. Q.	10	28	18	44	100

e. The Hamilton, Webster, and Hill-Huntington methods all give the same results, so one could argue that these yield the best apportionment.

41. a. The total population is 390 students, so with 10 committee positions to be apportioned, the standard divisor is 390 ÷ 10 = 39. This is used to compute the standard quota and the minimum quotas in the table below. Hamilton's method yields:

Group	Soc.	Pol.	Ath.	Total
Pop.	48	97	245	390
Std. Q.	1.23	2.49	6.28	10
Min. Q.	1	2	6	9
Frac. R.	0.23	0.49	0.28	1
Final A.	1	3	6	10

b. Jefferson's method begins as with Hamilton's. As noted in part **a**, the standard divisor is 39, so we try lower modified divisors until the apportionment comes out just right. By trial and error, the modified divisor of 35 is found to work. Note that this choice of the modified divisor is not unique, as other nearby values also work.

Group	Soc.	Pol.	Ath.	Total
Pop.	48	97	245	390
Std. Q.	1.23	2.49	6.28	10
Min. Q.	1	2	6	9
Mod. Q.	1.37	2.77	7.00	11.14
NMQ	1	2	7	10

c. Webster's method requires us to find a modified divisor such that the corresponding modified quotas round (not truncate) to numbers that sum to the desired 10 members. Inspecting the tables in parts **a** and **b**, we see that neither the standard nor modified quotas there work, so we must try other modified divisors. This time, we find that 38 is a suitable modified divisor. Note that this choice of the modified divisor is not unique, as other nearby values also work.

Group	Soc.	Pol.	Ath.	Total
Pop.	48	97	245	390
Std. Q.	1.23	2.49	6.28	10
Min. Q.	1	2	6	9
Mod. Q.	1.26	2.55	6.45	10.26
Rou. Q.	1	3	6	10

d. The Hill-Huntington method requires us to find a modified divisor such that the corresponding modified quotas, *rounded relative to the geometric mean*, yield numbers that sum to the desired 10 members. The standard divisor of 39 and standard quotas are already sufficient because they round (per the geometric means) to the desired apportionment. Thus there is no need to seek out a modified divisor in this case.

Group	Soc.	Pol.	Ath.	Total
Pop.	48	97	245	390
Std. Q.	1.23	2.49	6.28	10
Min. Q.	1	2	6	9
Geo. M.	1.41	2.45	6.48	-
Rou. Q.	1	3	6	10

The geometric means are for the whole numbers bracketing the standard quotas, namely: $\sqrt{1\times2}$ = 1.41, $\sqrt{2\times3}$ = 2.45, and $\sqrt{6\times7}$ = 6.48. The modified quotas (in this case the standard quotas) are compared to these, and hence 1.23 and 6.28 are rounded down to 1 and 6, respectively, whereas 2.49 is rounded up to 3.

e. The Hamilton, Webster, and Hill-Huntington methods all give the same result, and thus one could argue that these yield the best apportionment.

42. Refer to exercise 41 for a detailed explanation of the method of solution that yields the following apportionments.

a. Standard divisor = 62.75.

Dept.	Pol.	Fire	Para.	Total
Pop.	485	213	306	1004
Std. Q.	7.73	3.39	4.88	16
Min. Q.	7	3	4	14
Frac. R.	0.73	0.39	0.88	2
Final A.	8	3	5	16

b. Modified divisor = 60.

Dept.	Pol.	Fire	Para.	Total
Pop.	485	213	306	1004
Std. Q.	7.73	3.39	4.88	16
Min. Q.	7	3	4	14
Mod. Q.	8.08	3.55	5.10	16.73
NMQ	8	3	5	16

c. Modified divisor not necessary.

Dept.	Pol.	Fire	Para.	Total
Pop.	485	213	306	1004
Std. Q.	7.73	3.39	4.88	16
Min. Q.	7	3	4	14
Rou. Q.	8	3	5	16

d. Modified divisor not necessary.

Dept.	Pol.	Fire	Para.	Total
Pop.	485	213	306	1004
Std. Q.	7.73	3.39	4.88	16
Min. Q.	7	3	4	14
Geo. M.	7.48	3.46	4.47	-
Rou. Q.	8	3	5	16

e. All four methods give the same results.

43. Refer to exercise 41 for a detailed explanation of the method of solution that yields the following apportionments.

a. Note that the total "population" is 2.5 + 7.6 + 3.9 + 5.5 = 19.5 (million dollars). Standard divisor = 0.78.

Store	Bou.	Den.	Bro.	F. C.	Total
Pop.	2.5	7.6	3.9	5.5	19.5
Std. Q.	3.21	9.74	5.00	7.05	25
Min. Q.	3	9	5	7	24
Frac. R.	0.21	0.74	0.00	0.05	1
Final A.	3	10	5	7	25

b. Modified divisor = 0.76.

Store	Bou.	Den.	Bro.	F. C.	Total
Pop.	2.5	7.6	3.9	5.5	19.5
Std. Q.	3.21	9.74	5.00	7.05	25
Min. Q.	3	9	5	7	24
Mod. Q.	3.29	10.00	5.13	7.24	25.66
NMQ	3	10	5	7	25

c. Modified divisor not necessary.

Store	Bou.	Den.	Bro.	F. C.	Total
Pop.	2.5	7.6	3.9	5.5	19.5
Std. Q.	3.21	9.74	5.00	7.05	25
Min. Q.	3	9	5	7	24
Rou. Q.	3	10	5	7	25

d. Modified divisor not necessary.

Store	Bou.	Den.	Bro.	F. C.	Total
Pop.	2.5	7.6	3.9	5.5	19.5
Std. Q.	3.21	9.74	5.00	7.05	25
Min. Q.	3	9	5	7	24
Geo. M.	3.46	9.49	5.48	7.48	-
Rou. Q.	3	10	5	7	25

e. All four methods give the same results.

44. Refer to exercise 41 for a detailed explanation of the method of solution that yields the following apportionments.

a. Standard divisor = 1143.33.

Nbrhd.	G	W	C	Total
Pop.	4300	3040	2950	10,290
Std. Q.	3.76	2.66	2.58	9
Min. Q.	3	2	2	7
Frac. R.	0.76	0.66	0.58	2
Final A.	4	3	2	9

b. Modified divisor = 1000.

Nbrhd.	G	W	C	Total
Pop.	4300	3040	2950	10,290
Std. Q.	3.76	2.66	2.58	9
Min. Q.	3	2	2	7
Mod. Q.	4.30	3.04	2.95	10.29
NMQ	4	3	2	9

c. Modified divisor = 1200.

Nbrhd.	G	W	C	Total
Pop.	4300	3040	2950	10,290
Std. Q.	3.76	2.66	2.58	9
Min. Q.	3	2	2	7
Mod. Q.	3.58	2.53	2.49	8.58
Rou. Q.	4	3	2	9

d. Modified divisor = 1220.

Nbrhd.	G	W	C	Total
Pop.	4300	3040	2950	10,290
Std. Q.	3.76	2.66	2.58	9
Min. Q.	3	2	2	7
Mod. Q.	3.52	2.49	2.42	8.43
Geo. M.	3.46	2.45	2.45	-
Final A.	4	3	2	9

e. All four methods give the same results.

UNIT 12D

TIME OUT TO THINK

Pg. 666. Answers will vary depending on the congressional district. This would be a good topic for a discussion either during or outside of class.

Pg. 669. Answers will vary depending on how the districts are drawn. This would be a good topic for a discussion either during or outside of class.

QUICK QUIZ

1. **c.** The process of redrawing district boundaries is called redistricting.

2. **b.** This answer does the best job in summarizing the political importance of redistricting.

3. **b.** As shown in Table 12.22 in the text, house elections are decided, on average, by larger margins of victory.

4. **c.** If district boundaries were drawn in a random fashion, one would expect that Republicans would win about 56% of the house seats. Since they won only 15/32 = 47% of the seats, it appears that the district boundaries were set in a way that favored Democrats.

5. **b.** If district boundaries were drawn in a random fashion, one would expect that Republicans would win about 58% of the house seats. Since they won 21/32 = 66% of the seats, it appears that the district boundaries were set in a way that favored Republicans.

6. **c.** Gerrymandering is the drawing of district boundaries so as to serve the political interests of the politicians in charge of the drawing process.

7. **a.** If you concentrate most of the Republicans in a few districts (and essentially concede that they will win in those districts), you will stack the deck in the favor of the Democrats in all the remaining districts.

8. **b.** The courts have generally allowed even very convoluted district boundaries to stand as long as they don't violate existing laws.

9. **a.** If district lines are drawn in such a way as to maximize the number of, say, Democratic seats in the House, they must concentrate the Republican voters in a few districts, and these districts are going to elect Republican representatives (assuming voters vote along party lines).

10. **b.** In an election for a seat that, say, a Democrat is almost guaranteed to win, the real contest occurs in the primary election, rather than the general election. Primaries tend to draw smaller numbers of voters, and those with more clearly partisan interests, and this results in the election of a representative with more extreme partisan views.

DOES IT MAKE SENSE?

7. Makes sense. The district lines in that state are most likely drawn in such a way as to favor Democrats.

8. Makes sense. The practice of gerrymandering often produces districts where the percentage of voters in a particular party is not the same as the overall percentage of those voters in the state.

9. Does not make sense. If the practice of gerrymandering is alive and well in your state, you probably shouldn't expect that the percentage of voters from the various political parties is accurately reflected in the percentage of representatives from those parties that win elections.

10. Does not make sense. It is against the law to draw district lines where the populations differ by a large margin. In a state with 8 million people and

8 House seats, there should be roughly 1 million people per district.

11. Does not make sense. Current laws require that district lines should be drawn to produce contiguous districts.

12. Makes sense. To the extent that the practice of gerrymandering produces districts where the elections are noncompetitive (and therefore these districts elect representatives with more extreme views), the removal of the practice would presumably produce more districts that are competitive, which would result in a smaller number of representatives who hold extreme views.

BASIC SKILLS & CONCEPTS

13. **a.** In 1998, the percentage of votes cast for Republicans was $\frac{574}{574+407} = 59\%$, and for Democrats it was $\frac{407}{574+407} = 41\%$. In 2004, the percentage of votes cast for Republicans was $\frac{1126}{1126+598} = 65\%$, and for Democrats it was $\frac{598}{1126+598} = 35\%$.

b. In 1998, the percentage of House seats won by Republicans was 5/6 = 83%, and for Democrats it was 1/6 = 17%. In 2004, the percentage of House seats won by Republicans was 6/8 = 75%, and it was 2/8 = 25% for Democrats.

c. In both 1998 and 2004, the percentage of House seats won by Republicans was significantly larger than the percentage of votes they received, though the disparity was not as pronounced in 2004.

d. Because of the change noted in part **c**, it's plausible that redistricting had an effect on the distribution of representatives.

14. **a.** In 1998, the percentage of votes cast for Republicans was $\frac{558}{558+581} = 49\%$, and for Democrats it was $\frac{581}{558+581} = 51\%$. In 2004, the percentage of votes cast for Republicans was $\frac{3319}{3319+2212} = 60\%$, and for Democrats it was $\frac{2212}{3319+2212} = 40\%$.

b. In 1998, the percentage of House seats won by Republicans was 15/23 = 65%, and for Democrats it was 8/23 = 35%. In 2004, the percentage of House seats won by Republicans was 18/25 = 72%, and it was 7/25 = 28% for Democrats.

c. In both 1998 and 2004, the percentage of House seats won by Republicans was significantly larger than the percentage of votes they received.

d. It appears as though the district lines in 1998 were set up to favor Republicans, because roughly half of the votes cast were for Republicans, yet they won 65% of the seats. It's difficult to determine whether redistricting had an effect on the 2004 outcomes – more voters chose Republican candidates, and this would lead to more seats in the House.

15. a. In 1998, the percentage of votes cast for Republicans was $\dfrac{1040}{1040+592}=64\%$, and for Democrats it was $\dfrac{592}{1040+592}=36\%$. In 2004, the percentage of votes cast for Republicans was $\dfrac{1914}{1914+1366}=58\%$, and for Democrats it was $\dfrac{1366}{1914+1366}=42\%$.

b. In 1998, the percentage of House seats won by Republicans was 8/11 = 73%, and for Democrats it was 3/11 = 27%. In 2004, the percentage of House seats won by Republicans was 7/13 = 54%, and it was 6/13 = 46% for Democrats.

c. In 1998, the percentage of House seats won by Republicans was significantly larger than the percentage of votes they received. In 2004, the percentage of votes and seats were pretty close to one another.

d. Because of the change noted in part **c**, it's plausible that redistricting had an effect on the distribution of representatives.

16. a. In 1998, the percentage of votes cast for Republicans was $\dfrac{1608}{1608+2180}=42\%$, and for Democrats it was $\dfrac{2180}{1608+2180}=58\%$. In 2004, the percentage of votes cast for Republicans was $\dfrac{2209}{2209+3457}=39\%$, and for Democrats it was $\dfrac{3457}{2209+3457}=61\%$.

b. In 1998, the percentage of House seats won by Republicans was 13/31 = 42%, and for Democrats it was 18/31 = 58%. In 2004, the percentage of House seats won by Republicans was 9/29 = 31%, and it was 20/29 = 69% for Democrats.

c. In 1998, the percentage of House seats won by Republicans was the same as the percentage of votes they received. In 2004, the percentage of seats was a little lower.

d. Because of the change noted in part **c**, it's plausible that redistricting had an effect on the distribution of representatives.

17. a. In 1998, the percentage of votes cast for Republicans was $\dfrac{1472}{1472+1381}=52\%$, and for Democrats it was $\dfrac{1381}{1472+1381}=48\%$. In 2004, the percentage of votes cast for Republicans was $\dfrac{2565}{2565+2478}=51\%$, and for Democrats it was $\dfrac{2478}{2565+2478}=49\%$.

b. In 1998, the percentage of House seats won by Republicans was 10/21 = 48%, and for Democrats it was 11/21 = 52%. In 2004, the percentage of House seats won by Republicans was 12/19 = 63%, and it was 7/19 = 37% for Democrats.

c. In 1998, the percentage of House seats won by Republicans was very close to the percentage of votes they received. In 2004, the percentage of votes changed only by a small amount, yet the percentage of seats won went up by a significant margin.

d. Because of the change noted in part **c**, it's plausible that redistricting had an effect on the distribution of representatives.

18. a. The most likely distribution would be 5 Republican and 5 Democrat seats.

b. The maximum number of Republican seats that could be won is 9. In order to get a majority of Republican voters in as many districts as possible, you need to load up one district with Democrats. Each district has 600,000 people – imagine drawing district lines so that all 600,000 people were Democrats in a particular district. That district would elect a Democrat for its representative, but the remaining 9 districts could be drawn to have Republican majorities, and they would elect Republicans. (Note: With the assumption that voting is to take place along party lines, all you'd really need to do is move 1 Democrat from each of 9 districts into the remaining district, and then take 9 Republicans from that district and distribute them evenly across the other 9 districts. This would produce a Republican majority in 9 districts. Of course this assumes that each district begins with exactly 300,000 Republicans, and 300,000 Democrats). Reverse the above logic to convince yourself that the minimum number of Republican representatives is 1.

19. a. The most likely distribution would be 8 Republican and 8 Democrat seats.

b. The maximum number of Republican seats that could be won is 15. In order to get a majority of Republican voters in as many districts as possible, you need to load up one district with Democrats. Each district has 625,000 people – imagine drawing district lines so that all 625,000 people were Democrats in a particular district. That district would elect a Democrat for its representative, but the remaining 15 districts could be drawn to have Republican majorities, and they would elect Republicans. (Note: With the assumption that voting is to take place along party lines, all you'd really need to do is move 1 Democrat from each of 15 districts into the remaining district, and then take 15 Republicans from that district and distribute them evenly across the other 15 districts. This would produce a Republican majority in 15 districts. Of course this assumes that each district begins with exactly 312,500 Republicans, and 312,500 Democrats). Reverse the above logic to convince yourself that the minimum number of Republican representatives is 1.

20. a. The most likely distribution would be 5 Republican and 5 Democrat seats.
    b. The maximum number of Republican seats is 9, and the minimum number is 1. (Refer to exercise 18b; the logic is the same).

21. a. The most likely distribution would be 6 Republican and 6 Democrat seats.
    b. The maximum number of Republican seats is 11, and the minimum number is 1. (Refer to exercise 19b; the logic is the same).

22. a. The most likely distribution would be 10 Republican and 0 Democrat seats. This is due to the fact that with random district lines, one would expect a 70% majority in favor of Republicans in every single district, and as long as voting takes place along party lines, all of these districts will elect Republican representatives.
    b. From part **a**, we see that the maximum number of Republican seats is 10. In order to find the minimum number, first observe that each district has 500,000 people, and the entire state has 1,500,000 Democrats. A particular district will elect a Democrat only when the district has a Democrat majority. This requires at least 250,001 Democrats (and 249,999 Republicans), with the assumption that voting takes place along party lines (and that everyone votes). However, there are only 1,500,000 Democrats to spread around, and since $1,500,000 \div 250,001 = 5.999976$, the maximum number of districts where one could find a Democrat majority is 5. This implies that the minimum number of Republican seats is 5.

23. a. The most likely distribution would be 15 Republican and 0 Democrat seats. This is due to the fact that with random district lines, one would expect an 80% majority in favor of Republicans in every single district, and as long as voting takes place along party lines, all of these districts will elect Republican representatives.
    b. From part **a**, we see that the maximum number of Republican seats is 15. In order to find the minimum number, first observe that each district has 500,000 people, and the entire state has 1,500,000 Democrats. A particular district will elect a Democrat only when the district has a Democrat majority. This requires at least 250,001 Democrats (and 249,999 Republicans), with the assumption that voting takes place along party lines (and that everyone votes). However, there are only 1,500,000 Democrats to spread around, and since $1,500,000 \div 250,001 = 5.999976$, the maximum number of districts where one could find a Democrat majority is 5. This implies that the minimum number of Republican seats is 10.

24. There are several solutions. Perhaps the easiest to describe is one where the boundaries divide the state into eight rectangles, each 2 blocks wide and 4 blocks high.

25. There are several solutions. Perhaps the easiest to describe is one where the boundaries divide the state into 8 rectangles, each 4 blocks wide and 2 blocks high.

26. There are several solutions. Perhaps the easiest to describe is one where the boundaries divide the state into eight rectangles, each 2 blocks wide and 4 blocks high.

27. There are several solutions. Perhaps the easiest to describe is one where the boundaries divide the state into 8 rectangles, each 4 blocks wide and 2 blocks high.

28. Answers will vary, though it is certainly possible to find the required boundaries.

29. It is not possible to draw district boundaries that satisfy the conditions given. Three Democrats are needed in a single district for a Democrat majority, and thus a valid solution would require three Democrats in each of three districts, for a total of nine Democrats. But there are only eight Democrats in the state.

30. Answers will vary (there are several solutions).

31. Answers will vary (there are several solutions).

32. Yes, it is possible – draw boundaries so that three districts have 3 Republicans, and 2 Democrats (these districts will elect a Republican), and the other two will automatically elect a Democrat.

FURTHER APPLICATIONS

33. Answers will vary for the first three cases (there are several solutions). The last case, where 4 Republicans are elected, is not possible. Five Republicans are needed in a single district for a Republican majority, and thus a valid solution would require five Republicans in each of four districts, for a total of 20 Republicans. But there are only 18 Republicans in the state.

34. Answers will vary for the first three cases (there are several solutions). The last case, where 4 Republicans are elected, is not possible. Five Republicans are needed in a single district for a Republican majority, and thus a valid solution would require five Republicans in each of four districts, for a total of 20 Republicans. But there are only 18 Republicans in the state.

35. There are many solutions.

36. Solutions will vary.

37. It is not possible for one party to win every House seat for the situation described. To show this for the example provided (20 voters and four districts), note that 3 voters of the same party are required for a majority in a single district. Thus a majority in all four districts would require 12 voters of the same party, which is impossible, because there are only 10 such voters. This argument can be generalized to give a proof of the statement in the exercise.